W9-CSP-647

Recent Developments in Separation Science

Volume III
Part A

Editor

Norman N. Li, Sc.D.

Exxon Research and Engineering Company
Linden, New Jersey

CRC

Published by

CRC PRESS, Inc.
18901 Cranwood Parkway · Cleveland, Ohio 44128

Library of Congress Cataloging in Publication Data

Li, Norman N
Recent developments in separation science.

(CRC uniscience series)
Includes bibliographical references.
1. Separation (Technology) I. Title.
TP156.S45L5 660.2'842 72-88417
ISBN 0-8493-5031-X (Complete Set)
ISBN 0-87819-001-5 (Former Complete Set)

This book represents information obtained from authentic and highly regarded sources. Reprinted material is quoted with permission, and sources are indicated. A wide variety of references are listed. Every reasonable effort has been made to give reliable data and information, but the author and the publisher cannot assume responsibility for the validity of all materials or for the consequences of their use.

All rights reserved. This book, or any parts thereof, may not be reproduced in any form without written consent from the publisher.

© 1977 by CRC Press, Inc.

International Standard Book Number 0-8493-5031-X (Complete Set)
Former International Standard Book Number 0-87819-001-5 (Complete Set)
International Standard Book Number 0-8493-5481-1 (Volume III, Part A)
International Standard Book Number 0-8493-5482-X (Volume III, Part B)

Library of Congress Card Number 72-88417
Printed in the United States

PREFACE

It was about 5 years ago that we published our first two volumes. At that time, we did not have plans to publish additional volumes. Volumes I and II, which contain a total of 22 chapters, were therefore designed to cover practically all the important aspects of separation science and technology. Our readers' favorable responses in the past years have convinced us to make the book a multivolume series so that additional volumes can be published from time to time. This two-part volume is the first of several volumes that we plan to publish in the next few years.

We are very proud to note that in this volume (Parts A and B) we are able to present 15 chapters written by the leading authorities in separation science and technology. These chapters present discourses on unifying theories for separation processes, on the theories describing the interactions of fluid dynamics, interfacial phenomena, and mass transfer, and on a variety of separation methods and processes. The last category includes dynamically formed membranes, electrolytical purification, facilitated transport through membranes, gas absorption, ion exchange process, liquid clathrates, liquid membranes, supercritical extraction, ultrafiltration, and waste water treatment for fermentation processes.

The materials discussed in each chapter are, in general, the author's own research work and his critical review of the current state of art. The authors had complete freedom in choosing certain important areas for emphasis. As a result, some chapters treat the related chemistry or mathematics in more detail than others, and some deal more with the engineering and economics aspects of a separation process. Each chapter, consequently, possesses its own special feature and appealing points.

All the chapters were reviewed by Dr. E. W. Funk of Exxon and myself, with two chapters reviewed also by Professor R. W. Rousseau of North Carolina State University of Raleigh. I wish to thank both of them for their help. I would like to express my sincere appreciation also to the authors and the Staff of CRC Press for their effort in making Volume III possible. Special thanks are due to Ms. M. Magee and Ms. T. Weintraub of CRC Press for their editorial assistance.

Norman N. Li
Linden, New Jersey

THE EDITOR

Norman N. Li, Sc.D., heads the Separation Science Group at the Corporate Research Laboratories of Exxon Research and Engineering Company. He has numerous scientific publications and patents on topics of crystallization, extraction, blood oxygenation, enzyme membranes, water treatment, liquid membranes, and polymeric membranes. Of the many patents he holds, 21 alone deal with the basic invention and various applications of liquid surfactant membranes. He was a consultant on gas diffusion for the Apollo project and has given lectures at many universities and industrial research laboratories. Dr. Li teaches two short courses for the American Institute of Chemical Engineers, "New Separation Processes" and "Surface Chemistry and Emulsion Technology." He served as chairman of two Gordon Research Conferences, "Separation and Purification" and "Transport Phenomena in Synthetic and Biological Membranes," and of several symposia on separations for the American Chemical Society and the American Institute of Chemical Engineers.

CONTRIBUTORS

Jerry L. Atwood, Ph.D.
Department of Chemistry
University of Alabama
University, Alabama

Alan R. Berens, Ph.D.
B.F. Goodrich Co.
Research and Development Center
3recksville, Ohio

)ibakar Bhattacharyya, Ph.D.
)epartment of Chemical Engineering
Jniversity of Lexington
.exington, Kentucky

Ieinz-Günter Blaschke, Ph.D.
'arbenfabrik Bayer AG
.everkusen, West Germany

Ilf Brunke, D.Sc.
lenkel AG
üsseldorf, West Germany

nrico Drioli, Ph.D.
acolta di Ingegneria
ıstituto di Principi di Ingegneria Chimica
niversita degli Studi di Napoli
aples, Italy

ohn W. Frankenfeld, Ph.D.
xxon Reearch and Engineering Co.
inden, New Jersey

dward W. Funk, Ph.D.
xxon Research and Engineering Co.
.nden, New Jersey

. B. Grieves, Ph.D.
epartment of Chemical Engineering
niversity of Kentucky
exington, Kentucky

arold B. Hopfenberg, Sc.D.
epartment of Chemical Engineering
orth Carolina State University
aleigh, North Carolina

yrus Irani, Ph.D.
.xxon Research and Engineering Co.
.inden, New Jersey

Isao Karube, D. Eng.
Research Laboratory of Resources Utilization
Tokyo Institute of Technology
Tokyo, Japan

Takashi Koike, B.S.
Kyowa Hakko Kogyo Co. Ltd.
Tokyo, Japan

Russel J. Lander, M.S.
Department of Chemical and Biochemical Engineering
University of Pennsylvania
Philadelphia, Pennsylvania

Ho-Lun Lee, Ph.D.
Department of Chemical Engineering
University of Wisconsin
Madison, Wisconsin

Norman N. Li, Sc.D.
Exxon Research and Engineering Co.
Linden, New Jersey

Edwin N. Lightfoot, Jr., Ph.D.
Department of Chemical Engineering
University of Wisconsin
Madison, Wisconsin

R. N. Maddox, Ph.D.
School of Chemical Engineering
Oklahoam State University
Stillwater, Oklahoma

William S. Miller, B.S.
The Permutit Company
Research and Development Center
Princeton, New Jersey

Albert B. Mindler, B.S.
The Permutit Company
Research and Development Center
Princeton, New Jersey

Minoru Nagashima, M.S.
Kyowa Hakko Kogyo Co. Ltd.
Tokyo, Japan

Sadao Noguchi, B.S.
Kyowa Hakko Kogyo Co. Ltd.
Tokyo, Japan

Robert L. Pigford, Ph.D.
Department of Chemical Engineering
University of Delaware
Newark, Delaware

John A. Quinn, Ph.D.
Department of Chemical and Biochemical Engineering
University of Pennsylvania
Philadelphia, Pennsylvania

Joachim F. G. Reis, Ph.D.
Department of Chemical Engineering
University of Wisconsin
Madison, Wisconsin

Hirotoshi Samejima, Ph.D.
Tokyo Research Laboratory
Kyowa Hakko Kogyo Co. Ltd.
Tokyo, Japan

Karl Schügerl, Ph.D.
Institute for Technical Chemistry
Technical University of Hanover
Hanover, West Germany

Jerome S. Schultz, Ph.D.
Department of Chemical Engineering
University of Michigan
Ann Arbor, Michigan

T. Thomas Shih, Ph.D.
Chemical Research Laboratory
Allied Chemical Company
Morristown, New Jersey

Douglas R. Smith, M.S.
Department of Chemical and Biochemical Engineering
University of Pennsylvania
Philadelphia, Pennsylvania

Rolf Streicher, D.Sc.
Lurgi Mineralöltechnik GmbH
Frankfurt am Main, West Germany

Shuichi Suzuki, D.Sc.
Research Laboratory of Resources Utilization
Tokyo Institute of Technology
Tokyo, Japan

Mario S. Waissbluth, Ph.D.
Department of Biotechnology and Bioengineering
Center for Advanced Studies
National Polytechnic Institute
Mexico City, Mexico

TABLE OF CONTENTS

THE SYSTEMATIC DESCRIPTION AND DEVELOPMENT OF SEPARATIONS PROCESSES

H. L. Lee, E. N. Lightfoot, J. F. G. Reis, and M. D. Waissbluth

TABLE OF CONTENTS

INTRODUCTION

During the last decade there has been an enormous increase in the specific needs for physical separations, in the technology available for producing them, and also in the number of processes available in fully developed form.

The development of new processes has been especially impressive in the general areas of synthetic polymers, biological macromolecules, and colloidal particles. To mention just a few new or rapidly evolving processes we cite parametric pumping,[108,111,119] affinity chromatography,[26,39] polarization chromatography,[48,68] continuous chromatography[37,107] high-speed liquid chromatography,[33,80] zonal centrifugation,[3,19] continuous electrophoresis,[49,50,64,66] isotachophoresis,[25] dielectrophoresis,[62] separation by flow,[31] and spreading,[85] and a variety of membrane separations.[81,88,91]

We can also refer the reader to a number of relatively new journals and periodic reviews devoted entirely to separations, for example *Progress in Separation and Purification, Separation Science,* and *Separation and Purification Methods.*

The bulk of newly developed separations are still primarily confined to analytical and small-scale preparative applications. It is a major challenge to scale these operations up, particularly to meet the challenges of increasing energy and raw materials costs. Moreover, since the available number of possibilities is already very large, and since there are doubtless many processes yet to be discovered, even the systematic listing of possibilities becomes a major task. For example, it is suggested by Pauschmann that the number of potentially useful and qualitatively distinct separations is on the order of 10^4.

The organization and rationalization of all this material have proven to be a difficult task, and the available frameworks appear inadequate. An opportunity therefore exists for a long overdue restructuring of this classic field, and such a reorganization should take full advantage of recent advances in transport theory, the strategy of process design,[96,97] and the more ambiguous area of existing technology. The challenge is clearly to combine these hitherto largely unrelated areas in such a way as to facilitate the solution of important separations problems: the invention and development of new processes, the selection among existing processes, and the systematic study of separations as a scholarly discipline. Meeting this challenge is our major goal.

Substantial efforts have already been made in these directions, notably by Karger et al.,[59] Rony,[93] Giddings,[43] Pauschmann,[82] and De Clerk et al.[28] It is, however, our belief that a more powerful organization can be provided by the conservation and rate laws of transport phenomena, and we outline such an approach below. The rationale for this is of course that all separations are almost by definition transport processes and therefore described in detail by the equations of change.

This rationalization is, however, only partially correct. First, the very generality of the transport equations makes them unsuitable for distinguishing between individual processes; these distinctions lie primarily in the boundary conditions (including system geometry) and equations of state. Second, the essentially descriptive nature of transport phenomena makes this discipline a weak point of departure for any creative activity: invention, development, or design.

We must therefore build our transport-based description into a synthesis-oriented strategic framework flexible enough to accommodate a great deal of poorly organized information: chemical or physical, financial, and political. Our approach to this problem is fourfold. We begin by developing an essentially heuristic classification scheme which facilitates the listing of possibilities and choosing between alternatives. This is the primary concern of the present discussion. Second, we are beginning to devise a synthesis scheme for generating promising processes from our fundamental classification. Third, we are seeking efficient means for comparison of alternate schemes. Since the synthesis and comparison must encompass a very large number of possibilities, it will be most efficient to combine these two operations into a staged series or hierarchy of successively more accurate, and expensive, computational or experimental procedures. Finally we shall be interested in the implementation of the above ideas, by way of concrete examples, to test the utility of our ideas.

All of these activities must of course be based on a solid understanding of separation as a basic concept. In this paper we start with the definition of separation as a basic concept and then present a general morphological description. We next provide a detailed framework for the quantitative description of separations and suggest how one may use this framework and understanding of separations morphology for classification and synthesis.

THE STRUCTURE OF SEPARATIONS PROCESSES

Definitions of Separation and Separative Work

We begin here by considering the rather general separation process of Figure 1 in which a feed stream or sample is converted into an unspecified number of products. We first define separation qualitatively in terms of scaled feed and product compositions, and then go on to present two methods of characterizing separation quantitatively: purity, or separation indices, and effort, or separative power. Purity is of paramount interest to the user of separations processes, particularly in analytical applications, and considerations of purity have dominated the separations literature. The effort required to achieve a given separation is clearly also an important consideration, however, particularly to engineers, and greater attention to this aspect of our field seems overdue.

Separation in Terms of Scaled Composition Changes

We define a separations process as one in which a feed mixture F is converted to M product mixtures, as suggested in Figure 1. These product mixtures may be readily identifiable streams, as in a distillation process, or abritrarily selected regions, for example effluent fractions from a gas or liquid chromatograph or two-dimensional zones in paper chromatography.

In general, separation can be expressed in terms of composition changes, and we shall use here two measures of composition:*

$$x_i = \text{mole fraction of species i at any position and time} \quad (1)$$

and

$$X_i = x_i/x_{iF} = \text{relative molar fraction} \quad (2)$$

where x_{iF} is the mole fraction of species i in the feed. For a system of N species the compositions may then be expressed as the vectors

$$\underline{x} = (x_1, x_2, --- x_N) \quad (3)$$

$$\underline{X} = (X_1, X_2, --- X_N) \quad (4)$$

$$\underline{X}_F = 1 \quad (5)$$

Note that these are local or point compositions.

We next define average compositions of the M product streams as

$$\pi_{ij} = \text{the mole fraction of species i in product stream j taken as a whole} \quad (6)$$

and

$$\Pi_{ij} = \pi_{ij}/x_{iF} \quad (7)$$

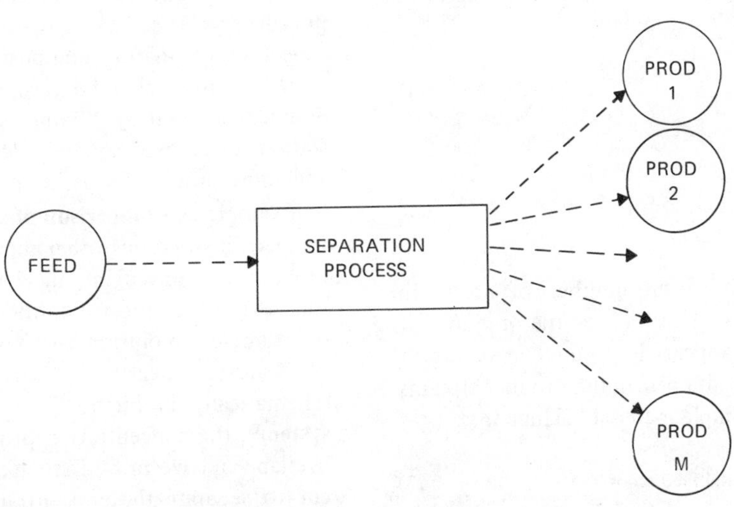

FIGURE 1. The nature of separation.

*It may on occasion be preferable to use mass or volume fractions.

We may therefore express product compositions as an N by M matrix, e.g.,

$$\underline{\underline{\pi}} = \begin{pmatrix} \pi_{11}, & \cdots & \pi_{1M} \\ \vdots & & \\ \pi_{N1} & \cdots & \pi_{NM} \end{pmatrix} \tag{8}$$

Note that the π_{ij} are averaged compositions, e.g., cup-mixing averages in flow systems, or volume averages in batch ones.

It is now clear that separation will occur whenever there is one element of Π for which

$$\Pi_{ij} \neq 1 \tag{9}$$

and that species k and ℓ will be separated to some extent whenever there is a product, for which

$$\Pi_{kj} \neq \Pi_{\ell j} \tag{10}$$

Equations 9 and 10 are sufficiently broad to include all measures of separation known to the authors, and they may clearly be written in other terms, for example, on a solvent-free basis or in mass or volume fractions. They are, in fact, too broad in that they are inherently qualitative, and we now turn our attention to quantitative measures of purity.

Separation Indices: Measures of Product Purity

We therefore now look at more specialized measures of separation, of which a great many have been proposed.[46,59,61,92,93]

One particularly useful example is the degree of segregation matrix $\underline{\underline{Y}}$ defined by

$$Y_{ij} \equiv r_j \Pi_{ij} / \sum_{\ell=1}^{M} r_\ell \Pi_{i\ell} \tag{11}$$

where

$$r_j = m_j / \sum_{\ell=1}^{M} m_\ell \tag{12}$$

and m_j equals the total number of moles in product mixture j. Thus Y_{ij} is the fraction of recovered i which appears in product mixture j. If all of the feed is contained in the product streams it follows from a simple material balance that

$$\sum_{\ell=1}^{M} r_\ell \Pi_{i\ell} = 1 \qquad \text{(total feed recovery)} \tag{13}$$

and

$$Y_{ij} = r_j \Pi_{ij} \qquad \text{(total feed recovery)} \tag{14}$$

Equations 13 and 14 will not be valid if there is chemical degradation or other product loss, or for transient situations. The degree of separation has proven a useful index, but it does not give a direct measure of relative segregation, which is often desired.

A more far-reaching index which does this is Rony's extent of separation ξ, defined as the magnitude of the determinant of $\underline{\underline{Y}}$:

$$\xi = |\det \underline{\underline{Y}}| \tag{15}$$

The physical significance of ξ may be seen most easily for a binary system where

$$\xi = |Y_{11}Y_{22} - Y_{12}Y_{21}| \tag{16}$$

Furthermore, for a binary system

$$Y_{11} = r_1\Pi_{11}/(r_1\Pi_{11} + r_2\Pi_{12}) \tag{17}$$

$$= 1 - Y_{12} \tag{18}$$

$$\xi = |Y_{11} - Y_{21}| = |Y_{22} - Y_{12}| \tag{19}$$

In this simple situation, then, ξ is just the difference in degrees of segregation into either of the two product mixtures.

This index has proven useful for comparing such dissimilar processes as stagewise distillation and zone melting. It is, however, only applicable where the number of components N to be separated is equal to the number of product streams M. If $N > M$ one may choose M particularly important species as key components and ignore the others in calculating composition. This is often done. It must also be recognized that a single number, as given by ξ, is not sufficient characterization for $N > 2$. Equation 15 is inadequate here and more powerful separation indices are needed.

Example 1: Comparison of separation indices – In specific situations other separation indices may prove more convenient, or at least more popular, than the above, and we consider one here by way of example: resolution to characterize separation of Gaussian peaks. In this situation, shown schematically in Figure 2 for a one-dimensional system*, the concentration profiles of two species overlap, and we must first decide upon a line of cut to separate the concentration field into two product mixtures. The proper positioning of this line may present a difficult decision in some cases,

*A three-dimensional Gaussian distribution is discussed in Example 2.

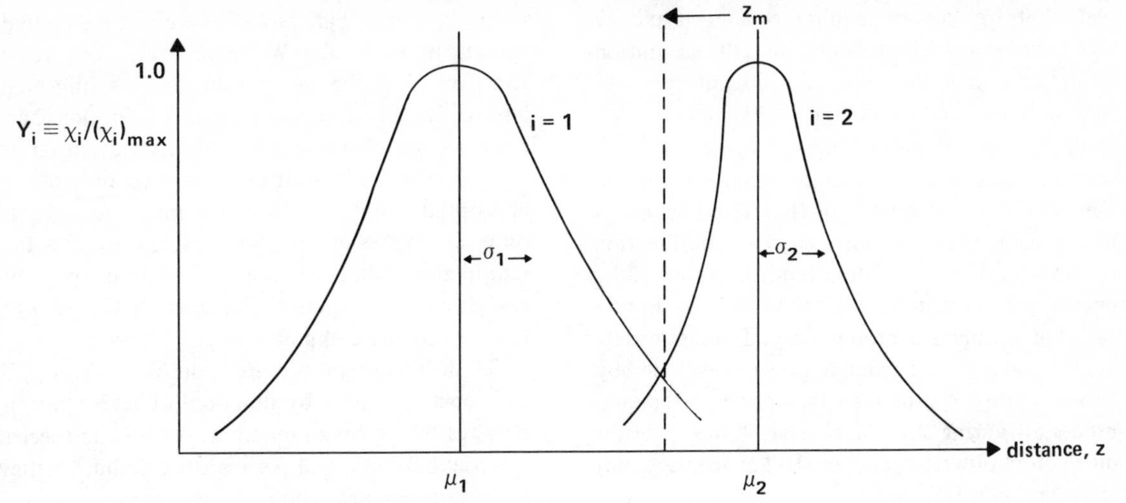

FIGURE 2. A simple one-dimensional separation.

but it is frequently satisfactory to separate at the point of equal fractional loss of major constituent, i.e., at the intersection of the normalized concentration distributions. This point is designated as z_m in Figure 2. Separation in such a system is frequently characterized in terms of the resolution R, usually defined[59] by

$$R \equiv \frac{1}{2} \cdot \frac{|\mu_1 - \mu_2|}{\sigma_1 + \sigma_2} \qquad (20)$$

where μ_1, μ_2 are the positions of the concentration maxima of solutes 1 and 2 and σ_1, σ_2 are the standard deviations about these two means. The fraction of the major constituent which is contained in the respective product mixtures is* then P(R) where

$$P(R) = \frac{1}{\sqrt{2\pi}} \int_{-\infty}^{R} e^{-z^2/2} dz \qquad (21)$$

is the normal probability integral.

It follows from Equations 11 and 19 that

$$Y_{ii} = 1 - Y_{ij} = P(R) \qquad (i = 1, 2; j \neq i) \qquad (22)$$

and

$$\xi = 2P - 1 \qquad (23)$$

A few representative comparisons of these indices are given in Table 1.

*See for example Reference 1, Section 26.2.8.

TABLE 1

Comparison of Separation Indices for Symmetrical One-dimensional Gaussian Separations*

R	P	Y_{ii}	ξ
0	0.5	0.5	0
0.25	0.691	0.691	0.383
0.5	0.841	0.841	0.683
0.75	0.933	0.933	0.866
1.0	0.977	0.977	0.954
1.25	0.994	0.994	0.988

*Note that

$P_3 < P(x) < P_1$

$$P_1 = \frac{1}{2}\left[1 + \sqrt{1 - \exp(-2x^2/\pi)}\right]$$

$$P_3 = \frac{1}{2}\left[1 + \sqrt{1 - \exp(-2x^2/\pi) - \frac{2(\pi - 3)}{3\pi^2} x^4 e^{-x^2/2}}\right]$$

Separative Power and the Value Function: Measures of Effort

One frequently needs a mechanism-independent measure of separator performance which combines the requirements of purity and productivity, and which is independent of product and feed compositions. No one such measure is best in all circumstances, and as a result quite a variety has evolved. The most general and unambiguous is minimum requirement of thermodynamic free energy, and this is normally also the most useful in the early stages of process design, for providing estimates of feasibility. Experience shows, however, that free-energy requirements are typically very minor contributors to overall separation effort* and that they normally do not correlate very well with either energy or equipment cost. Engineers have therefore turned to more specialized measures, and the most common are required numbers of transfer units or theoretical stages. A less widely used measure is the amplification function of Rony.[93] These tend, however, to be excessively specialized and to ignore the importance of optimizing productivity. The less widely known concept of separative power, developed by Dirac** for comparing isotope fractionation processes during the Manhattan Project, seems much more powerful, and we shall concentrate our attention on it here.

Discussions of separative power are made here in connection with the simple binary splitter of Figure 3 and confined to systems of only one valuable component (binary or pseudo-binary systems). The apparatus pictured splits a feed stream F into "product" and "waste" streams P and W, respectively; F, P, and W refer to molar stream rates for a continuous process or molar amounts for a batch process. This figure can be adapted to stagewise countercurrent apparatus by considering F as the combined input streams to any stage, and to continuous countercurrent processes by considering the splitter to represent a differential section of the apparatus.

Referring to this figure we define the separative power of this basic unit as

$$\delta U = PV(y) + WV(z) - FV(x) \quad (24)$$

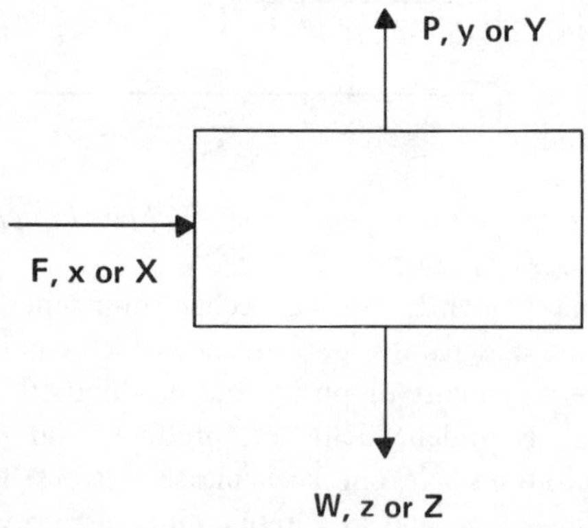

FIGURE 3. A simple binary splitter.

where x, y, and z are mole fractions of the desired species in F, P, and W, respectively. The value function V is the molar value of the indicated stream. It remains to complete this definition, but, since we are characterizing streams only in terms of composition, V must be a function only of the appropriate mole fraction. We must now determine an expression for V(x) which satisfies the requirement that δU be a function only of equipment and system characteristics, and not feed or product compositions.

To do this we must write P and W in terms of F and replace y and z by functions of x; this in turn requires two types of relations: overall and species material balances, and performance characteristics of the process unit. Those chosen here are

$$P = \theta F \quad (24a)$$

$$W = (1 - \theta)F \quad (24b)$$

and

$$x = y\theta + z(1 - \theta) \quad (25)$$

with

$$Y = \gamma X \quad (26)$$

$$Z = \beta X \quad (27)$$

where

$$X = x/(1 - x) \quad (28)$$

$$Y = y/(1 - y) \quad (29)$$

$$Z = z/(1 - z) \quad (30)$$

Here θ is known as the cut while γ and β are called enrichment ratios. Use of mole ratios rather than mole fractions introduces some mathematical difficulty, and the form of Equations 26 and 27 specializes our discussion considerably. However, there are a great many systems for which the enrichment ratios may be considered composition independent, and it is important to provide useful specific examples. It should be possible to parallel the discussion below for other performance characteristics.

We now wish to use the above relations to eliminate P, W, y, and z from Equation 23, and it may be seen immediately that our system is overdetermined. We may thus eliminate*** the cut θ by noting that

*As a specific example less than $2 \times 10^{-3}\%$ of the power consumption of a typical uranium-enrichment centrifuge is needed to supply the free energy of separation.[58]

**Usually referenced simply as "P.A.M. Dirac, British MS, 1941." Separative work and the associated concept of the value function are, however, discussed in a number of more easily available works. These include Cohen,[20] Olander,[78] and Shachter et al.[100]

***The cut θ is introduced primarily because of its importance in later discussions.

$$y = \frac{Y}{1 + Y} = \frac{\gamma X}{1 + \gamma X} \tag{31}$$

etc., and therefore that

$$\frac{X}{1 + X} = \left(\frac{\gamma X}{1 + \gamma X}\right)\theta + \left(\frac{\beta X}{1 + \beta X}\right)(1 - \theta) \tag{32}$$

and

$$\theta = \left(\frac{1 - \beta}{\gamma - \beta}\right)\left(\frac{1 + \gamma X}{1 + X}\right) \tag{33}$$

$$(1 - \theta) = \left(\frac{1 - \gamma}{\beta - \gamma}\right)\left(\frac{1 + \beta X}{1 + X}\right) \tag{34}$$

It follows that

$$\delta U/F = \left(\frac{1 - \beta}{\gamma - \beta}\right)\left(\frac{1 + \gamma X}{1 + X}\right) V\left(\frac{\gamma X}{1 + \gamma X}\right) + \left(\frac{1 - \gamma}{\beta - \gamma}\right)\left(\frac{1 + \beta X}{1 + X}\right) V\left(\frac{\beta X}{1 + \beta X}\right) - V(x) \tag{35}$$

which is our desired result. It only remains to find an expression for V(x) making δU independent of composition.

Careful inspection of Equation 35 will show that the form of V(x) depends on the ratio of β to γ, and that obtaining a general solution is a formidable problem; it does not appear to have been solved at the time of writing. Fortunately, however, essentially equivalent solutions exist for two very important special cases, and we shall confine discussion to these:

1. Antisymmetric enrichment: $\beta = 1/\gamma$ so that

$$Y = \alpha Z \tag{36}$$

with

$$\alpha = \gamma^2 \tag{37}$$

and

$$\theta = (1 + \sqrt{\alpha}X)/(1 + \sqrt{\alpha})(1 + X) \tag{38}$$

2. Small enrichment ratios:

$$\gamma - 1 << 1$$

$$\beta - 1 << 1$$

so that

$$Y = \alpha Z \tag{39}$$

with

$$\alpha - 1 << 1 \tag{40}$$

and θ is arbitrary.

The antisymmetric case is of particular importance in cascades, and we shall have more to say about it in the third section of this chapter. We note here only that the local reflux in any cascade can be set to meet the requirements of Equations 36 to 38 and that such a cascade (known as ideal) is the most efficient possible by the criteria normally used. Our first special case thus provides a performance standard for any linear cascade. The small-enrichment limit is similarly important in continuum contactors since differential segments of such a contractor always provide small enrichment ratios. We return to this point immediately after giving expressions for V(x) for these two limiting situations.

The antisymmetric case is treated by Cohen* who shows that

$$V(x) = C\left(\frac{\sqrt{\alpha} + 1}{\sqrt{\alpha} - 1}\right)\frac{(2x - 1)\ln\left[\left(\frac{x}{1 - x}\right)\Big/\left(\frac{x_0}{1 - x_0}\right)\right]}{\ln\sqrt{\alpha}} + A\left(\frac{1 - x_0}{x_0}\right) + B(1 - x) \tag{41}$$

where A and B are arbitrary constants, C is $\delta U/F$, and x_0 is an arbitrary reference concentration. The simplest and most symmetric choice is to set x_0 equal to one half, B equal to zero, and

$$V = (2x - 1)\ \ln\ [x/(1 - x)] \tag{42}$$

Then

$$\delta U/F = \frac{(\sqrt{\alpha} - 1)\ \ln\alpha}{2(1 + \sqrt{\alpha})} \tag{43}$$

Cohen suggests, however, that for any specific separation problem it may prove more convenient to set x_0 equal to the feed concentration and to define both feed and waste streams to have zero value. This last definition requires establishing a

*Cohen defines his enrichment ratio α as Y/X, but this choice is inconvenient because it is ordinarily strongly dependent on θ. The ratio Y/Z used in Equation 41 is often independent of θ, at least in the first approximation. For the antisymmetric situation consider here

$$Y/Z = (Y/X)^2$$

but this simple relation holds only when θ is given by Equation 38.

waste composition in advance, but in any event the specific choices made are clearly matters of taste, hence inarguable.

The value function is important in relating engineering effort to changes in composition. Thus, for a cascade of constant α, separative work δU is proportional to the sums of stage overflows and an ideal cascade is that which minimizes this sum. The value function is particularly useful for estimating the effect of changing feed or product specifications, but it also facilitates comparison between alternate processing procedures. It is most helpful in the intermediate stages of design, before accurate economic estimates are feasible, for concentrating attention on "reasonable" configurations.

The results for small enrichment may be obtained from Equation 35 by* using the truncated series expressions:

$$\ln\gamma \doteq \epsilon - \frac{\epsilon^2}{2} \tag{44}$$

$$\epsilon = (\gamma - 1) \tag{45}$$

and

$$\ln\beta \doteq \epsilon - \frac{\epsilon^2}{2} \tag{46}$$

$$\epsilon = (\beta - 1) \tag{47}$$

which yield:

$$V = (2x - 1)\ \ln\,[x/(1 - x)] \tag{48}$$

$$\delta U/F = \frac{1}{2}\,\theta\,(1 - \theta)(\alpha - 1)^2 \tag{49}$$

It may be seen that Equation 48 is identical with Equation 42 and that Equation 49 is consistent with Equation 43. Now, however, α and θ are mathematically independent.** We find then that the choice made for V(x) is a surprisingly useful one, and we shall have several occasions to make use of it below. We shall find the concepts of separative power and value useful from many standpoints in comparing alternate processes, and also for estimating the maximum separation potential of a given type of equipment. It will be helpful for this type of estimation to establish one further concept, that of volumetric value production rate, and we conclude our discussion by doing this. (This discussion is taken with only minor modifications from Olander.[78])

The value as defined by Equations 42 or 48 is a property of the fluid in a thermodynamic sense, and, just as for any other property it is possible to write a conservation statement for the value in the moving fluid. The "value transport equation" so obtained is very similar to the entropy transport equation which plays a fundamental role in non-equilibrium thermodynamics; it may be written as

$$\frac{\partial(cV)}{\partial t} + \nabla\cdot\mathbf{N}_V = R_V \tag{50}$$

In Equation 50, c is the total concentration of the fluid, V is the value of a unit amount of fluid, and $\mathbf{N}_V$ is the vector flux of value. The rate of production of value per unit volume of fluid is denoted by R_V. This quantity is related to the separative power of a unit of volume τ by

$$\delta U = \int_\tau R_V\, d\tau \tag{51}$$

Just as in the transport of matter, the transport of value can be broken up into a diffusive term $\mathbf{J}_V^\star$ and a convective term:***

$$\mathbf{N}_V = \mathbf{J}_V^\star + cv^\star V \tag{52}$$

Inserting the above equation into Equation 50 yields

$$c\frac{\partial V}{\partial t} + cv^\star\cdot\nabla V + \nabla\cdot\mathbf{J}_V^\star = R_V \tag{53}$$

where the overall mass continuity equation

$$\frac{\partial c}{\partial t} + \nabla\cdot(cv^\star) = 0 \tag{54}$$

has been used (we have assumed that the average molecular weight of the fluid is everywhere uniform).

We now need to develop an expression for the diffusive component of the value flux, $\mathbf{J}_V^\star$. The property called value does not "diffuse" in the same sense that molecules or heat diffuse. Rather, value is transported due to the interdiffusion of the two species in the mixture which are denoted by A and B. The value flux due to molecular transport by diffusion may be expressed by

*Alternate derivations which are simpler if one considers only the small enrichment case are given by Olander[78] and by Shachter et al.[100]

**In any actual separator the observed value of α will generally depend on θ, however.

***See Reference 11, Chapter 16. Here v* is the molar average mixture velocity, $\mathbf{N}_V$ is the flux of value relative to the coordinate system, and $\mathbf{J}_V^\star$ is the corresponding flux relative to $v^\star$.

$$J_v^\star = J_A^\star \bar{\bar{V}}_A + J_B^\star \bar{\bar{V}}_B \tag{55}$$

where $J_A^\star$ and $J_B^\star$ are the diffusive fluxes of A and B, i.e. fluxes relative to $v^\star$. By analogy to energy transport by interdiffusion in multicomponent systems[11] and entropy transport in a moving fluid, the quantities $\bar{\bar{V}}_A$ and $\bar{\bar{V}}_B$ are identified with partial molal values. The partial molal value is defined as follows: Consider a volume of fluid containing n_A moles of A and n_B moles of B. The total value of this region of fluid, V_{tot}, is

$$V_{tot} = (n_A + n_B)V(x_A) \tag{56}$$

where V is the value function and x_A is the mole fraction of component A. The partial molal value of components A and B are then given by

$$\bar{\bar{V}}_A = (\partial V_{tot}/\partial n_A)_{n_B} \tag{57}$$

and

$$\bar{\bar{V}}_B = (\partial V_{tot}/\partial n_B)_{n_A} \tag{58}$$

It follows that

$$\bar{\bar{V}}_A = V(x_A) + (1 - x_A)(dV/dx_A) \tag{59}$$

$$\bar{\bar{V}}_B = V(x_A) - x_A(dV/dx_A) \tag{60}$$

Substituting Equations 59 and 60 into Equation 55 results in

$$J_v^\star = J_A^\star\,(dV/dx_A) \tag{61}$$

where we have used the fact that $J_A^\star + J_B^\star = 0$.[11] The divergence of $J_V^\star$ is

$$\nabla\cdot J_v^\star = \nabla\cdot\left[J_A\left(\frac{dV}{dx_A}\right)\right] = \left(\frac{dV}{dx_A}\right)\nabla\cdot J_A + J_A\cdot\nabla\left(\frac{dV}{dx_A}\right) \tag{62}$$

Since the value function depends only upon composition x_A, the gradient of V or its derivative may be expressed by

$$\nabla V = \left(\frac{dV}{dx_A}\right)\nabla x_A \tag{63}$$

$$\nabla\left(\frac{dV}{dx_A}\right) = \left(\frac{d^2V}{dx_A{}^2}\right)\nabla x_A \tag{64}$$

Substituting Equations 62 to 64 into Equation 53 yields

$$R_v = J_A^\star\cdot\nabla x_A\left(\frac{d^2V}{dx_A{}^2}\right) + \underline{\underline{\left[c\frac{\partial x_A}{\partial t} + cv^\star\cdot\nabla x_A + \nabla\cdot J_A^\star\right]}}\left(\frac{dV}{dx_A}\right) \tag{65}$$

Now the bracketed term in Equation 65 is identically zero by virtue of the species continuity equation, and

$$R_v = (J_A^\star\cdot\nabla x)\ \frac{d^2V}{dx^2} \tag{66}$$

Note that we have so far made no assumption as to the concentration dependence of the value function, and therefore we are not limited by the above expressions. If we now put Equation 48 into Equation 65 we obtain the specific result

$$R_v = (J_A^\star\cdot\nabla x)/[x(1-x)]^2 \tag{67}$$

which is the expression normally used. It is shown in Example 10 that this simple result is extremely powerful for estimating maximum separation potentials of proposed processes.

Characterization of Concentration Distributions

Determination of species concentration distributions is one of the primary problems facing us, and there is no one most effective approach to solving it. Rather there are four levels of organization on which we can proceed and which we designate here as:

1. Molecular
2. Continuum
3. Pseudo-continuum
4. Discrete

Description at each of these levels is obtained from its immediate predecessor by a process of contraction, and as a result this listing is in decreasing order of amount of information provided. However, since obtaining information about diffusing systems often requires considerable effort, it is desirable in practice to settle for the least amount needed to solve the problem at hand. Each of these levels thus has its merits.

The Molecular Level

On the molecular level, the physical system is characterized not by species concentration distributions, but by a set of particle position vectors, $\{\mathbf{x}_1, \mathbf{x}_2, \ldots \mathbf{x}_N\}$, where N is the total number of molecules. One must then calculate the trajectories of individual molecules by describing their interactions with each other and any confining surfaces. This molecular approach is normally too tedious to be of practical interest, but it can be both desirable and practicable when intermolecular spacings are appreciable relative to system dimensions.* This is most likely to occur for rarefied gases in microporous systems, as, for example, in fractionation of isotopes by effusion[8,9,100] or molecular distillation.[7] Even here, however, the formalisms of the continuum level often prove useful, as in the estimation of mass diffusivities in the Knudsen flow range.[30,34,35]

When the trajectories of the particles become indescribably complex due to particle interactions, it is necessary to adopt a statistical approach. The trajectory of a typical particle i is then represented by an ensemble distribution function $f(\mathbf{x}_i)$ which, by the ergodic hypothesis

$f(\mathbf{x}_i)d\mathbf{x}_i$ = Fraction of time in which particle i exists between the position $\mathbf{x}_i$ and $\mathbf{x}_i + d\mathbf{x}_i$, over a period of time small compared to the time scale of interest (68)

For N-particle trajectories, we have an N-particle distribution function $F(\mathbf{x}_1, \mathbf{x}_2, \ldots \mathbf{x}_N)$. For nonequilibrium systems, this distribution function changes with time, and the equation describing its evolution can be found in standard texts on statistical mechanics (e.g., Reference 16, Chapter 7).

In separation technology the molecular approach is rarely used, but it definitely has its place. Examples include electromagnetic separations in plasmas[7] for which no continuum description is adequate, the design of effusion equipment,[100] and the estimation of interphase mass-transfer rates in molecular distillation (see Reference 15, Chapter 2, pp. 13–31).

An analog of the molecular approach is sometimes used in the processing of particulate material. An example of current interest is the recovery of metallic objects from solid wastes by magnetic forces via induced electrical currents. (For the theory see Reference 36, Vol. 2, p. 16–5)

The macroscopic species concentration can be obtained from the species distribution function by a process known as contraction, as follows:

$$c(\mathbf{x}, t) = \frac{1}{\tilde{N}} \sum_{\substack{i = i \\ \text{(all molecules)}}} \int_{-\infty}^{\infty} F(\mathbf{x}_1, \mathbf{x}_2, \ldots \mathbf{x}_N, t)\, \delta(\mathbf{x}_i - \mathbf{x})\, d\mathbf{x}_1 \ldots d\mathbf{x}_N \tag{69}$$

where c is in moles per unit volume, $\tilde{N}$ is Avogadro's number, and $\delta(\mathbf{x})$ is the Dirac delta function. The molecular level of description, in terms of the set of coordinates $\{\mathbf{x}_1, \mathbf{x}_2, \ldots \mathbf{x}_N\}$, is now replaced by a continuum description, in terms of the spatial position vector **x** only.

The Continuum Level

It is possible to obtain a continuum equation of change for the species concentration by integrating the equation governing the evolution of the system distribution function $F(\mathbf{x}_1, \mathbf{x}_2, \ldots \mathbf{x}_N, t)$ (e.g., see Reference 54, p. 459). However, this equation of change, known as the species continuity equation, is more easily obtained from continuum arguments (Reference 11, Chapter 18). The result is

$$\frac{\partial c_i}{\partial t} + (\nabla \cdot c_i \mathbf{v}_i) = R_i \tag{70}$$

Here

c_i = Macroscopically observable molar concentration of solute species i (71)
$\mathbf{v}_i$ = Macroscopically observable velocity of species i (72)
∇ = Gradient operator (73)
R_i = Rate of appearance of species i by chemical reaction (74)

Equation 70 is quite general, but it does not give us a great deal of insight; it is therefore useful to consider the various contributions to the species velocity $\mathbf{v}_i$.

We therefore write

$$\mathbf{v}_i = \bar{\mathbf{v}}_i + \mathbf{v}_i' \tag{75}$$

where

$\bar{\mathbf{v}}_i$ = Contributions from macroscopically observable phenomena: fields or forces acting on the solute i and the bulk motion of the fluid in which it is suspended
$\mathbf{v}_i'$ = "Random" contributions from Brownian motion

We shall see in a later section that Equation 75 is acceptable in a wide variety of situations, and further that the Brownian contributions can usually be approximated as

*Effective simulation procedures are under active development for interacting molecules; this field is known as molecular hydrodynamics.

$$v_i' = -\mathscr{D}_{im} \nabla c_i \quad (76)$$

where $\mathscr{D}_{im}$ is an effective binary diffusivity for species i in the mixture. Then we have

$$\frac{\partial c_i}{\partial t} + (\nabla \cdot c_i \bar{v}_i) - (\nabla \cdot \mathscr{D}_{im} \nabla c_i) = R_i \quad (77)$$

which is a form of Fick's law.

We next expand the divergence of the species molar flux $c_i \bar{v}_i$ to write

$$\frac{\partial c_i}{\partial t} + (\bar{v}_i \cdot \nabla c_i) + c_i(\nabla \cdot \bar{v}_i) - (\nabla \cdot \mathscr{D}_{im} \nabla c_i) = R_i \quad (78)$$

which is, for the moment, our desired result. It will be shown below that each of the terms in Equation 78 has a simple useful physical significance and hence that this particular form is a convenient basis for describing separation morphology.

Equation 77 can be modified to describe the diffusional interactions characteristic of multicomponent systems and additional diffusional driving forces (Reference 70, Chapter 3). As so modified, it, along with its companions the equations of motion and energy,[11] will serve as the fundamental basis for almost all quantitative descriptions of separation. Normally the transport and equilibrium properties appearing in these equations may be considered as functions only of thermodynamic state, and the accuracy of the predicted continuous profiles of concentration, velocity, and temperature are significantly limited only by the accuracy with which these properties are known.

All that is needed to obtain the desired profiles is to integrate the differential equations of change for suitable boundary conditions and equations of state. This may be done with acceptable accuracy for a very wide variety of systems; means for doing so are discussed at length in standard texts.

The Pseudo-continuum Level

There are, however, many situations for which it is difficult or inconvenient to integrate the equations of change. Among the most important of these are geometric and flow complexities. Examples include turbulent flow and multiphase flow through packed beds. Convective dispersion (Taylor dispersion[109]) in laminar duct flow is probably the most familiar example in which flow-induced complexities make the pseudo-continuum approximations worthwhile. Diffusion with single-phase flow in packed beds, characteristic of chromatographic and fixed-bed leaching operations, represents a situation in which both difficulties exist.

In all cases the recommended procedure is to carry out an additional contraction. One replaces the local concentrations, velocities, and temperatures by volume or time averages over a representative unit cell, at least one of whose dimensions is small compared to those of the system. The specific way in which one does this depends upon the goals of the endeavor and the nature of the system.

For turbulent flow (Reference 11, Chapters 5, 12, and 20) the unit cell is taken in time rather than in space, and in Darcy flow[13,101] it is a volume element corresponding to one representative region in the porous medium. In both cases the description retains its dimensionality, but information on local variations is lost.

For Taylor dispersion and mass transfer in packed columns the averaging is normally taken in space over the whole flow cross section. The spatial dimensions of the model are thereby reduced from three to one.

In all cases the final result of the contraction is forced* into an expression bearing at least some resemblance to Equation 77. As a specific example most diffusional formulations in widespread use fit the general form:

$$\frac{\partial \bar{c}_i}{\partial t} + \nabla \cdot [\underline{\underline{R}}_0 \cdot \langle v_i \rangle \bar{c}_i] \doteq \nabla \cdot [\underline{\underline{\epsilon}} \cdot \nabla \bar{c}_i] + \bar{w}_i^{(m)} \quad (79)$$

Here

$$\bar{c}_i = \frac{1}{\tau} \int_\tau c_i d\tau \quad (80)$$

$$\langle v_i \rangle = \frac{1}{\tau} \int_\tau v_i d\tau \quad (81)$$

$\bar{w}_i^{(m)}$ = molar rate of transport to the phase of interest per unit volume (82)

and ∇ is now understood to be a gradient operator for the pseudo-continuum produced by the smoothing represented by Equations 80 and 81. The integrals in these equations are for a unit cell with volume τ.

The volumetric rate of input of species i to the

*Similar contractions are used in the descriptions of momentum and energy transport.

phase of interest $\bar{w}_i^{(m)}$ represents a variety of possible effects. It can be used to describe production (or consumption) of species i by chemical reaction, either homogeneous or at phase boundaries. One example of reaction at phase boundaries which is increasing rapidly in importance is affinity chromatography.[26,39] More important for our purposes, however, is diffusional transport across phase boundaries, which behaves as a homogenous source at the pseudo-continuum level. One could of course simply average species concentrations over all co-existing phases, but this is only a useful procedure when one can assume local equilibrium between these phases. When this is not possible it is necessary to consider each phase separately and allow for interphase transport via $\bar{w}_i^{(m)}$.

Equation 79 is often more useful than Equation 77 because $\langle v_i \rangle$ is easily determined and $\bar{w}_i^{(m)}$ can be written in the form

$$\bar{w}_i^{(m)} = k_c a(\bar{c}_i - \bar{c}_i^*) \tag{83}$$

where k_c is an experimentally evaluated mass-transfer coefficient, a is the interfacial area per unit volume in the unit cell, and $\bar{c}_i^*$ is the concentration in the phase of interest in thermodynamic equilibrium with the surrounding phase at its average concentration $\bar{c}_i$. With the product $k_c a$ treated as a system parameter, it is now unnecessary to consider the boundaries within the unit cell.

The parameters $\underline{\underline{\epsilon}}$ and $\underline{\underline{R}}_0$, which correspond to the dispersion coefficient ϵ and retardation factor R_f of chromatography, are second-order tensors. These parameters are not state properties, since they depend on geometry and flow conditions. In addition they may be position and orientation dependent.

Fortunately, it is often found that Equation 79 can be simplified without total loss of utility and that the parameters appearing in the simplified equation can be estimated without undue theoretical or experimental difficulty. We return to this problem in a later section.

It is most important at this early stage of our discussion to note that, qualitatively at least, the general characteristics of Equation 79 are very similar to those of Equation 77. We can thus discuss separation morphology for both continuous and pseudo-continuous systems in terms of this simpler expression; we do this in a following section.

The Discrete Level

Here we carry spatial contraction to its limit by averaging over the entire system volume. This reduces our system to a point and our description to that of the macroscopic balances (Reference 11 Chapters 7, 15, and 22).

Then for mass transfer we obtain the very simple relation:

$$\frac{dm_{i,\,tot}}{dt} = -\sum_{j=1}^{N} w_{ij} \tag{84}$$

Here

$m_{i,\,tot}$ = Total mass of species i within the system at any time t (85)

w_{ij} = Rate at which mass of i leaves in any of the N streams j from the system. (86)

w_{ij} is normally given by

$$w_{ij} = Q_j \pi_{ij} \tag{87}$$

where

$$Q_j = \text{total molar flow rate of stream j} \tag{88}$$

The definition of π_{ij} has been given in Equation 6.

It is clear that information relating the species concentrations in various streams (transfer functions) is needed to use Equation 84, and this must be supplied at a more detailed level. Equation 84, however, is important in the analysis of cascades and networks which are best described in terms of their discrete morphology.

The Morphology of Separations Processes

The space-time patterns of species concentration distributions provide one useful basis of classifying separations processes, which we shall refer to as morphology. It is the purpose of this section to develop a morphological classification system, and to do so on the basis of the continuity equation already introduced as Equation 11. We begin with a qualitative introduction to this approach and proceed to a formal description of space-time patterns. We complete our discussion by presenting a classification scheme.

An Introduction to Separations Morphology

We begin here by considering the very simple types of separation produced by gravitational settling of macroscopic particles in a continuum, and by showing that this single separation mechanism can be used to produce a wide variety of morphologically distinct separations processes. We

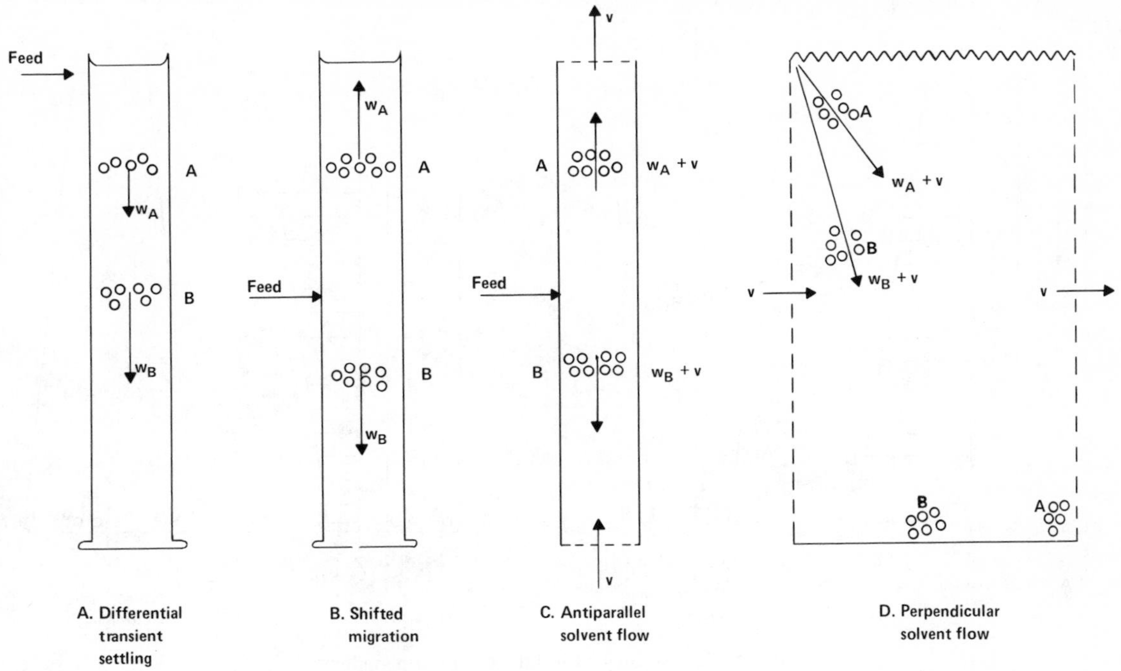

FIGURE 4. Settling with uniform shifts.

then go on to show that separations processes based on quite different mechanisms can be morphologically identical.

Variants on Gravitational Settling

We begin by considering a two-dimensional settling operation shown schematically in Figure 4A. Here small amounts of two different kinds of particles, A and B, with each uniform as to size, shape, and density, are introduced to the top of a quiescent column of solvent. If the solvent is less dense than either, the two types of particles will settle, but at different rates. Two distinct bands will then move down the column at different velocities in such a way as to produce a one-dimensional transient separation. In this fundamental mode of operation the solvent velocity **v** is zero and the species velocities relative to **v**, $\mathbf{w}_A$, and $\mathbf{w}_B$ are parallel, constant, and of different magnitudes. This fundamental separation can now be modified via changes in the above three velocities (shift operations) or increasing either the amount of particles fed or the interval over which they are introduced (superposition operations).

We begin by noting that if the fluid density were intermediate between those of A and B the two particles would move in opposite directions (shifted migration – see Figure 4B). Now one can also use continued introduction of feed to produce a steady one-dimensional binary separation. This in turn can be accomplished by continued introduction of feed pulses (superposition).

We next note that a similar result can be obtained by moving the solvent upward at a speed V intermediate between the two settling velocities (opposed convection – see Figure 4C).

Either of these two modifications may be described as an antiparallel velocity shift, and it is clear that only two components can be separated continuously in this manner. However, a multicomponent steady two-dimensional separation can be produced by moving fluid to the right (perpendicular shift – see Figure 4D).

All of the above operations involve only steady uniform shifts, and it is often desirable to use more complex modifications. We consider here by way of example simple steady shifts which are nonuniform in space: focusing, antifocusing, and filtration. We begin by noting that two simple situations will focus particles of the above types; i.e., bring them all to very nearly the same horizontal position irrespective of their starting point. These are

1. Use of a suspending fluid whose density increases in the direction of the gravitational field **g** (density focusing, see Figure 5A)
2. Solvent flow opposed to the gravitational

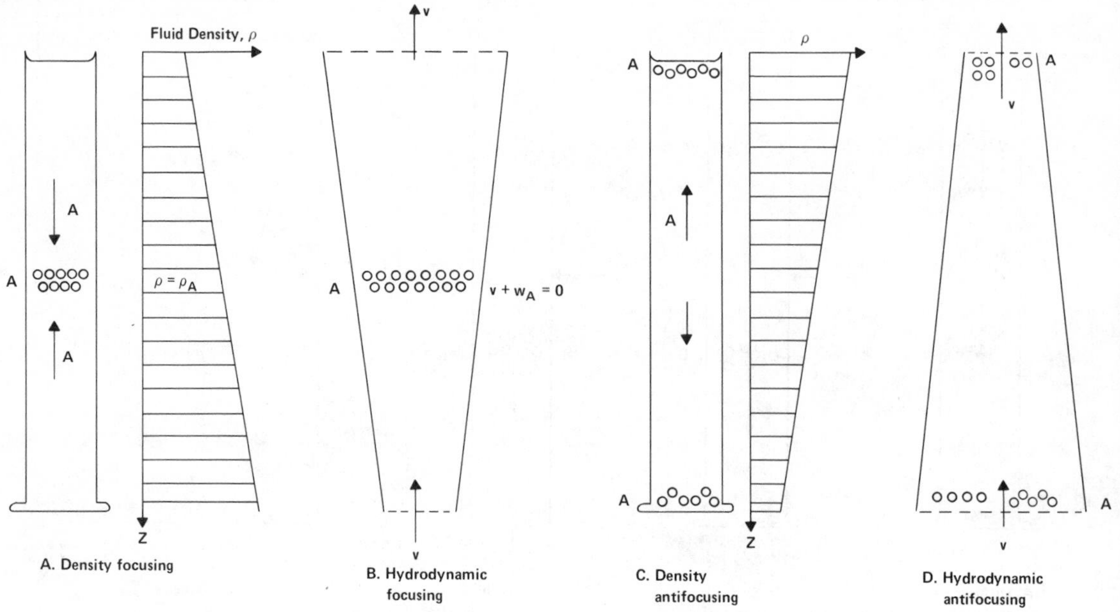

FIGURE 5. Settling with shifts of uniform gradients.

field but decreasing upward (hydrodynamic focusing (see Figure 5B).

We can also perform antifocusing, causing particles to avoid any metastable horizontal position by reversing these density or velocity gradients (see Figures 5C and 5D). All of these operations can be produced by a uniform gradient of particle velocity.

Higher-order shifts are also possible, and perhaps the most familiar of these is filtration, shown schematically in Figure 6. Here the velocity of the particles removed by the filter drops very abruptly to zero. In most cases this change can be closely approximated as a step function, but aerosol filtrations are considerably more gradual.

Settling of a concentrated mass of particles is also complex, because settling velocity decreases with increasing particle concentration. As suggested in Figure 7, this concentration dependence of migration velocity produces antifocusing at the lower edge of the particle band and focusing at the upper.

All of the above operations can be described, at least in their essentials, by assuming the particles to be falling always at their terminal velocities. However, another widely used variant of gravitational settling, jigging, depends on settling transients. This process, very complex in practice, can be explained in its major features via the diagrams of Figure 8. A jig in this case is a horizontal screen moving up and down in a cyclic manner and carrying a bed of mixed particles on its surface as it moves up. This apparatus and the screen trajectory are shown in parts A and B of the figure. The screen drops only a short distance in each cycle, but it moves faster than any particles can follow. The particles then accelerate toward an effective terminal velocity, but they cannot attain this limit before being stopped by the plate.

Now it is characteristic of all hydrodynamic particles that they start falling through fluid at an accelerating rate dependent only upon their density relative to that of the fluid

$$\frac{dv}{dt} = \left[\frac{\rho_S - \rho_F}{\rho_S}\right] g \tag{89}$$

where ρ_S and ρ_F are the solid and fluid densities, respectively. In this early period, the differences in position depend only upon differences in density, whereas for longer times of fall size and shape play major roles. Particles are then segregated primarily by density and only secondarily by size. Successful jigging clearly depends on operating in the transient period.

All* of the above variants on settling are used industrially on a very large scale, and they all

*Except the antifocusing of Figures 5B and 5D.

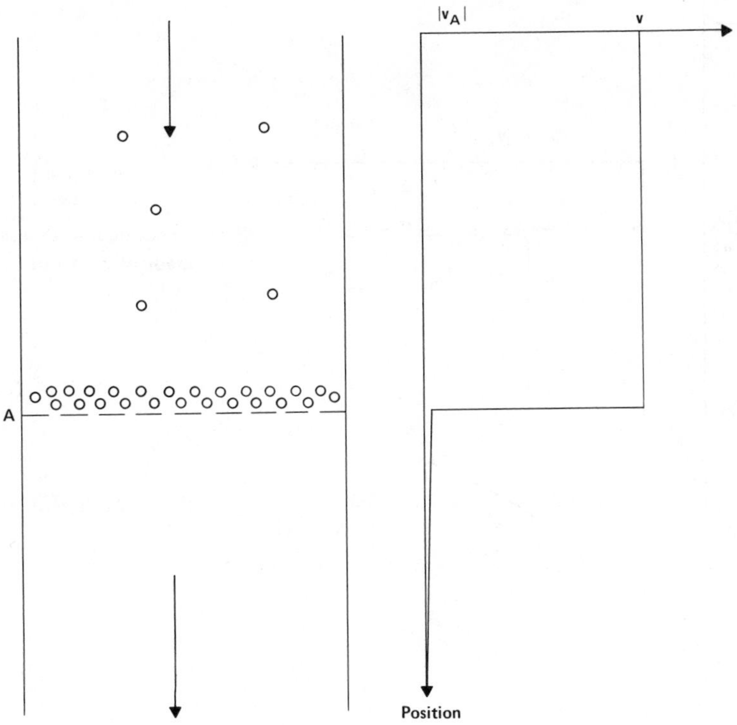

FIGURE 6. Filtration across an impermeable septum.

differ significantly from each other. These differences in turn are morphological in nature, so we now have one reason for using such a basis of classification: the making of distinctions. We next show that morphology can also be used to relate separations produced by different mechanisms.

Analogs of Gravitational Settling

Here we list some representative separations analogous to the settling operations just described. Our purpose here is primarily promotional – to demonstrate the utility of the morphological approach. The problem of making a complete listing is left to a later effort.

1. Differential settling (Figure 4A): essentially all chromatographic operations, differential electrophoresis,[10,10a] and so forth
2. Hindered settling (Figure 7): displacement chromatography, where the same localized focusing and antifocusing typically appear, and allied fixed-bed processes such as saturation and regeneration
3. Steady binary separations: binary distillation, gas absorption, and the other familiar countercurrent unit operations
4. Focusing operations: isoelectric focusing and a wide variety of volatility-based focusing in multicomponent distillation. Hydrodynamic focusing could also be used in electrophoresis, perhaps to good advantage, but we are not aware of this having been done as yet.
5. Perpendicular shifts: two-dimensional, usually paper, chromatography. It should be noted here that such shifts need not be rectilinear.[5]
6. Filtration: zone melting.[83] Here the freezing surface acts analogously to the filter septum and the bar of material to be refined moves relative to it. Less exotic but much more important analogs of filtration are such phase changes as evaporation and precipitation or crystallization. Here the phase boundary acts as a septum, just as for zone melting, but system geometry tends to be much more complex.
7. Jigging: relaxation electrophoresis. This possibility, which appears to be a novel one, is a means we propose for separating proteins with equal steady electrophoretic mobilities but different relaxation times. Originated as an electrophoretic analog to jigging, it depends on the fact that a protein requires a measurable time to

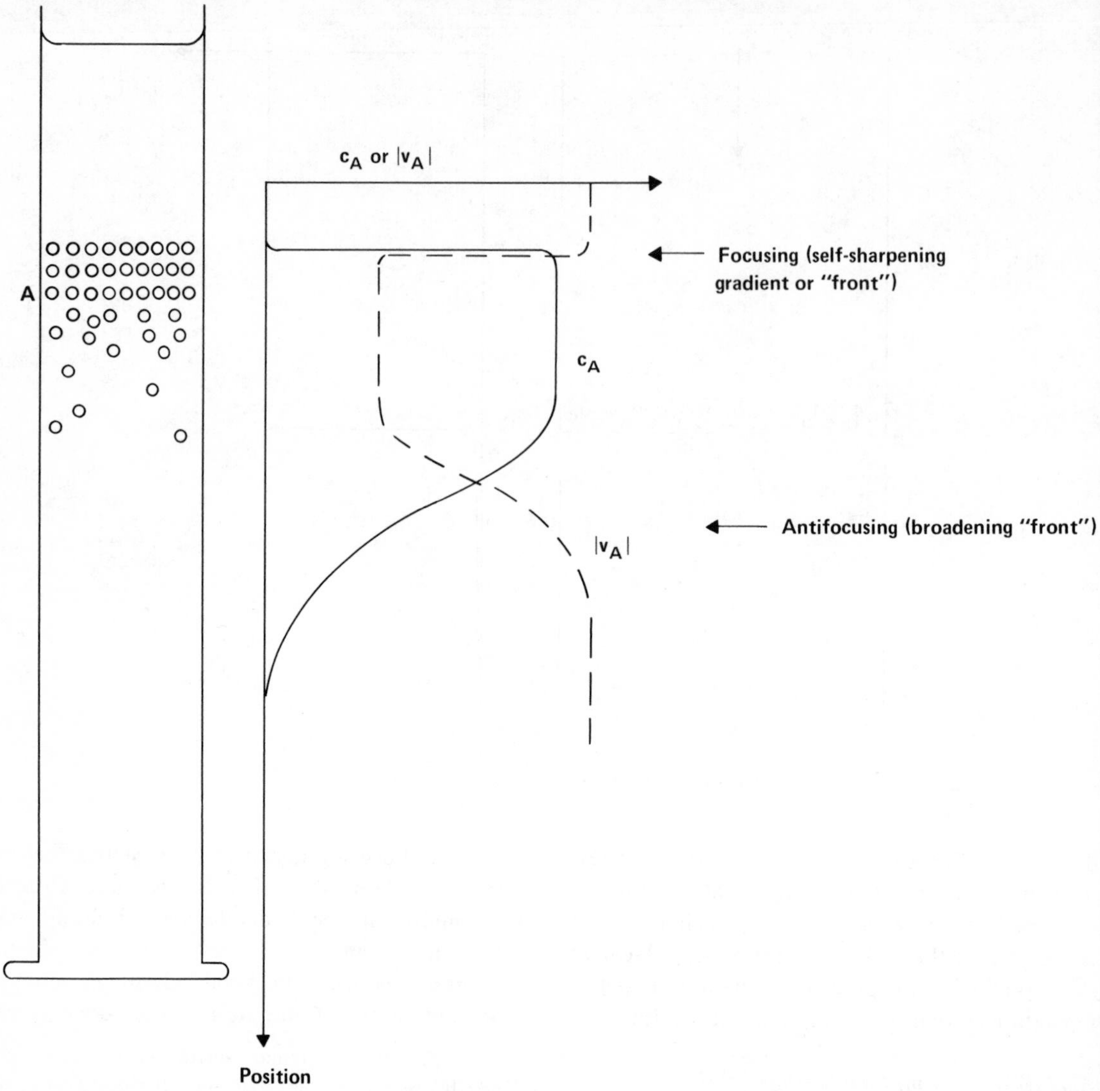

FIGURE 7. Hindered settling.

respond to the imposition of an electric field.[76] This is indicated in Figure 9A where the electrophoretic velocities of two proteins, A and B, are plotted against time since establishment of a field with constant strength E. If a biased square wave is used rather than a constant field, as suggested in Figure 9B, it is possible to stay in the transient-response region and take advantage of the velocity differences which occur here. Although this concept has yet to be tested, it seems promising. Characteristic protein relaxation times are such that frequencies on the order of 10 kHz, easily obtained in commercially available equipment, should suffice. Pseudo-continuum equivalents of relaxation also exist. One example is oscillation of partition coefficients with a period comparable to the time constant for lateral equilibration. This last example is chosen to show the utility of any systematic classification for innovation by analogy – finding new processes simply by looking for empty spots in a classification matrix.

We now develop the above ideas, starting from the species continuity equation.

Space-time Patterns of Species Concentration Distribution

Here we use the species continuity equations noted earlier to explain the key features of solute distributions, and we concentrate our attention primarily at the microscopic continuum level. This

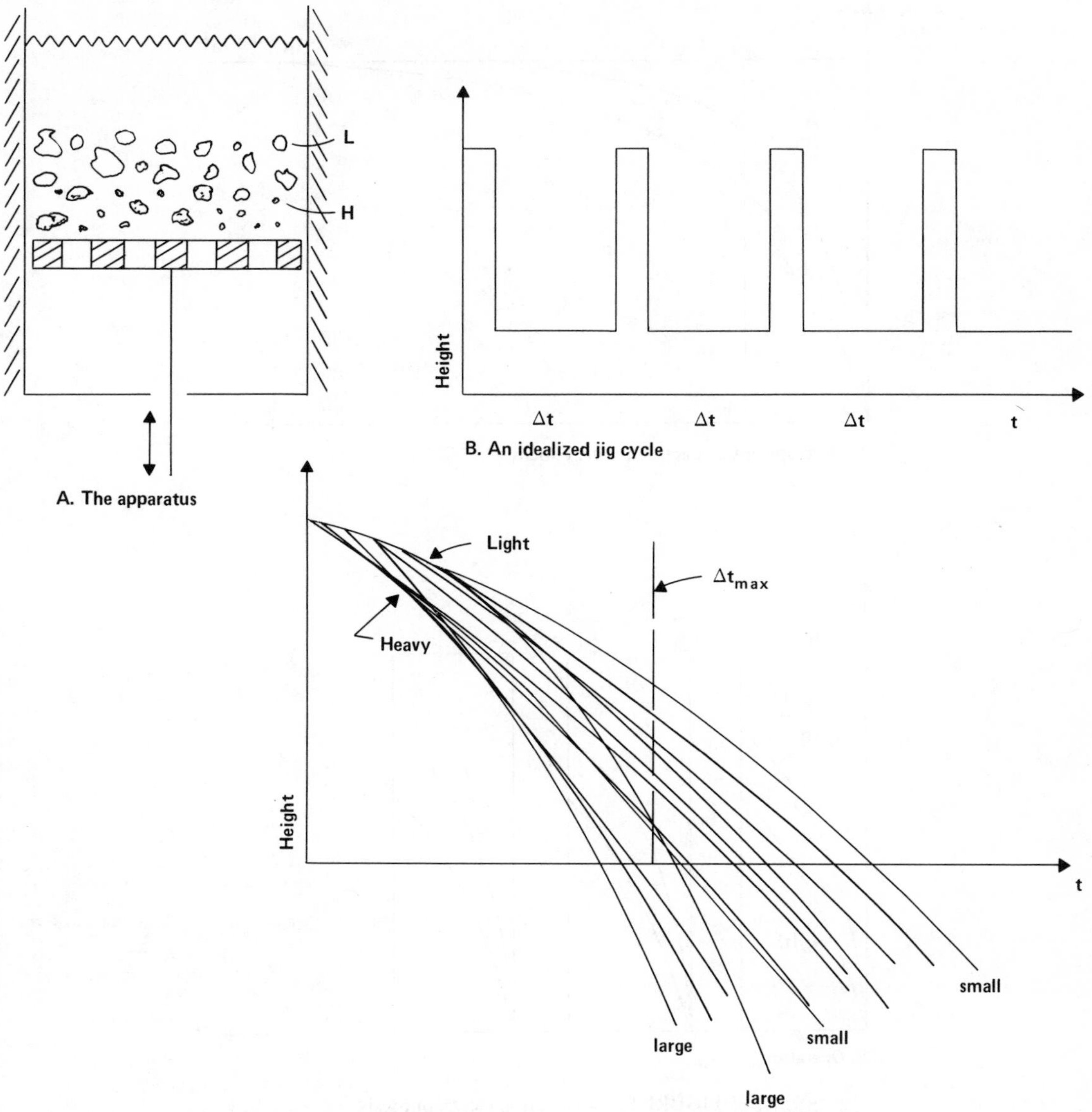

FIGURE 8. Jigging. In Figure A, H and L refer to heavy and light particles, respectively.

is convenient not only because of the general importance of this level of description, but also because conclusions obtained from it often apply with only minor modifications to description at the other levels.

Space-time Patterns at the Microscopic Continuum Level

We begin by looking at the evolution of a differential feed pulse in a space-time continuum. To aid in visualization (see Figure 10) we limit ourselves to two spatial dimensions and put the feed point at $(x_0, y_0, 0)$; extension to three dimensions is mathematically straightforward but difficult to draw.

We are primarily interested in the trajectories of the center of mass for each solute, shown by the heavy lines emanating from $(x_0, y_0, 0)$ in the figure and the distribution of solute about the centers of mass. The center of mass μ_{i1} of species i is defined for any time t as the first moment of mass with respect to position in the (x, y) plane:

$$\mu_{il} \equiv \frac{1}{M_i} \int_{\tau} x c_i d\tau \qquad (90)$$

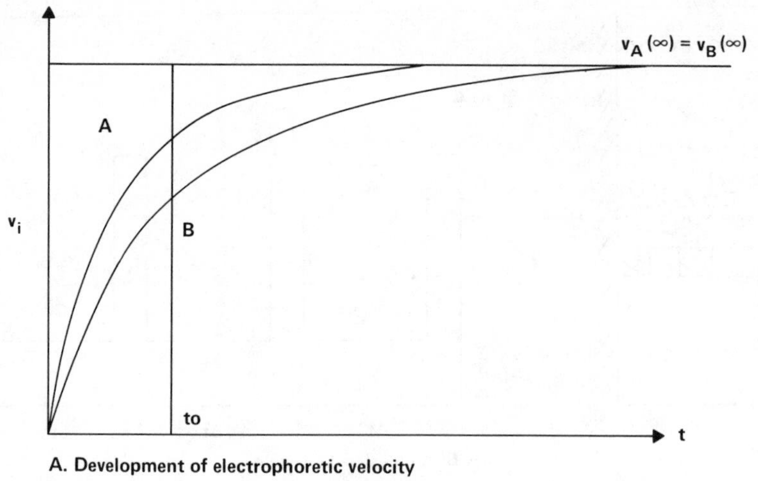

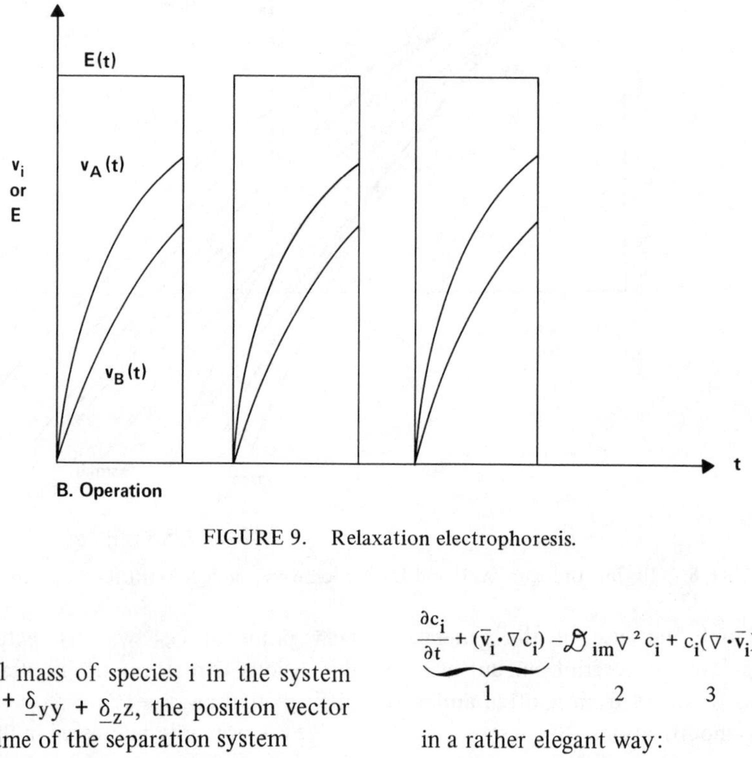

FIGURE 9. Relaxation electrophoresis.

where

M_i = Total mass of species i in the system
x = $\underline{\delta}_x x + \underline{\delta}_y y + \underline{\delta}_z z$, the position vector
τ = Volume of the separation system

The distribution about μ_{il} is given by surfaces including fixed fractions f_i of M_i and which for any time are closed curves of constant species concentration. We refer to these as f-envelopes, and clearly the zero-envelope is the trajectory of μ_{il}.

The position of the center of mass and the shapes of the f-envelopes are described by the species continuity equation

$$\underbrace{\frac{\partial c_i}{\partial t} + (\bar{v}_i \cdot \nabla c_i)}_{1} - \underbrace{\mathcal{D}_{im} \nabla^2 c_i}_{2} + \underbrace{c_i(\nabla \cdot \bar{v}_i)}_{3} = 0 \tag{91}$$

in a rather elegant way:

1. The trajectory of the center of mass in our space-time coordinates depends only upon Term 1 in the above equation, as averaged over the system volume: the center of mass moves at unit velocity in time and the average velocity

$$<v_i> = \int_\tau c_i \bar{v}_i dV \Big/ \int_\tau c_i d\tau \tag{92}$$

through space. Here τ is system volume.

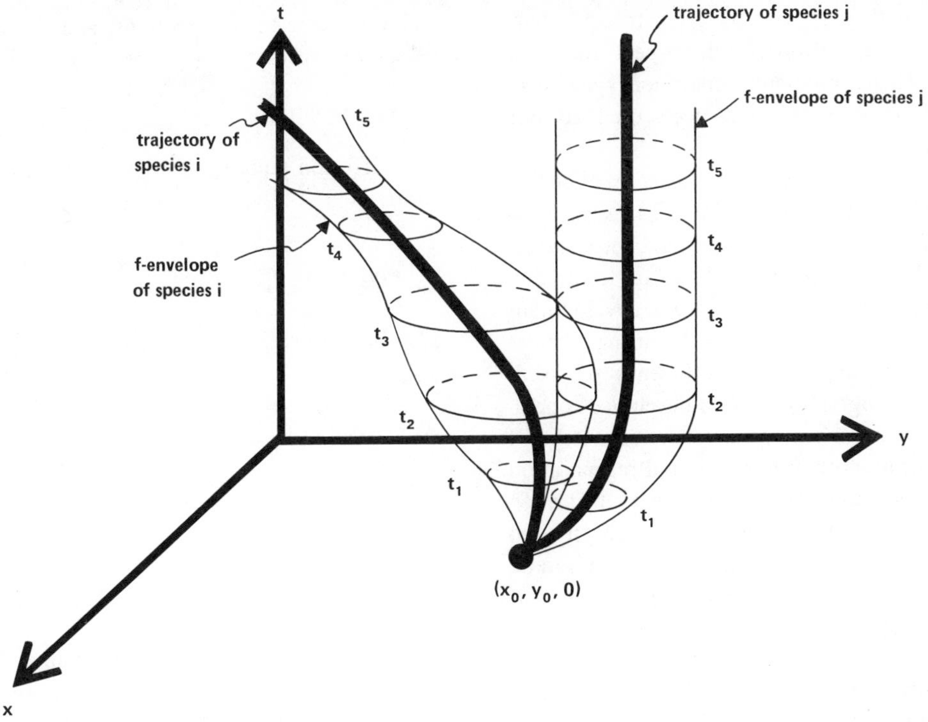

FIGURE 10. Trajectories and f-envelopes for separating species i and j from a common differential feed pulse.

2. The expansion or contraction of the f-envelopes is described by Terms 2 and 3, and these are quite different in character.

Term 2, which describes Brownian dispersion, always leads to expansion of the envelopes, typically with the square root of time in the absence of confining surfaces.

Term 3 describes the combined effect of the solvent and migration velocities, which will be described in the third major section of this chapter, and this can lead to either expansion or contraction of the f-envelopes: If $(\nabla \cdot \bar{v}_i) > 0$, the Brownian spreading is further enhanced, but if $(\nabla \cdot \bar{v}_i) < 0$ it is opposed. It is $(\nabla \cdot \bar{v}_i)$ which induces the focusing or antifocusing discussed previously, and we shall see in the next example that its effect is profound.

Separations work tends to be organized according to these three numbered terms, and in decreasing order of priority.

Most interest is centered around separating the trajectories as described by Term 1 of Equation 91, i.e., in providing separation of the first moments or the centers of mass with respect to position, or more simply just first-moment separations. In considering separability at this level, one example of which is considered in Figure 10, one need not worry about the complexities associated with Brownian dispersion or focusing. Term 1 is sufficient, for example, to describe the familiar retardation or R_f values of differential chromatography.

Normally, however, one is also interested in the degree of separation of the f-envelopes, and even in the simplest systems this requires consideration of the Brownian forces. It should also be recognized from the section on definitions that some separation occurs when corresponding f-envelopes fail to overlap, even if center-of-mass trajectories are identical. The most effective of such separations differ in the second moments of mass with respect to position and are referred to as second-moment separations.* These are useful in some circumstances, e.g., in annular electrophoresis,[86,112] immunodiffusion,[57] and in separation by spreading.[85] These have so far been investigated in systems of cylindrical or spherical sym-

*The characterization of separations by moments, is, however, ambiguous. Thus, symmetrical spreading species-dependent rates about a point can be converted mathematically to a first-moment separation simply by using radius as a measure of position.

metry where they can be converted to equivalent first-moment separations (with respect to radial distance). Higher-moment separations are also possible, but have not yet been used to our knowledge.

Focusing has received the least explicit attention of the three major factors in separation morphology, but it is of widespread importance. Examples include accumulations of trace impurities in distillation columns[61] and development of hot* spots in gas absorbers. Focusing is most important for improving the efficiency of fixed-bed sorption operations: Well-developed operations like water softening may take advantage of focusing during both exhaustion and regeneration (for theory see Cooney[21] and Lightfoot et al.[73] and Cooney.[21-23]) Focusing has also been used very successfully in a variety of electrophoretic operations.[18,51,79,115] It seems probable that the full potentiality of focusing has yet to be realized.

To illustrate the above points we now consider several examples.

Example 2: Steady migration in a three-dimensional continuum – We consider the introduction of m_i moles of solute species i as a compact pulse to the coordinate origin of Figure 11 at zero time. The diffusing medium is quiescent and very large in all directions, and the migration velocity of species i

$$\bar{v}_i = v_0 = \text{a constant} \tag{93}$$

The diffusion equation for species i then takes the form

$$\frac{\partial c_i}{\partial t} + (v_0 \cdot \nabla c_i) = \mathcal{D}_{im} \nabla^2 c_i \tag{94}$$

and the boundary and initial conditions may be written as:

As $r \to \infty$

$$c_i \text{ and } \nabla c_i \to 0 \tag{95}$$

At $t = 0$

$$c_i = m_i \delta(x)\, \delta(y)\, \delta(z) \tag{96}$$

where r is the distance from the origin and δ is the Dirac delta function. We may simplify this description by introducing the position vector **p** via

$$\mathbf{p} = \mathbf{r} - v_0 t \tag{97}$$

where

$$\mathbf{r} = \delta_x x + \delta_y y + \delta_z z \tag{98}$$

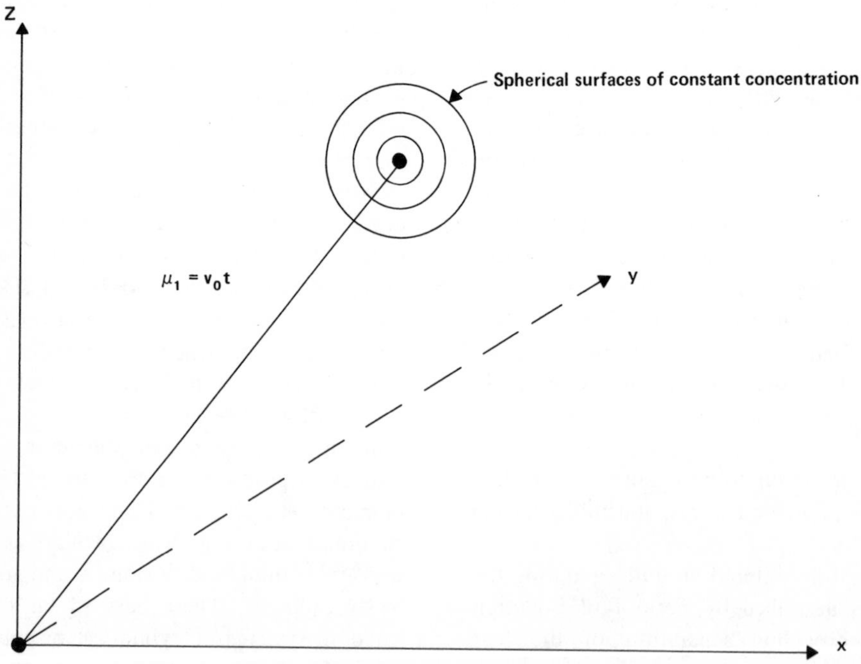

FIGURE 11. Instantaneous solute distribution for migration from a point source.

*Heat, or more properly enthalpy, is analogous to a diffusing species and hot spots decrease separability in a binary process in somewhat the same way trace accumulation does.

Integration now gives:*

$$c_i = \frac{m_i}{8(\pi \mathscr{D}_{im} t)^{3/2}} e^{-(p^2/4\mathscr{D}_{im} t)} \tag{99}$$

Our system is now completely described, and it only remains to determine the trajectory, dispersion, and focusing characteristic of this system. We begin by noting that the position of the center of mass at any time is

$$\mathbf{p}_{CM} \equiv \int_V c_i \mathbf{p}\, dV \Big/ \int_V c_i\, dV \tag{100}$$

where V is the volume of the diffusing system. It may be seen from the symmetry of Equation 99 that

$$\mathbf{p}_{CM} = 0$$

$$\boldsymbol{\mu}_1 = \mathbf{v}_0 t \tag{101}$$

It may now be seen that $\boldsymbol{\mu}_1$ does represent the trajectory of a point moving at velocity $\mathbf{v}_0$ in space, and "unit velocity" in time, as claimed in the text.

We next note that

$$(\nabla \cdot \bar{\mathbf{v}}_i) = (\nabla \cdot \mathbf{v}_0) = 0 \tag{102}$$

as written implicitly in Equation 4. There is therefore no focusing.

There are a number of ways to express dispersion, including Equation 99 itself. However, we shall see that for estimating separations of any two species the distribution of solute in a single rectangular coordinate direction, say x in Figure 11, is of primary interest. We may therefore write**

$$\frac{\partial m_i}{\partial x} = \int_{-\infty}^{\infty} \int_{-\infty}^{\infty} c_i\, dy\, dz \tag{103}$$

where dm_i is the mass of i contained between two planes perpendicular to the x-axis and a distance dx apart. We may rewrite Equation 103 as

$$\frac{\partial m_i}{\partial x} = \frac{m_i}{8(\pi \mathscr{D}_{im} t)^{3/2}} e^{-\frac{(x - v_{0x} t)^2}{4\mathscr{D}_{im} t}} \int_{-\infty}^{\infty} \int_{-\infty}^{\infty} e^{-y^2/4\mathscr{D}_{im} t} e^{-z^2/4\mathscr{D}_{im} t}\, dy\, dz \tag{104}$$

*Reference 17, Section 10.2.

**Note that this integration is carried out at constant t.

where v_{0x} is the x-component of $\mathbf{v}_0$. The result of this double integration is

$$\partial m_i/\partial x = (m_i/\sqrt{4\pi \mathscr{D}_{im} t}) \exp\left\{-\frac{(x - v_{0x} t)^2}{4\mathscr{D}_{im} t}\right\} \tag{105}$$

which is just the Gaussian distribution function, with standard deviation

$$\sigma = \sqrt{2\mathscr{D}_{im} t} \tag{106}$$

The properties of this function and its relation to resolution are already discussed in Example 1.

Example 3: One-dimensional migration with nonuniform species velocity: Focusing — We have just seen that if the migrational velocity is uniform the resolution increases with the square root of time. We show here that a further substantial improvement can be obtained by using a nonuniform species velocity. More specifically, we show that under the proper conditions species concentration profiles asymptotically approach a constant shape so that resolution ultimately increases linearly with time. One separation process described by the model to be presented below is isoelectrofocusing.[18] In this process the nonuniform species velocity is induced by a pH gradient; species are focused at their isoelectric points. We start by writing the species continuity equation in the basic form

$$\frac{\partial c_i}{\partial t} = -(\nabla \cdot c_i \mathbf{v}_i) \tag{107}$$

Splitting the migration velocity $\mathbf{v}_i$ into the molar-average velocity $\mathbf{v}^\star$ and the relative migration velocity $\mathbf{v}_i^r$, we may write, from Equations 75 and 76,

$$c_i v_i = c_i v^* - \mathscr{D}_{im} \frac{\partial c_i}{\partial z} + c_i v_i^r \tag{108}$$

for our one-dimensional migration. If we define

$$Z = z - v^\star t \tag{109}$$

combining Equations 107 and 108 gives, in the coordinate system defined via Equation 109,

$$\frac{\partial c_i}{\partial t} = \frac{\partial}{\partial Z}\left[c_i v_i^r - \mathscr{D}_{im} \frac{\partial c_i}{\partial Z}\right] \tag{110}$$

Integration of Equation 110 for arbitrary variation of velocity with position and time is clearly not possible, but it is beneficial to examine the limiting behavior of this expression.

More particularly we seek asymptotic solutions defined by:

$$c_i = c_{Tr}(Z, t) + c_\infty(Z) \tag{111}$$

with

$$c_{Tr} \to 0 \text{ as } t \to \infty \tag{112}$$

It is clear from this definition that

$$\frac{d}{dZ}\left[c_\infty v_i^r - \mathcal{D}_{im}\frac{dc_\infty}{dZ}\right] = 0 \tag{113}$$

The required boundary conditions are

$$c_\infty, \frac{dc_\infty}{dZ} = 0 \tag{114}$$

as

$$|Z| \to \infty \tag{115}$$

and

$$\int_{-\infty}^{\infty} c_\infty \, dZ = m_i/S \tag{116}$$

where m_i is the number of moles of i fed to the system and S is the cross section. Furthermore asymptotic solutions of the type postulated will only be possible if v_i^r, c, and $\mathcal{D}_{im}$ are independent of time.

We may now integrate formally Equation 113 to obtain

$$\frac{dc_\infty}{dZ} = \frac{c_\infty v_i^r}{\mathcal{D}_{im}} + \frac{K_1}{\mathcal{D}_{im}} \tag{117}$$

where K_1 is an integration constant.

It appears immediately from Equations 114 and 115 that K_1 must be zero and that the term $c_\infty v_i^r/\mathcal{D}_{im}$ must vanish at large $|Z|$. We may then integrate Equation 117 to obtain

$$\ln c_\infty = \int_0^Z \frac{v_i^r \, dz}{\mathcal{D}_{im}} + \ln c_\infty^\circ \tag{118}$$

where c_∞° is the value of c_∞ at Z = 0. Equation 118 may be rewritten as

$$c_\infty = c_\infty^\circ \exp\left[\int_0^Z \frac{v_i^r}{\mathcal{D}_{im}} dz\right] \tag{119}$$

If, besides Equations 114, 115, and 116, we also require the distribution of c_∞ to be nonuniform, we see that only a restricted range of functions of Z is acceptable for $v_i^r/\mathcal{D}_{im}$. Among these are

$$(v_i^r/\mathcal{D}_{im}) = -A|Z|^a Z \tag{120}$$

where

$$a > -1 \tag{121}$$

$$A > 0 \tag{122}$$

One clearly acceptable solution is a = 0 for which the concentration profile approaches the normal error curve.

$$c_\infty = c_\infty^\circ e^{-AZ^2} \tag{123}$$

The situation described in this example is said to produce focusing since the asymptotic profile of Equation 123 is approached even if the initial distribution is more diffuse than this asymptotic limit.

Space-time Patterns at Other Levels of Description

Equation 90 is valid only at the microscopic continuum level and as a result different bases must be found for other levels of description. We do not consider these differences large enough to justify repeating material previously mentioned for each of these situations, but some are worth noting; we summarize these below.

The Molecular Level

Description at the molecular level must deal with each particle separately so that the concept of diffusion appears to have little meaning, and in any event each such situation needs to be handled as a special case. However, in any large-scale separation, effects much like diffusion occur, and dispersion is an important consideration. Perhaps the best developed large-scale separation which must be described in terms of molecular trajectories is the fractionation of isotopes in a cyclotron (or calutron). The reader is referred to the literature on this process[8] for an instructive example.

The Pseudo-continuum Level

This differs from the microscopic continuum level in the presence or $\underline{\underline{R}}$, the tensorial nature of $\underline{\underline{R}}$ and $\underline{\underline{\epsilon}}$, and in the complex significance of the "homogeneous reaction" term. The complexity of

$\underline{\underline{R}}$ and $\underline{\underline{\epsilon}}$ are more important to the quantitative calculation of profiles than to the essentially qualitative needs of morphological classification. We therefore defer discussion of these quantities and concentrate our attention on the reaction term, which most often represents interphase transport between phases occupying the same (pseudo-continuum) space.

Since the trajectories of the solutes generally differ in the two phases, split trajectories are common. That is, individually identifiable portions of a feed pulse may behave so differently that they should be treated separately. Very common examples are provided by countercurrent contactors with feed streams entering in the central region of the apparatus, e.g., a continuous distillation column. Here entering solute is split between one portion which moves upward and another which moves down, and it is desirable to construct separate trajectories and f-envelopes for each portion.

The Discrete Level

We reserve the term discrete for chains or networks of identifiable processing units joined by pumps and ducts serving only as transport devices. We also subdivide these systems into two categories:

1. Cascades or networks of repeating units (centrifuges, mixer-settlers, etc.), sometimes differing in size but always similar in function
2. Sequential processing systems similar only in the general sense that each major subunit carries out some separative task

The first of these categories is much more susceptible to generalizations or systematic analysis, and we concentrate our attention on it. Sequential processing is, however, very common in separations work, and it can also be approached systematically. We say a few words about this subject at the end of the section.

To a sufficiently myopic observer the morphology of cascades and networks is very similar to that of continuum or pseudo-continuum systems. Thus a distillation column is quite comparable to a continuous countercurrent absorber or a unidirectional electrophoresis cell in which the solvent is convected antiparallel to the electrolytic current. Two-dimensional networks are closely comparable to simpler cross-flow operations, and so forth. By smoothing out the discontinuities between adjacent units one may in principle obtain a one-to-one correspondence between discrete and continuous processing systems.

For simple cascades of identical repeating units this correspondence is also obtained in practice: most distillation columns are, for example, effectively one-dimensional.

In the case of difficult separations, however, even a simple linear cascade becomes two-dimensional,* in the sense of having a variable "width." That is, either the size of individual units will vary over the length of the cascade or two or more identical units may be placed in parallel within the cascade. Almost all isotope fractionations are carried out in such tapered cascades, and width is typically greatest at the feed point. These are more effective in terms of separative power** than the uniform or square cascades more familiar from unit operations texts.

The most effective of all are the so called ideal cascades, designed to avoid remixing of partially separated streams. More specifically, in an ideal cascade the compositions of the streams entering any stage are identical. Thus for the systems of Figure 12

$$y_{n-1} = x_{n+1} \tag{124}$$

where

y_{n-1} = Mole fraction of reference species in the overflow from stage n − 1

x_{n+1} = Mole fraction of reference species in the underflow from stage n + 1

In practice ideal tapers are difficult to construct, and compromises are made. Cascade design is discussed at length in the isotope fractionation literature, for example in the studies by Cohen[20] or Shachter et al.[100] We merely point out here that an ideal cascade minimizes the sum of stage overflows for a given amount of separative work.

Extensive two- or three-dimensional discrete networks are rare,[116;117] primarily because linear cascades suffice for the binary or pseudo-binary separations which have dominated engineering practice. However, these more complex mor-

*Similar modifications may be useful at the continuum and pseudo-continuum levels, but they are presently rare.
**See section entitled "Definitions of Separation and Separative Work."

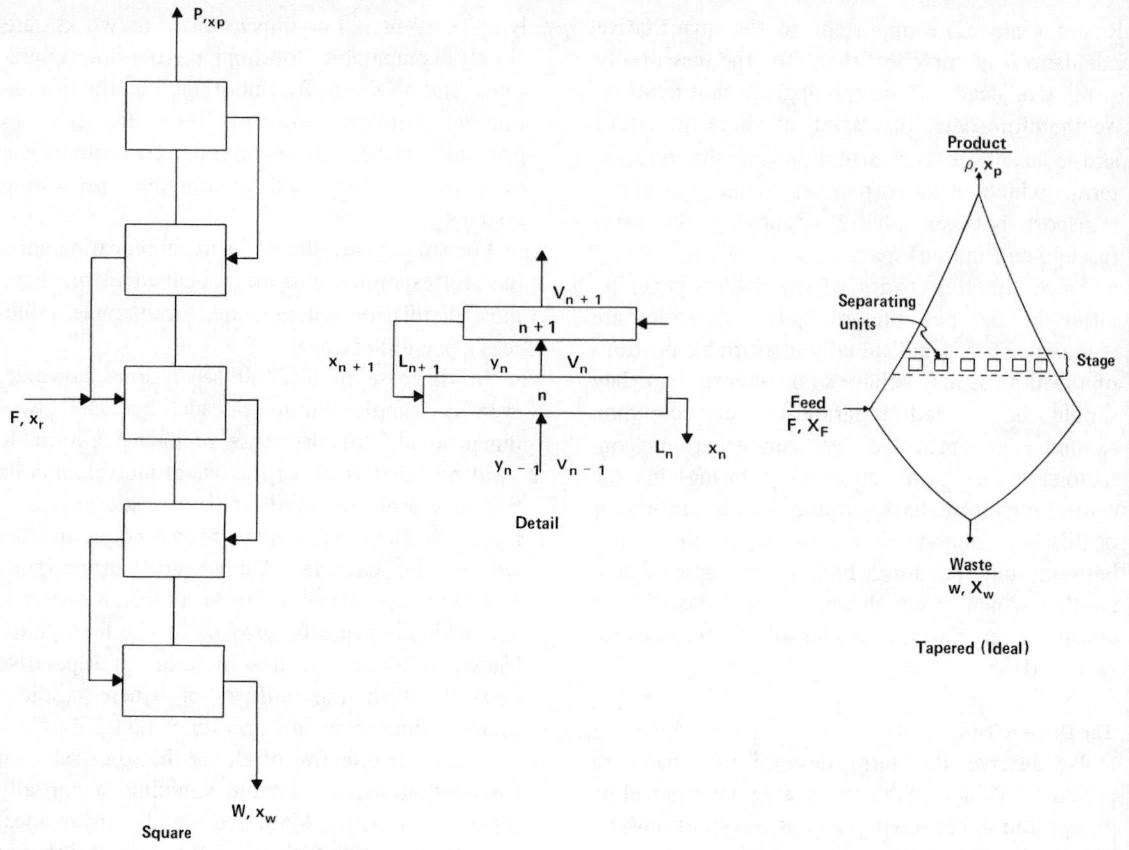

FIGURE 12. Pictorial representation of cascades.

phologies are useful for multicomponent separations and may come into wider use. These are more difficult to optimize, but an extension of ideal cascade theory to so-called matched abundance ratio networks has been provided by de la Garza et al.[40,41]

Cascade theory also seems useful, at least as a heuristic guide, in the design of complex sequential processes, for example preparation of a single solute in high purity from a complex crude mixture. In these situations one must remove a variety of impurities, ranging from solvent to inert solids, and must decide both upon the individual processing steps and their ordering in the separation sequence. In general it is desirable to remove first the impurities present in larger amounts, and this is roughly equivalent to minimizing the sum of stage overflows.

More complex and less symmetric morphologies also arise in discrete systems, and one example is shown in Figure 13: integration of the three U.S. plants for the enrichment of uranium (from Reference 7). These very complex situations are really outside the scope of our discussion, however, and are more properly in the province of process design.

Morphological Classes of Separations

We now build on the above discussion to provide a morphological basis for classifying separations processes. In doing this we are much influenced by the work of H. Pauschmann,[82] who was among the first to see the possibilities inherent in such a procedure.

The basis for this effort is the intuitive belief, gained from surveys such as that provided previously, that one can make useful distinctions without going into great detail. Most particularly we feel that this can be done without integration of the defining conservation equations. This is, however, a matter for judgement, and our suggestions cannot yet be considered as definitive.

It should be recognized that there are many aspects to morphology and that we can cover only a few here. We begin by emphasizing the importance of feed superpositions and trajectory shifts at

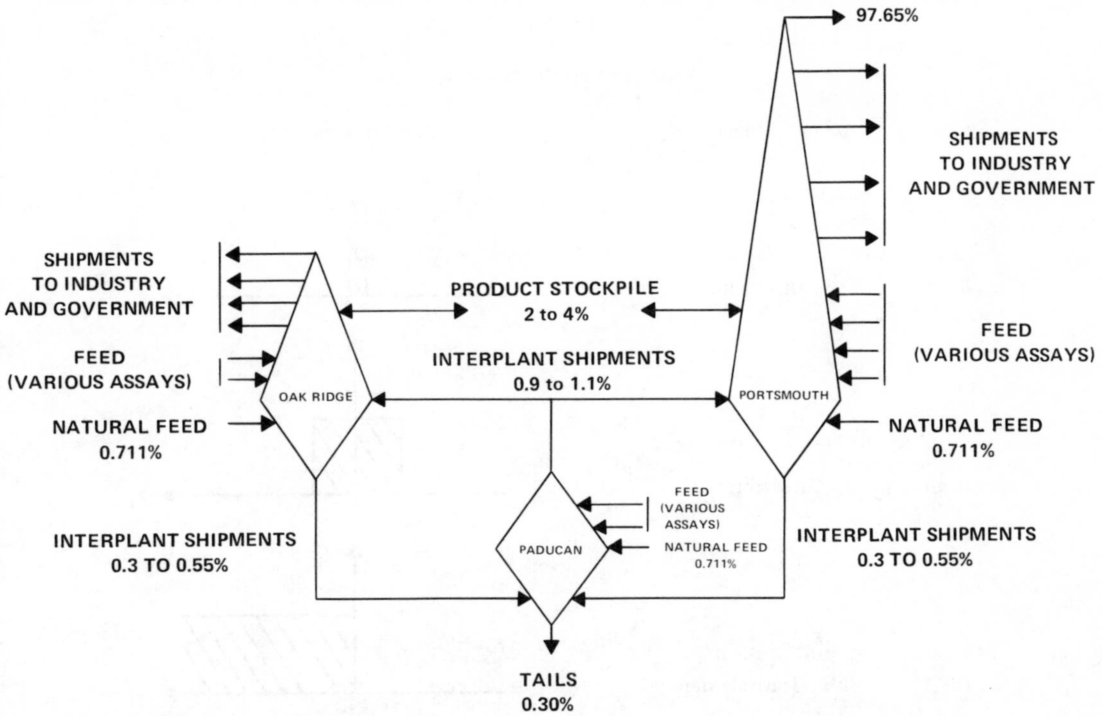

FIGURE 13. Mode of operation for gaseous diffusion plants (% values are weight % U-235).

the microscopic continuum level, and then show how these concepts can be exploited at the industrially important pseudo-continuum level.

Feed Patterns and Species Velocities at the Microscopic Continuum Level

We start by assuming the most important separations parameters to be the pattern of feed introduction and the trajectories of the centers of mass of at least two solutes which are to be separated one from the other. Dispersion characteristics and separator shape are considered to be of secondary importance.

With this assumption the requirements for a morphological description reduce to three quantities:

$\mathfrak{F}$ = A suitable approximate representation of feed distribution in the four-dimensional space-time separations continuum

$\mathbf{U}_i, \mathbf{U}_j$ = Corresponding representations of the velocities of the centers of mass of two representative solute species i and j

We choose here to express $\mathfrak{F}$ and each component of the velocities in terms of multiplicative descriptors:

$$\mathfrak{F} = f_1 f_2 f_3 f_4 \tag{125}$$

$$(U_i)_k = (g_1 g_2 g_3 g_4)_{ik} \tag{126}$$

Here the numerical subscripts refer to the three spatial dimensions and time; the appropriate f_n or g_n describe the dependence of the indicated quantity on the corresponding coordinate. Subscript k refers to the component of the velocity vector $\mathbf{U}_i$.

A very wide variety of descriptors can be used, but we shall limit ourselves to those given in Table 2 and to products of them. We shall also adopt two conventions:

1. The sign of each function is as shown in pictorial representations, unless it has an overline in which case its sign is reversed.
2. A negative value of f_i denotes a tendency to remove solute from a given phase, either by chemical reaction or interfacial mass transport.

The components (x_1, x_2, x_3) can refer to any spatial coordinate system.

TABLE 2

Feed and Velocity Descriptors

Symbol*	Name	Pictorial representation
$\delta(x_i)$	Dirac impulse	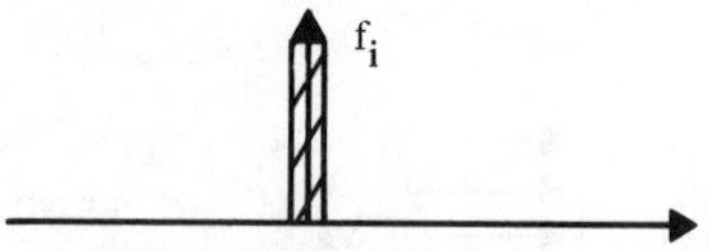
$\Pi(x_i)$	Rectangle	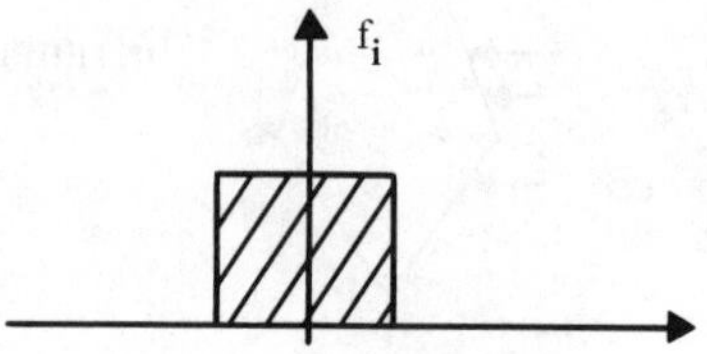
$H(x_i)$	Heaviside step	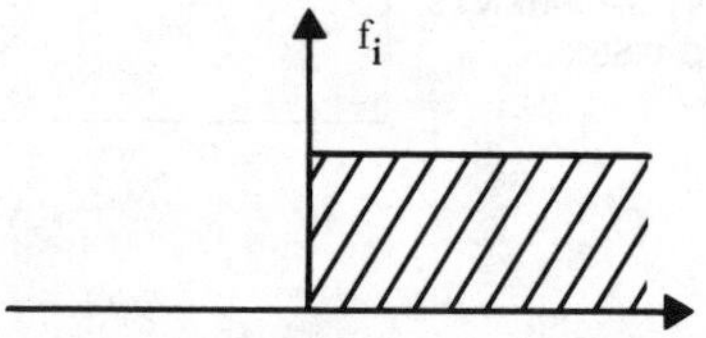
$\mathrm{sgn}(x_i)$	Signum	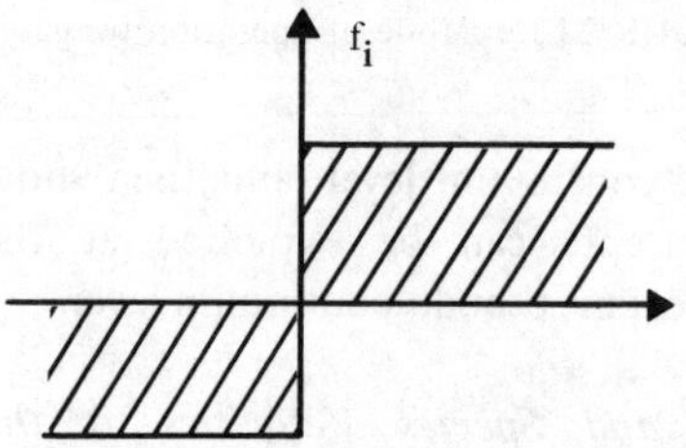
$A(x_i)$	Alternation	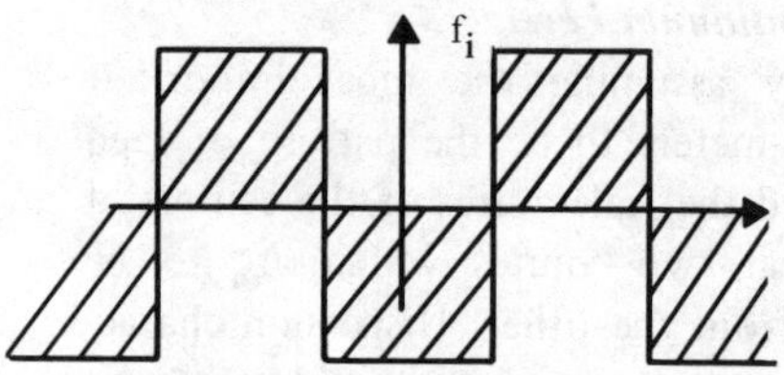
$G(x_i)$	Gradient	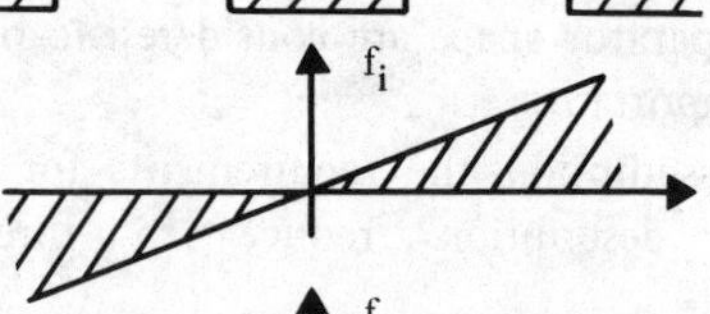
1	Unity	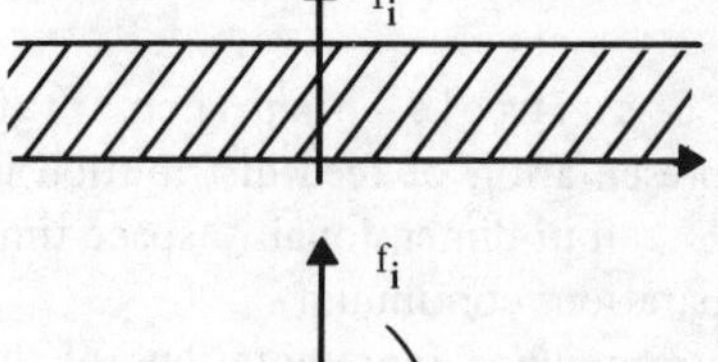
0	Zero	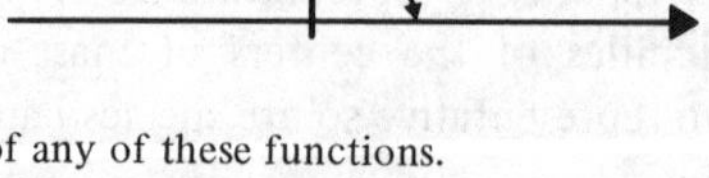

Note: An overline, e.g., $\widetilde{G}$, will be used to denote the negative of any of these functions.

*See, for example, Reference 120.

The simplest operation from a morphological standpoint is a one-dimensional differential chromatography. Here

$$m = m_0 = \begin{cases} \mathfrak{F} = \delta(x)\,\delta(y)\,\delta(z)\,\delta(t) & (127a) \\ U_i = \delta_x & (127b) \\ U_j - U_i = \delta_x & (127c) \end{cases}$$

where m is system morphology and the subscript zero refers to the fundamental operating mode. Note that our morphological scheme is qualitative. There is therefore no magnitude provided in any part of the description. Equation 127a states that the feed is a concentrated pulse introduced to the coordinate origin at time zero. Equations 127a to 127c describe the differential settling of Figure 4A, and by extension differential chromatography and all of the other analogs described in that section.

Modifications of the feed descriptors produce altered morphologies as suggested in Table 3. The first of these appears to differ only quantitatively from the fundamental mode and hence to be in contradiction in our neglect of quantitative differences. However, the distinction is really between infinitesimal and finite, and this is a big difference. It is in fact as big as the difference between Π and H mathematically, and it has important physical significance: finite column loadings tend to produce solute-solute interactions which can be important. The third operation is an important one in which all solutes are displaced by some agent, e.g., enthalpy or a slower-migrating species. The solutes to be separated then approach an asymptotic state in which they all move at the same speed as a series of adjacent bands, often with only rather narrow mixed zones between them. An example is displacement chromatography. The fourth operation represents a rare situation in which the feed schedule is different for each species: gradient elution of a preformed sorbate band. Here a mixed feed is tightly bound to the proximal end of a separation system, and the various components are released one by one by progressively changing the solvent fed to the system.

Representative velocity modifications are shown in Table 4. To save space, restrictions on feed patterns are not shown; they are simple and can be supplied by the reader for himself.

The first example is the simple binary separation already discussed, perhaps the most familiar of all separations to chemical engineers. It may now be noted that this useful separation can be achieved in two ways:

1. Movement of the two solutes to be separated relative to the solution can be in opposite directions and steady separation achieved even for a stationary solution or solvent.
2. If the relative motion of the solutes is in the same direction but different magnitude, the separation requires opposition by a convective (bulk) velocity intermediate in magnitude between the two migration velocities.

We find then a need to distinguish between migration and convection once we are interested in the mechanisms responsible for a given morphology. This important distinction is made in the section entitled "Mechanisms of Separation."

The second example is an alternate to Example 4 of Table 3. Here the elution is considered sequential so that the solutes start their motions at different times. The third example is a very common form of gradient elution in which the speeds of all species are increased in a monotonic fashion with time. We do not distinguish at this time between uniform and nonuniform increases

TABLE 3

Modification of Feed Descriptors

	$\mathfrak{F}$	Physical process described*
1	$\delta(x)\,\delta(y)\,\delta(z)\,\Pi(t)$	High-load fixed-bed separations
2	$\delta(x)\,\delta(y)\,\delta(z)\,H(t)$	Continuous separations ($U_j = -U_i$)
3	$\delta(x)\,\delta(y)\,\delta(z)[\overline{\text{sgn}}(t)\,\Pi(t)]$	Displacement operations
4	$\delta(x)\,\delta(y)\,\delta(z)\,g(t)_i$	Gradient elution of a preformed band

*U_i, $U_j = \underline{\delta}_x$ except as noted.

TABLE 4

Modification of Velocity Descriptors

	U_i	U_j	Physical process described
1	$\underline{\delta}_x$	$-\underline{\delta}_x$	Antiparallel shift (steady binary separation)
2	$\underline{\delta}_x H(t)$	$\underline{\delta}_x H[t - t_0(j)]$	Sequential elution of a preformed band
3	$\underline{\delta}_x g(t)$	Same	Spatially uniform gradient elution
4	$\underline{\delta}_x \bar{g}(x)$	Same	Transient focusing
5	$\underline{\delta}_x + \underline{\delta}_y$	Same	Perpendicular shift (steady multicomponent separation)
6	$\underline{\delta}_x \bar{g}(x) + \underline{\delta}_y$	Same	Steady focusing
7	$\underline{\delta}_x g(x) + \underline{\delta}_y$	$\underline{\delta}_y$	Partial elimination by antifocusing
8	$\underline{\delta}_x [1 - H(x)]$	$\underline{\delta}_x$	Transient filtration
9	$\underline{\delta}_x [1 - H(x)] + \underline{\delta}_y$	$\underline{\delta}_x$	Steady filtration
10	$\underline{\delta}_x [1 + A(t)]$	Same	Transient jigging
11	$\underline{\delta}_x [1 + A(t)] + \underline{\delta}_y$	Same	Steady jigging

because the specific schedule of velocity increases is best decided late in the design process. Classification schemes, on the other hand, are more useful for initiating this process.

The fourth and sixth examples represent processes which require velocity gradients $\partial v_i/\partial x_i$ less than zero. It has already been shown that this situation leads to a localization of solute, and in Example 3 that focusing will occur irrespective of Brownian motion just so long as $|\partial v_i/\partial x_i|$ does not decrease with concentration. (It is in part for this reason that we have chosen not to include dispersion in our discussion of morphology.) The seventh example shows a possibility, not yet implemented to our knowledge, for reducing contamination by one solute through antifocusing.

The fifth, eighth, and ninth operations have already been touched on and do not appear to require discussion here.

The descriptor [1 + A(t)] of the last two examples does require attention. We take it here to represent a biased cyclic process. That is, the symmetric cyclic process described by A(t) is biased by superposition of a steady component represented morphologically as unity. The result is an oscillatory flow with a non-zero time average. It could be argued, perhaps justifiably, that only the time-averaged result need be represented in a morphological classification. It is our view, however, that the oscillatory nature of this process should be represented explicitly since it is necessary to its success.

A more serious problem is that of redundancy, since many combinations of the above descriptors are not unique. The magnitude of this problem is most easily seen by referring to the work of Pauschmann, who obtains an extremely large number of combinations ($\sim 10^5$) with a much more limited set of descriptors. Fortunately, we can make a very substantial improvement by always taking the fundamental mode in the x_1-direction and any shifts or superpositions not parallel to x_1 first in the x_2-direction. Next we note that three-dimensional morphologies are exceedingly rare and have very limited utility. Most of our morphology can then be expressed in the three-dimensional (x_1, x_2, t) continuum. In these simple ways redundancy can be avoided. We shall return to this point, and also to the related problem of minor distinctions later.

Aspects of Morphology Peculiar to Pseudo-continuum Descriptions

Whereas pseudo-continuum processes look much like their true continuum counterparts, especially from a morphological viewpoint, there are at least two important fundamental differences: the much larger number of characteristic concentrations and velocities in different phases, and the transport of solutes between phases. We touch on these briefly here by an example and postpone a definitive treatment until later. We also note that pseudo-continuum descriptions of Taylor dispersion, transport in turbulent flow, and transport through beds of inert solids are morphologically identical to those of corresponding continuum processes. We concentrate our attention on systems of two active phases, as these are both the simplest and the most important in practice.

For simplicity we begin by examining one-dimensional paper chromatography as a pseudo-continuum example of the fundamental morphological mode (see Figure 14). In Part A of this figure we show the trajectories and velocities of three solutes (i,j,k) and their observable velocities

$$v_i = \alpha_i v_i^f + (1 - \alpha_i)\, v_i^p = \alpha_i v_i^f \qquad (128)$$

where

v_i = Observable velocity of species i
α_i = Fraction of species i in fluid phase, f
v_i^f = Velocity of i in the fluid phase
v_i^p = 0 = Velocity of i in the "paper" phase

We have then a transient multicomponent separation of the type first considered in the subsection on separations morphology.

We can convert this to a steady binary separation by reversing the direction of any solute velocity, and we now have at least two ways of doing this:

1. Providing an upward migration of at least one species in either or both of the phases of magnitude greater than $\alpha_i |v_i^f|$,

2. Moving the paper phase upward at a speed greater than $\alpha_i |v_i^f|$

Both of these approaches are used, e.g., column electrophoresis in the first case or any of the common two-phase countercurrent processes in the other. The end result is the same in both cases and is just the antiparallel shift shown in Part B of the figure.

One may also use a perpendicular shift of either of the above types to produce the steady multicomponent separation of Part C of the figure. We are not yet ready to discuss apparatus geometry, but we show in Figure 15 two means of providing

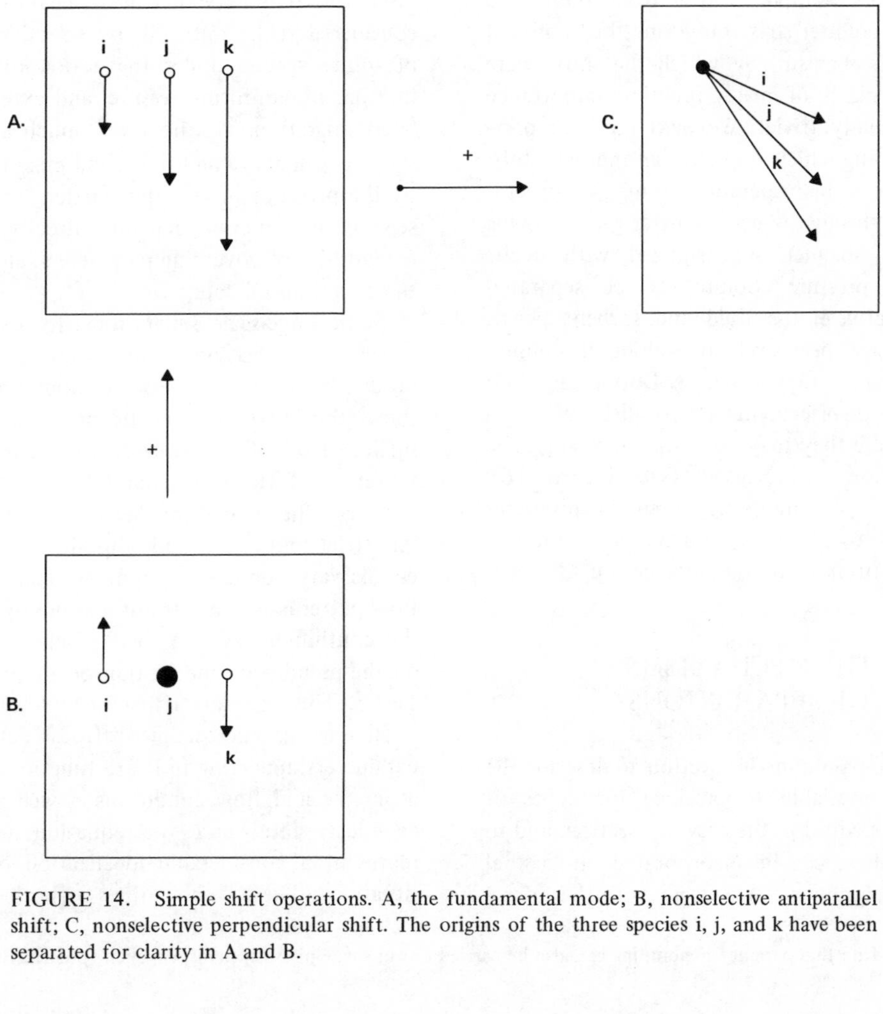

FIGURE 14. Simple shift operations. A, the fundamental mode; B, nonselective antiparallel shift; C, nonselective perpendicular shift. The origins of the three species i, j, and k have been separated for clarity in A and B.

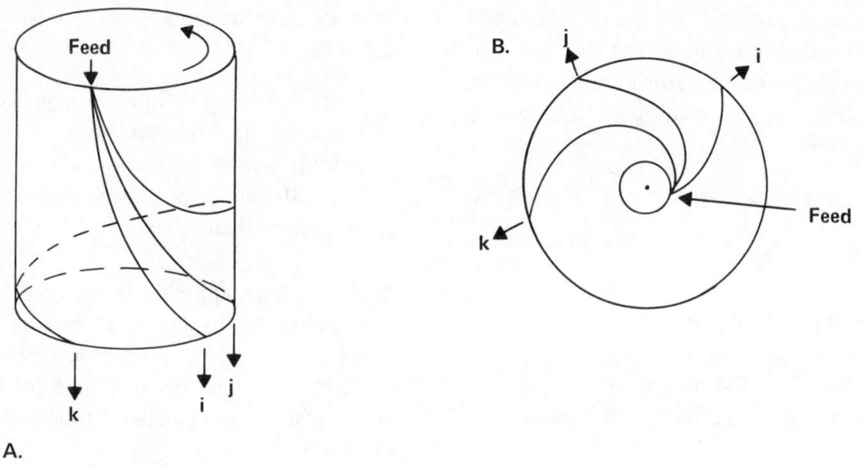

FIGURE 15. Implementation of the perpendicular shift concept. In A, solvent is fed uniformly to the upper ring and feed at one point. In B, solute is fed uniformly to the inner ring and feed at one point. Both processes are continuous.

perpendicular shifts without running out of paper. Both have been used.[5,107]

The above examples differ from their true continuum counterparts only in the physical means, or mechanism, by which the shifts were produced. This is of major practical importance but conceptually trivial. We next consider parametric pumping which results in an indirect shift. We illustrate* this operation using a sorbent-coated tube through which a carrier gas is moving in a cyclic manner synchronized with cyclic changes of pressure. Solutes to be separated distribute between the fluid and sorbent phase, and the average species velocities along the column are also given by Equation 128. During each half cycle species displacements are parallel, but over a complete cycle they may be antiparallel, since the flow direction is reversed (see Figure 16). Morphologically, parametric pumping processes are identical to all steady, binary, and unidirectional separations but the mechanism is quite different.

THE MECHANISMS OF SEPARATIONS

It is our purpose in this section to describe the mechanisms available to produce the types of separations outlined in the previous section, and to show how these can be incorporated into actual separations equipment. We begin with the microscopic continuum formulation which we shall consider as fundamental for reasons already discussed. It is here that most separations can be considered to be initiated, by selective migration of solute species under the action of Brownian motion, nonuniform pressure, and external fields. Such migrations are, however, much affected by system boundary conditions, and most particularly by the presence of selective barriers; the degree of separation achieved depends directly upon the magnitudes of governing parameters, and hence on the equations of state.

Some large-scale separations, for example settling, centrifugation, and electrophoresis, are produced primarily by species migration, and for these this first portion of our discussion will suffice. Normally, however, convective augmentation of diffusional separations is required to produce the scales of separation needed for industrial purposes, and this in turn typically entails very complex equipment geometry and/or flow patterns which it is not feasible to describe at the continuum level. We will discuss these based on the pseudo-continuum transport equation given earlier. This equation is useful but not nearly so reliable as the microscopic diffusion equation: the parameters appearing in it are functions of system geometry and flow conditions as well as physicochemical state, and the equation will always represent a considerable idealization of the real situation. These ambiguities arise because the

*We shall later find that parametric pumping can also be carried out in single-phase systems, via cyclic polarization.

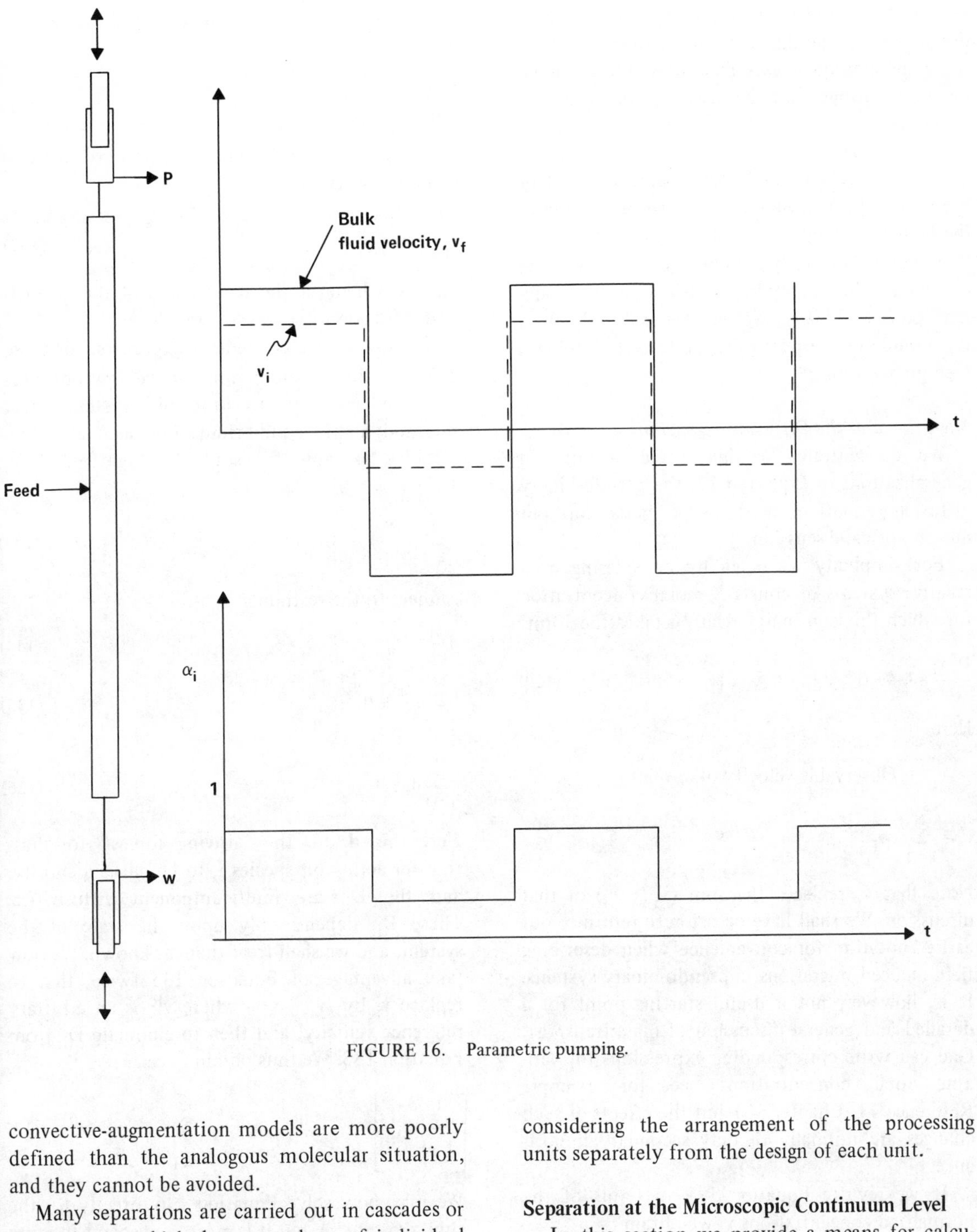

FIGURE 16. Parametric pumping.

convective-augmentation models are more poorly defined than the analogous molecular situation, and they cannot be avoided.

Many separations are carried out in cascades or networks in which large numbers of individual processing units are interconnected. Examples include stagewise contactors such as distillation columns and multistep separations such as the preparation of highly purified pharmaceuticals from crude sources. It has been found desirable in such cases to specialize the design effort by considering the arrangement of the processing units separately from the design of each unit.

Separation at the Microscopic Continuum Level

In this section we provide a means for calculating product concentrations, hence degree of separation, from feed composition and the physical and chemical characteristics of the separation system. We do this by first writing an appropriate continuity relation for each species in terms of the molar diffusion flux, and then relating the diffusion fluxes to the mass-transfer driving forces tending to produce them. We then show in subsequent sections how these fundamental relations may be used to practical advantage.

Even though we find a surprisingly large variety of driving forces available for separation, most of the selectivity of highly specific processes arises in the boundary conditions and equations of state. It is therefore critically important that these be considered thoroughly in the development of any new process. Finally, we will touch briefly on a less well-defined aspect of separations technology: feed preparation.

Migration and the Diffusion Equations

We concentrate in this initial section on generalizations of Equation 77, the pseudo-binary diffusion equation used as a basis for our morphological discussion.

For simplicity we begin by considering non-reactive systems of constant molar concentration for which this continuity relation takes the form:

$$\frac{D^{\star}x_i}{Dt} = \frac{\partial x_i}{\partial t} + (\mathbf{v}^{\star} \cdot \nabla x_i) = -(\nabla \cdot x_i[\mathbf{v}_i - \mathbf{v}^{\star}]) \tag{129}$$

Here

$\mathbf{v}_i$ = Observable velocity of species i

$$\mathbf{v}^{\star} = \sum_{i=1}^{N} x_i \mathbf{v}_i$$

Note that $\mathbf{v}_i$ replaces the sum $(\bar{\mathbf{v}}_i + \mathbf{v}_i')$ of that discussion. We shall have occasion to return to our earlier notation for convenience when describing field-induced migrations in pseudo-binary systems. It is, however, not a useful starting point for a detailed and general discussion of mass transport. One can write corresponding expressions for variable total concentration (see for example Reference 11, Chapter 18), but the effects of such changes are normally of only secondary importance.

If we rewrite Equation 129 in terms of the normalized concentrations χ_i we obtain

$$\frac{D^{\star}\chi_i}{Dt} = -(\nabla \cdot \chi_i[\mathbf{v}_i - \mathbf{v}^{\star}]) \tag{130}$$

This equation describes the change of χ_i in an element of fluid moving with the local molar-average velocity, and this is an adequate measure of changes in the χ_i. Since the Π_{ij} depend directly on the χ_i, we may in general expect separation whenever

$$\frac{D^{\star}\chi_i}{Dt} \neq 0 \tag{131}$$

Furthermore species i and j will be separated one from the other when

$$\frac{D^{\star}\chi_i}{Dt} \neq \frac{D^{\star}\chi_j}{Dt} \tag{132}$$

that is, whenever the divergences of the normalized diffusion fluxes $\chi_i(\mathbf{v}_i - \mathbf{v}^{\star})$ differ.

We now seek a convenient expression for these diffusion fluxes, and in doing so we limit ourselves for the moment to isotropic systems near thermodynamic equilibrium. For such a system (see for example the study by Lightfoot,[70] p. 163):

$$\sum_{j=1}^{N} \frac{x_i x_j}{\text{Đ}_{ij}} \mathbf{v}_j = \mathbf{d}_i \tag{133}$$

subject to the restraints

$$\text{Đ}_{ij} = \text{Đ}_{ji} \tag{134}$$

$$\sum_{j=1}^{N} \frac{x_j}{\text{Đ}_{ij}} = 0 \tag{135}$$

$$\sum_{j=1}^{N} \mathbf{d}_i = 0 \tag{136}$$

Here the $\mathbf{d}_i$ are the "driving forces" for mass transfer acting on species i, to be defined shortly, and the Đ_{ij} are multicomponent diffusivities. These Đ_{ij} depend only upon the state of the system, and we shall treat them as known. We now take advantage of Equation 135 twice, first to replace $\mathbf{v}_j$ by $(\mathbf{v}_j - \mathbf{v}^R)$ where $\mathbf{v}^R$ is an arbitrary reference velocity, and then to eliminate Đ_{ii} from Equation 133. We thus obtain:

$$\left[\sum_{\substack{j=1 \\ \neq i}}^{N} \frac{x_j}{\text{Đ}_{ij}}\right] x_i(\mathbf{v}_i - \mathbf{v}^R) = \mathbf{d}_i + x_i \sum_{\substack{j=1 \\ \neq i}}^{N} \frac{x_j}{\text{Đ}_{ij}} (\mathbf{v}_j - \mathbf{v}^R) \tag{137}$$

We may now solve Equation 136 directly for the flux $x_i(\mathbf{v}_i - \mathbf{v}^R)$, but it is more convenient to write a slightly modified expression.

$$x_i(\mathbf{v}_i - \mathbf{v}^R) = -D_{im}\mathbf{d}_i + x_i(\mathbf{V} - \mathbf{v}^R) \tag{138}$$

$$D_{im} = \left[\sum_{\substack{j=1 \\ \neq i}}^{N} \left(\frac{x_j}{\text{Đ}_{ij}}\right)\left(\frac{1}{1 - x_i}\right)\right]^{-1} \tag{139}$$

$$\mathbf{V} - \mathbf{v}^R \equiv \sum_{\substack{j=1 \\ \neq i}}^{N} \left(\frac{x_j D_{im}}{Ð_{ij}}\right)(\mathbf{v}_j - \mathbf{v}^R) \quad (140)$$

This rather improbable set of expressions turns out to be quite convenient with $\mathbf{v}^R$ set either to the molar average velocity or to zero. This is seen by considering the special case of all $Ð_{ij}$ equal for which

$$x_i(\mathbf{v}_i - \mathbf{v}^R) \doteq -D_{im}\mathbf{d}_i + x_i \sum_{j=1}^{N} x_j(\mathbf{v}_j - \mathbf{v}^R) \quad (141)$$

since

$$Ð_{ij} \doteq D_{im}$$

Then

$$x_i\mathbf{v}_i = -D_{im}\mathbf{d}_i + x_i \sum_{j=1}^{N} x_i\mathbf{v}_i \quad (\mathbf{v}^R = 0) \quad (142)$$

$$x_i(\mathbf{v}_i - \mathbf{v}^\star) = -D_{im}\mathbf{d}_i \quad (\mathbf{v}^R = \mathbf{v}^\star) \quad (143)$$

Equations 142 and 143 have the same form as Fick's first law for binary systems and reduce to the binary form for N = 2. Here we let i = A and J = B so $Ð_{ij} = Ð_{AB}$ and

$$x_A(\mathbf{v}_A - \mathbf{v}^\star) = -D_{AB}\mathbf{d}_A \quad (N = 2) \quad (144)$$

They are also satisfactory for pseudo-binary systems, those in which one species, designated as the solvent S, is predominant. Then

$$x_i(\mathbf{v}_i - \mathbf{v}^\star) \doteq -Ð_{is}\mathbf{d}_i \quad (x_j << x_S) \quad (145)$$

The great bulk of separations processes are analyzed on the basis of either Equations 144 or 145. This usually works well because the solute-solute diffusional interactions expressed in the term $(\mathbf{V} - \mathbf{v}^R)$ are generally of only secondary importance. There are, however, exceptions of importance, and we shall touch on some of them later.

For the moment we shall assume Equation 145 to be a satisfactory approximation and put it into Equation 130. We thus obtain:

$$\frac{D^\star x_i}{Dt} \doteq -\left[\nabla \cdot \frac{Ð_{is}}{x_F}\mathbf{d}_i\right] \quad \left[\begin{matrix}\text{negligible solute-solute} \\ \text{diffusional interaction}\end{matrix}\right] \quad (146)$$

It follows from this simple equation that the primary causes of separation are spatial variations in the diffusional driving forces $\mathbf{d}_i$. We therefore take a close look at these in the next section.

We now review a representative list of "forces" tending to move one diffusing species relative to the others, and we begin with those obtained from linear irreversible thermodynamic analysis.[29,54] These are by far the most commonly encountered, and they are usually the most effective. There are, however, many others of at least occasional importance, and we touch on two additional types by way of example: those involving nonlinear effects and those encountered in nonisotropic systems.

It is now well known that for isotropic systems not far from equilibrium one may write

$$\mathbf{d}_i = \mathbf{d}_i^\bullet \equiv x_i \nabla_{T,p} \ln \gamma_i x_i + (c_i\bar{V}_i - \alpha\omega_i)\nabla p/c\mathcal{R}T$$

$$+ \frac{x_i \nu_i \mathfrak{F}}{RT} \nabla\phi + k_{io}\nabla T \quad (147)$$

Here

γ_i	=	Molar activity coefficient of i, with thermodynamic activity
c	=	Total molar concentration
c_i	=	cx_k = molar concentration of species i
$\bar{V}_i$	=	Partial molal volume of species i
ω_i	=	Mass fraction of species i in mixture
p	=	Hydrostatic pressure
ν_i	=	Ionic charge on species i, e.g., −2 for $SO_4^=$
ϕ	=	Electrostatic potential
T	=	Absolute temperature
k_{io}	=	A thermal diffusion ratio which, like the $Ð_{ij}$, is a system property
$\mathcal{R}$	=	The international gas constant
$\mathfrak{F}$	=	Faraday's constant

The coefficient α is unity in free solution and zero for mobile species in membrane transport. The reasons for this difference in formulation are discussed by Lightfoot, Reference 70 Section III.1.4. Equation 147 is a rather powerful one in forming the basis for describing concentration, pressure, electro-, and thermal diffusion. We return to it at the end of the section, in Example 8. First, however, we wish to point out that other, less familiar, effects can contribute to diffusion. There are a very large number of these, in principle, but not all will be equally important. We discuss a few of the more likely by way of example.

Particularly notable among these are effects excluded from the usual irreversible thermodynamic analyses because they are not linearly related to the diffusion fluxes. Examples familiar from electrodynamics include forces on charged particles moving across a magnetic field and of electric or magnetic induction.* It is intuitively attractive merely to add such terms to the $\mathbf{d}^{\bullet}$, for example by writing

$$\mathbf{d}_i = \mathbf{d}_i^{\bullet} + \frac{x_i \nu_i \mathcal{F}}{\mathcal{R}T} [\mathbf{v}_i \times \mathbf{B}] + \frac{x_i \Gamma_i^k}{\mathcal{R}T} [\mathbf{P}^k \cdot \nabla \mathbf{P}^k] - \frac{\omega_i}{\mathcal{R}T} \{[\mathbf{I} \times \mathbf{B}]/c + \Gamma_{Tot}^k [\mathbf{P}^k \cdot \nabla \mathbf{P}^k]\} \quad (148)$$

where

$\mathbf{B}$	=	Magnetic induction
Γ_i^M, Γ_i^E	=	Species magnetic or electrical susceptibility,
P^M, P^E	=	Respectively, magnetic induction **B**, or the electric field E
$\mathbf{I}$	=	Local current density
Γ_{Tot}	=	Bulk susceptibility

The first added term in Equation 148 is the basis of mass spectrometry, and it is important in magneto-electrophoresis.[65] The second term is used, for example, in analysis of such paramagnetic materials as oxygen and in dielectrophoresis.[87] It remains to justify the detailed form of Equation 148.

A second possibly important class of diffusion phenomena not covered in ordinary irreversible thermodynamic analysis is that of orientable particles; these are excluded on the basis of anisotropy. A rather complete kinetic theory is, however, available for suspensions of monodisperse orientable Brownian particles in an isotropic solvent,[14] and it should be possible to extend this to more complex situations should the occasion arise.

For binary systems of position-independent diffusivity, diffusional behavior is described by the following modification of Equation 146:

$$x_A(\mathbf{v}_A - \mathbf{v}^{\star}) = \underline{\underline{Đ}}_{AB} \cdot \mathbf{d}_A \quad (149)$$

Here the $\mathbf{d}_A$ are those of Equations 147 or 148, but the scalar diffusivity of Equation 144 is replaced by a tensorial equivalent,

$$\underline{\underline{Đ}}_{AB} = \begin{bmatrix} Đ_{xx} & --- & Đ_{xz} \\ | & & \\ & \text{———} & Đ_{zz} \end{bmatrix} \quad (150)$$

This tensor is symmetric so that

$$Đ_{ij} = Đ_{ji} \quad (151)$$

but the magnitudes of the $Đ_{ij}$ depend both on the shape of the asymmetric particle and the strength and direction of the orienting field.

The degree of orientation in any situation depends upon a Langevin parameter[14]

$$L = \epsilon/kT \quad (152)$$

where ϵ is a measure of molecular alignment energy and k is Boltzmann's constant. As one example, for a dipolar molecule aligned by an electric field E, it is convenient to define

$$\epsilon = \mu_\epsilon E \quad (153)$$

where μ_ϵ is the molecular dipole moment. When L is small relative to unity, the randomizing effect of Brownian motion dominates system behavior, and $\underline{\underline{Đ}}_{AB}$ approaches the usual scalar result

$$\underline{\underline{Đ}}_{AB} \rightarrow Đ^{\circ}_{AB} \underline{\underline{\delta}} \qquad (L \rightarrow 0) \quad (154)$$

where $\underline{\underline{\delta}}$ is the unit tensor and the superscript degree indicates the Brownian limiting magnitude: the nondiagonal elements of $\underline{\underline{Đ}}_{AB}$ disappear, and the three diagonal elements become equal. For ellipsoids of revolution[14] alignment becomes effective at $L \sim 10$. For macroscopic particles μ_ϵ tends to be large and a high degree of alignment can be readily achieved. We consider one such situation immediately below.

Example 4: Pressure Diffusion of Skew Particles – Normally one is led to promising separations by order-of-magnitude calculations such as those presented in the next major section. Sometimes, however, we must depend almost entirely on qualitative arguments, and we consider one such situation here: the hydrodynamic resolution of enantiomorphic crystal pairs (optical isomers). All optically active molecules lack a plane of symmetry, and the mirror-image relation of enantiomorphic pairs suggests that they will move in different directions, as permitted by Equation 151, when subjected to the same diffusional driving forces. However, to take

*See for example Reference 16.

advantage of this possibility on a macroscopic scale requires a degree of molecular alignment not easily achieved in practice.

It is, however, well known that the molecular asymmetry is maintained in macroscopic crystals, which also exhibit mirror-image symmetry. This is indicated in Figure 17 where an enantiomorphic crystal pair is shown schematically. Their Brownian effects are negligible, and they act as hydrodynamic particles when suspended in a fluid.

For isolated particles moving at low Reynolds number relative to a quiescent fluid, their hydrodynamic behavior is particularly simple and can be described by two equations[52]

$$F = \mu D[\underline{\underline{K}} \cdot v] + \underline{\mu D^2 [\underline{\underline{C}}_R^T \cdot \omega]} \quad (155)$$

$$T = \mu D^2 [\underline{\underline{C}}_R \cdot v] + \underline{\mu D^3 [\underline{\underline{\Omega}} \cdot \omega]} \quad (156)$$

Here μ is fluid viscosity, and D is a characteristic particle length. Equation 155 states that the force **F** exerted by the particle on the fluid is proportional both to its velocity **v** and rate of rotation **ω** relative to the fluid. Equation 156 states a similar relation for the torque, applied at an arbitrary but definite point R in the particle. The proportionality factors are tensorial constants characteristic of particle shape, and in the case of $\underline{\underline{C}}_R$, of R: the translational tensor $\underline{\underline{K}}$, the coupling tensor $\underline{\underline{C}}_R$, and the rotational tensor $\underline{\underline{\Omega}}$.

A macroscopic separation requires control of rotation, and the simplest way to do this is to eliminate it, i.e., eliminate the underlined terms in Equations 155 and 156. We see immediately that to do this will require a torque equal to $\mu D^2 [\underline{\underline{C}}_R \cdot v]$. If such a torque can be applied, any force acting on the particle will produce a motion according to the relation

$$F = \mu D[\underline{\underline{K}} \cdot v] \qquad (\omega = 0) \quad (157)$$

Furthermore one can readily extend the hydrodynamic theory of diffusion (see for example Reference 70, p. 59) to this situation and write, for no rotation:

$$\underline{\underline{Ð}}_{AB} = (kT/\mu D)\underline{\underline{K}}^{-1} \qquad (T \neq 0\,!) \quad (158)$$

Thus the symmetry of $\underline{\underline{K}}$ will carry over into $\underline{\underline{Ð}}_{AB}$.

As a simple example we consider free settling of the particles in the presence of our orienting torque. Then if we designate a particle as "A" and the solvent as "B" we find the driving force to be that of pressure diffusion, and:

$$x_A x_B (v_B - v_A) = \left(\frac{\phi_A - \omega_A}{c\mathcal{R}T}\right) \frac{kT}{\mu D} \underline{\underline{K}}^{-1} \nabla p \quad (159)$$

(free settling) $\downarrow$ $(x_B \to 1; \nabla p \to -\rho g)$

$$(v_B - v_A) = \frac{2}{3} \pi R^2 \frac{(\rho_B - \rho_A)}{\mu} g \underline{\underline{K}}^{-1} \quad (160)$$

Here ρ_A and ρ_B are particle and fluid densities, respectively, ϕ_A is the volume fraction of solution occupied by the particles, and

$$R = \left[\frac{3}{4\pi} V_{part}\right]^{1/3} \quad (161)$$

This is a generalization of Stokes' law to asymmetric particles, and this may be seen immediately by recognizing that for a sphere

$$\underline{\underline{K}}_{sphere} = 3\pi \underline{\underline{\delta}} \quad (162)$$

Putting Equation 162 into Equation 160 yields

$$v_B - v_A = \frac{2}{9} \frac{R^2}{\mu} (\rho_B - \rho_A) g \quad (163)$$

which is a well-known form of Stokes' law.

To implement the ideas implicit in this development, the apparatus of Figure 17 is suggested: a rotating drum with a horizontal axis filled with a nonsolvent liquid. Rotation of the drum provides the near equivalent of an inclined plane for the crystals to fall along and helps to orient the particle: the three torque components needed to align the particle are provided by the gravitational-hydrodynamic dipole – between the centers of gravity and hydrodynamic reaction – and the drum wall. Rotation is thus eliminated, as required.

Presence of the drum wall greatly complicates the fluid mechanic picture and may well preclude a quantitative analytic description. However, qualitatively the picture is much the same as before, even at finite Reynolds numbers, and particles with no plane of symmetry will in general exhibit a horizontal velocity component. Furthermore the mirror-image nature of enantiomorphic pairs ensures that this horizontal motion will be in opposite directions, thus producing a separation.

This exception is borne out in practice: all the model pairs shown in Figure 18 separate readily in rotating drums. Encouraging results have

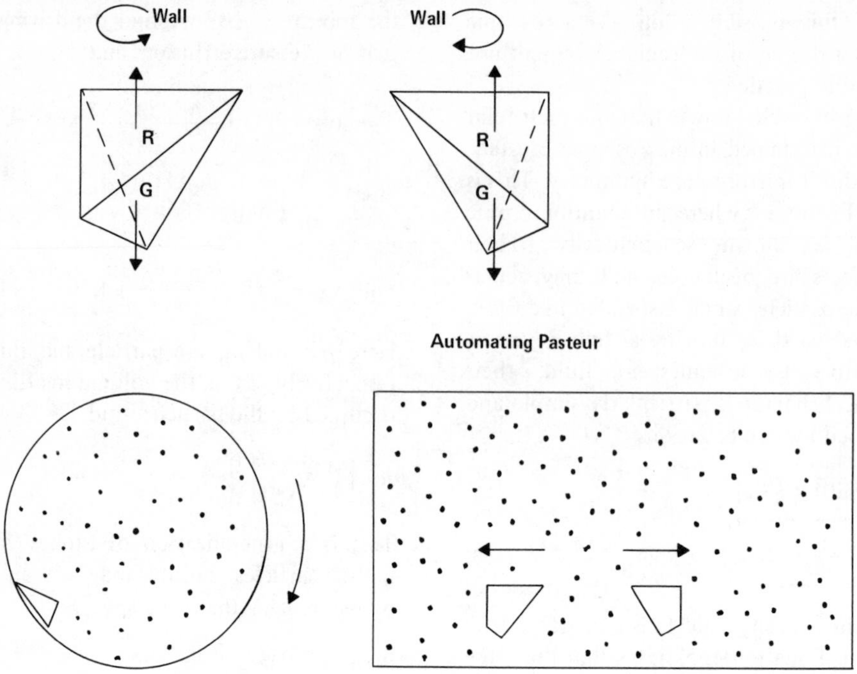

FIGURE 17. Hydrodynamic resolution of optical isomers.

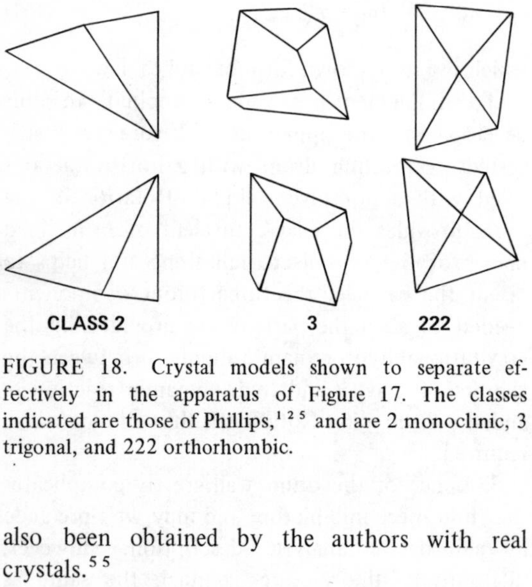

FIGURE 18. Crystal models shown to separate effectively in the apparatus of Figure 17. The classes indicated are those of Phillips,[125] and are 2 monoclinic, 3 trigonal, and 222 orthorhombic.

also been obtained by the authors with real crystals.[55]

Barriers and the Roles of Boundary Conditions

Very frequently the species dependence of the flux divergence

$$(\nabla \cdot x_i[v_i - v^\star]) \tag{164}$$

needed to produce separation arises at system boundaries. Examples range from very old processes like evaporation of sea water to such exciting new possibilities as affinity chromatography and a variety of membrane processes. In addition to these selective boundaries, totally impermeable surfaces are needed to define equipment geometry and to contain the separation system. All these varied situations enter our description mathematically as boundary conditions needed for integrating the appropriate equations of change.

The simplest cases are totally impermeable surfaces (including surfaces of symmetry) for which

$$x_i(v_i - v^\star)|_s = 0 \tag{165}$$

where the subscript s refers to conditions at the surface. More interesting are selectively permeable phase boundaries and selective membranes, the latter of which are most conveniently considered here as surfaces of discontinuity. The separations characteristics of both these types of selective surfaces are provided by combinations of thermodynamic and transport considerations. Although they have much in common we shall consider the two in turn.

For simplicity we shall limit detailed discussion to transport perpendicular to system boundaries, but it must be recognized that anomalous solute motion can also take place parallel to them. Examples include capillary rise[74] and species-dependent spreading of hydrocarbons at air-water boundaries.[85]

True Phase Boundaries

Even though the interfacial region between immiscible phases is very thin, one should always start out by considering it of finite extent; we do this here. In most separations processes, however, it can be treated as a mathematical surface across which discontinuities of composition, electrostatic potential, and (if one phase is rigid) pressure can occur, and which offers no resistance to transport itself.

Many substances concentrate at phase boundaries in macroscopically measurable amounts, and this segregation can be highly species selective. It leads on a true molecular scale to a wide variety of adsorption phenomena in solid-fluid systems and to foam fractionation at liquid-gas interfaces. It also leads to froth flotation processes and to (sometimes highly undesirable) stabilizing of emulsions. There are also persistent reports of finite transport resistance across true phase boundaries, but these are hard to substantiate. In most cases such resistance seems to result from presence of surfactants.

Fortunately there are a very large number of situations for which none of the above complications is important. For these, interfacial behavior is described by:

$$\ln \frac{\gamma_{i1}\, x_{i1}}{\gamma_{i2}\, x_{i2}} + \frac{\nu_i \mathcal{F}}{\mathcal{R}T}(\phi_1 - \phi_2) + \frac{(\bar{V}_i)_{avg}}{\mathcal{R}T}(p_1 - p_2) = 0 \qquad (166)$$

$$T_1 = T_2 \qquad (167)$$

where the subscripts 1 and 2 refer to conditions on either side of the interface. Equations 166 and 167 are statements of interphase thermodynamic equilibrium.*

However, the presence of an interface tends to result in development of diffusional boundary layers in the two adjacent phases, and these have a profound effect, both on mass-transfer rates and on selectivity. Intraphase transfer rates can normally be expressed in terms of lumped-parameter transfer coefficients, which in turn are characteristically only slightly species dependent. However, the transfer coefficients in the two phases often differ markedly, and their relative effect on a given solute in turn depends strongly on the equilibrium distribution, Equation 166: Transport rates tend to be most strongly influenced (or controlled) by the phase of lesser solubility. Selectivity in boundary-layer transport thus results from an interaction between thermodynamic and transport phenomena. The basis for its prediction is found in standard references (e.g., Reference 71).

Membranes

Selectively permeable membranes are increasingly attractive for initiating separations, but unfortunately membrane transport is an exceedingly complex subject from all points of view, except macroscopic geometry and the insignificance of transients. Membranes are typically anisotropic, they are often in irreproducible metastable or unstable thermodynamic states, and they cannot always be treated as continua from a diffusional standpoint. Moreover they are available in such a bewildering variety that no one reference can be considered as representative (see, however Reference 56). There are, however, some relatively simple special situations which arise frequently enough in separations technology to justify discussion here.

The simplest situation is binary diffusion across a membrane acting as a homogeneous continuum. For it,

$$N_i = \mathcal{D}_{im}\bar{c}_i \Delta \ln (a_i)_{Tot}/\delta^\circ \qquad (168)$$

where

$\mathcal{D}_{im}$	=	A mean diffusivity for i through the membrane
$\bar{c}_i$	=	Average of the interfacial molar concentrations of species i in the membrane phase
$(a_i)_{Tot}$	=	$(a_i)_{T,p} \exp (p\bar{V}_i/\mathcal{R}T)$
δ°	=	Solute-free membrane thickness

The quantity $(a_i)_{Tot}$ is continuous across solution-membrane interfaces. It is important to note here that no correction need be made for convection (see Section 17.2, p. 522, of Reference 11) if the membrane thickness is measured in some standard state, for example on a permeant-free

*The estimation of activity coefficient is discussed by Abrams and Prausnitz,[2] and Fredenslund et al.,[38] available data are presented by Gmehling and Onken.[47,47a]

basis as suggested here. The diffusivity $\mathcal{D}_{im}$ is, however, an integral one and is thus dependent upon the distribution of permeant in the membrane.

The next simplest situation is pseudo-binary diffusion in which the various permeants are assumed to have no effect on each other. Since swelling will affect transport, pseudo-binary treatments must be limited to low permeant concentrations. If in addition the permeants are nonreactive and nondissociating one may write

$$N_i = (\mathcal{D}_{im}/\delta)\,\Delta c_i \tag{169}$$

Where Δc_i is the change in species concentration within the membrane and δ is the membrane thickness. This simple expression is widely used.

Next in complexity are pseudo-ternary approximations for either charged or uncharged membranes (see Reference 70). The most widely used expressions for uncharged pseudo-ternary systems are those of Kedem and Katchalsky[60] and Staverman.[102] These prove to be of very limited validity, however, even though useful for many situations of biological interest.[72] Transport in charged membranes is almost always described in terms of the Nernst-Planck equations,[53] even though these may be seriously inadequate:[70] It is difficult to obtain enough information for a truly satisfactory description.

Magnitudes of Separation Parameters and Equations of State

The importance of approximate analysis can hardly be overestimated at any stage in the design of separations. Although highly refined quantitative calculations are frequently necessary in the later stages of the design process, they almost always play a secondary role. The critical questions normally concern the orders of magnitude of driving forces, equipment dimensions, purity requirements, and other tolerances, and of course productivity. It is also vital to identify key problem areas at the outset of any investigation.

We suggest the utility of simple calculations in Table 5 where we compare characteristic strengths of various diffusional forces relative to the randomizing effects of Brownian motion. These are typical of the kinds of comparisons which must be made in practical situations and are of particular importance in determining process conditions.

Although the relative magnitudes of the individual contributions to the $\mathbf{d}_i$ vary widely, it is nonetheless useful to compare them for representative situations. This is done in Table 5 for the indicated situations by calculating the field or equivalent required to equal a fractional activity gradient $\nabla_{T,p} \ln a$ of one reciprocal centimeter.

To save space no calculations are shown for the bulk of these entries, but the results shown are accessible from the cited references. Calculations are given below for pressure diffusion by way of example. First, however, we note that most of the less familiar processes require very large gradients for the situations considered here. This is of course the primary reason for their unfamiliarity, and their effective utilization remains a challenge. In general this challenge may be met either by providing a novel equipment configuration, capable of producing large gradients, or by using particularly favorable physicochemical conditions.

Example 5: Characteristic magnitudes in pressure dissusion — We now return to pressure diffusion and begin by noting that the $\mathbf{d}_i$ for pressure diffusion may be written as

$$\mathbf{d}_i^{(p)} = \frac{\nabla p}{c\mathcal{R}T}\left(c_i\bar{V}_i - \frac{\rho_i}{\rho}\right) \tag{170}$$

where c is total molar concentration, $c_i = cx_i$ is molar concentration of species i, ρ is mass density, and ρ_i is the mass concentration of species i. This expression is simplest for low-density gases since for these

$$c\mathcal{R}T = p \tag{171}$$

$$c_i\bar{V}_i = x_i \tag{172}$$

Furthermore, for a binary system, of species A and B,

$$\rho_A/\rho = x_A M_A/(x_A M_A + x_B M_B)$$

where M_i is the molecular weight of species i. If the fractional difference in molecular weights is small we may use the approximation:

$$\rho_A/\rho \doteq x_A\left[1 - x_B\left(\frac{M_B - M_A}{M_A}\right)\right] \tag{173}$$

Then

$$\frac{1}{x_A}\mathbf{d}_A \doteq (\nabla \ln p)\,x_B\,\frac{M_B - M_A}{M_A} \equiv 1\ \text{cm}^{-1} \tag{174}$$

and

TABLE 5

Characteristic Magnitudes of Diffusional Driving Forces

Driving force	d_i/x_i	Gradient and magnitude	Examples and references
Concentration gradient	$\nabla_{T,p} \ln a_i$	$\nabla_{T,p} \ln a_i \equiv 1\ cm^{-1}$	Polarography, as at a dropping mercury electrode where ionic fluxes are diffusion controlled
Pressure gradient Aqueous solutions	$\frac{\nabla p}{\mathcal{R}T}\left(\bar{V}_i - \frac{M_i}{\rho}\right)$	$\nabla p \doteq 1.42$ atm/cm = 1470 "g"	Fractionation of aqueous protein solutions, calculated for dilute serum albumin in water
Binary Ideal gases*	$\nabla \ln p\left(1 - \frac{\omega A}{x_A}\right)$	$\nabla \ln p \doteq 10^2\ cm^{-1}$	Fractionation of uranium isotopes
Electric field	$\frac{\nu_i F}{\mathcal{R}T} \nabla \phi$	$\nabla \phi = 25$ mV/cm	Electrophoresis
Temperature gradient	$\frac{k_{io}}{x_i} \nabla \ln T$	$\nabla T = 1.1 \times 10^3\ °C/cm$	Calculated for equimolar mixture of methanol and water (liquid at 313 D (see Ref. 11, Table 18.4-1)
Magnetic field	$\frac{\nu_i F}{\mathcal{R}T} [\mathbf{v_i} \times \mathbf{B}]$	$\mathbf{B} = 25 \times 10^6$ G	Calculated for univalent ion at velocity of 10 cm/sec (see Ref. 65 and 121)
Electric field gradient**	$[\mathbf{m}_i^E \cdot \nabla \mathbf{E}]$	$\nabla \mathbf{E} = 2 \times 10^4\ V/cm^2$	Calculated for a fully aligned molecule of 50,000 mol wt and dipole of 600 D (requiring ca. 2×10^4 V/cm) (see Ref. 62)
Magnetic field gradient**	$[\mathbf{m}_i^M \cdot \nabla \mathbf{B}]$	$\nabla \mathbf{B} = 80$ G/cm	Fractionation of liquid oxygen, etc. Calculated for fully aligned K_3FeF_6 in water (6 μB at 2 MG)

*ω_i = Mass fraction of species i. See text.
**Here $\Gamma_i^k \mathbf{p}^k$ has been replaced by $\mathbf{m}_i^k$, the effective dipole moment of species i. This is a more general expression which reduces to that in Equation 148 for small fractional alignment. See for example Reference 123.

$$\nabla \ln p \sim \frac{M_A}{M_B - M_A} \frac{1}{x_B} \tag{175}$$

This expression is quite adequate for describing the separation of uranium isotopes in the form of UF_6 by ultracentrifugation. Here for equimolar mixtures $\nabla \ln p \sim 10^2$/cm.

For dilute aqueous solutions $c \sim 18^{-1}$ g-mol/cm^3 and

$$c\mathcal{R}T = 18^{-1} \times 82.07 \times 298.16 \doteq 1360 \text{ atm} \tag{176}$$

at 25°C. The large magnitude of this reference pressure is the primary drawback to ultracentrifugation in liquids. For dilute solutions we may also write

$$\rho_i/\rho \doteq M_i x_i/M_w \tag{177}$$

It follows that

$$\mathbf{d}_i \doteq (\nabla p/1360 \text{ atm})(c\bar{V}_i - M_i/M_w)x_i \tag{178}$$

and for $\mathbf{d}_i/x_i$ of one reciprocal centimeter

$$\nabla p = (1360 \text{ atm})/(c\bar{V}_i - M_i/M_w) \text{ cm} \tag{179}$$

We may further note that for almost all globular proteins

$$\bar{V}_i \doteq (0.75 \pm 0.01) M_i \text{cm}^3/\text{g} \tag{180}$$

Then for a protein of 69,000 mol wt,

$$|\nabla p| \doteq \left|(1360 \text{ atm/cm})/(69{,}000)\left(\frac{0.75}{18} - \frac{1}{18}\right)\right| = 1.42 \text{ atm/cm} \tag{181}$$

The acceleration required to produce this pressure gradient

$$a = \frac{1}{\rho}\nabla p \doteq [(1.42)(1.013 \times 10^6)/(1)] \text{ cm/sec}^2 \tag{182a}$$

$$= 1.44 \times 10^6 \text{ cm/sec}^2 \tag{182b}$$

$$a/g = (1.44 \times 10^6/980) \doteq 1467 \quad (182c)$$

Thus the required acceleration is almost 1500 times that produced by the gravitational force per unit mass, g.

The magnitude of this result, along with the inverse dependence on molecular weight, has limited the use of pressure diffusion in aqueous solutions. There are now commercially available laboratory centrifuges producing accelerations up to 500,000 times the acceleration of gravity, however, and these will undoubtedly lead to greatly increased use of pressure diffusion at a molecular level. This process also looks very promising for the gas-phase fractionation of uranium isotopes (as UF_6).[78]

It should also be noted that hydrodynamic particles can be viewed as "molecules" of very large molecular weight. It then follows from the above development that Brownian motion is unimportant in such operations as settling, filtration, and centrifugation. This is of course just what is observed.

Feed Preparation and Ingenuity

No matter how systematically one approaches a problem there comes a time when he must rely on ingenuity, intuition, and personal experience. We choose to emphasize this aspect of separations design in terms of feed preparation, since this is a particularly difficult aspect to treat systematically. By preparation we mean a preliminary processing which produces no separation itself but which increases the effectiveness of later steps in the process which do.

Perhaps the oldest of all such pretreatments are purely mechanical: crushing and grinding.* These processes tend to be ignored in modern chemical engineering curricula because they are difficult to describe systematically, but they are of primary importance in separations processes. They not only facilitate such processes as leaching or oxidation, but they may also detach desired materials, such as iron oxide, from the inert material in which they are imbedded. This latter process clearly facilitates separation by differential settling or other means. Froth flotation techniques and conversion of naturally occurring uranium compounds to gaseous UF_6 are other familiar examples of putting raw materials into more easily separable forms.

Equally important and almost as old are chemical pretreatments. These are too numerous and varied for inclusion here, but they must not be overlooked.

There are also many more recent examples, and we consider two here.

Example 6: Sorting of Solid Wastes by Color – As material resources become more expensive there is increasing incentive to recover valuable materials from solid wastes. One such material is glass. Of the total amount of glass being used today, roughly 60% is colorless. Reprocessing of the recovered glass to form clear glass therefore requires a separation of the colored glass from the colorless one. The property difference to be exploited in the separation is naturally the color of the glass. However, since no effective means yet exists for selectively moving ground glass according to its color, it is necessary to transform the color characteristic into one more easily exploited. The actual process developed is as follows. Glass is first ground to fine particle size, which is then irradiated under an infrared lamp source. The particles are thus selectively heated according to their color, and hence their optical absorptivity. After a specified period of time they are sprayed with an organic adhesive which above certain temperature binds strongly to the glass. The glass mixture treated in this way can be separated by froth flotation.

A similar process can be applied to the removal of impurities from rock salt. These impurities consist of ferric or magnesium salts which are darkly colored. The rock salt can be layered on top of a conveyor belt which is completely covered with an adhesive material. The solids are again heated with an infrared light source so that strong bonds are formed between the impurities and the adhesive. As the belt turns around the purified rock salt falls off and is collected.

Example 7: Protein separation by SDS-complexing – Interaction between the hydrophobic groups of protein with surfactant such as sodium dodecyl sulfate (SDS) in solution results in the formation of complexes, in which a single protein molecule binds a large number of surfactant molecules. The anionic surfactant thus contributes a large amount of negative charge to the protein molecule, so that protein charge becomes insignificant. The charge to mass ratio of different protein complexes are therefore nearly the same, and the

*A modern counterpart is the cell lysis needed in the isolation of intracellular enzymes.

total charge on each protein molecule is now dependent primarily on molecular weight with shape a secondary factor. This forms the basis for electrophoretic separation of proteins according to molecular weights. In solution it is believed that the electrophoretic mobility of these protein complexes are virtually the same.[124] This makes it necessary to perform the electrophoresis on a polyacrylamide gel. The mobility of the complexes in the gel is found to be inversely proportional to the logarithm of the protein molecular weights. In solution of low ionic strength, however, there is reason to believe the electrophoretic mobilities of the protein complexes are largely dependent on the total charge on each complex. It is therefore possible to separate them using the technique of electropolarization chromatography.[89]

Separation at the Pseudo-continuum Level

Although all separations are initiated by the diffusional processes discussed above, these are seldom capable of producing the separation distances required for large-scale applications. This can be seen very simply by considering Einstein's expression for the mean distance $\bar{\delta}$ traveled by a solute molecule in a time t by concentration diffusion with a diffusivity $\mathcal{D}$:

$$\bar{\delta} = \sqrt{4\mathcal{D}t} \tag{183}$$

For a typical liquid system where $\mathcal{D} \sim 10^{-5}$ cm^2/sec, the distance traveled in an hour is only about

$$\bar{\delta}\,(1\ \text{hr}) \sim 0.4\ \text{cm} \quad \text{(liquid)} \tag{184}$$

Even for a gas with $\mathcal{D} \sim \frac{1}{3}\ cm^2/sec$

$$\tilde{\delta}\,(1\ \text{hr}) \sim 70\ \text{cm} \quad \text{(gas, 1 atm)} \tag{185}$$

which is small relative to most practical requirements.

It is therefore normally necessary to augment the primary diffusional separation by convection, that is by a macroscopically observable flow. This is most naturally done by superimposing a nonuniform velocity profile on a nonuniform concentration profile, with the gradients of concentration and velocity at right angles to the flow. This can be described symbolically by the descriptor

$$D = G_1 c_i + G_1 v_2 \tag{186}$$

which states that the system is dominated by a concentration gradient in the x_1-direction, accompanied by a convective flow which is in the x_2-direction, but which varies in strength in the x_1-direction. In the section immediately below we consider means by which this type of behavior can be produced.

Experience shows that convective augmentation normally leads to a degree of geometric complexity making detailed integration of the diffusion equation either cumbersome or impossible. We must therefore seek means of avoiding unnecessarily detailed descriptions while retaining the ability to predict macroscopically observable behavior to the degree possible. We deal with this problem of modeling at the pseudo-continuum level in a following section. This section is, however, largely formal in nature.

Convective Augmentation of Diffusional Separations

We begin here by considering a representative group of separations, to illustrate the possibilities available and the problems of classification and description to be expected. We emphasize the fundamental, or one-dimensional chromatographic, mode in this discussion, and it should be understood that all other modes discussed previously are possible.

All separation mechanisms described above can be combined with convection to produce enhanced separations, but not all are examples of convective augmentation. Free-flow electrophoresis, for example, merely represents a perpendicular shift converting unsteady one-dimensional migration into a steady two-dimensional process: The flow does not increase the separation distance, and, in fact, because of Taylor dispersion, it actually decreases resolution.[90]

Most of the convective augmentation processes involve polarization phenomena in that a steady state is more or less closely approached in the x_1-direction. Furthermore, as in all polarization phenomena bounding surfaces play a dominant role, whether they are impermeable, freely permeable, or permselective. We may classify convectively augmented separations here by the natures of these surfaces, the polarizing force, and the type of convection. The surfaces may be categorized as

1. Impermeable surfaces (to solutes being separated) only; single-phase separations
2. At least one freely permeable surface at which discontinuities in physical properties, parti-

cularly chemical activity coefficients, occur; two-phase separations

3. Membrane processes, which may be looked on as three-phase systems

It may be seen from the previous section that a wide variety of polarizing forces exists, but in practice spatial variations of the thermodynamic activity coefficient are the most important. We therefore consider here only two categories for polarization: thermodynamic and diffusional. In the present discussion we shall pay very little attention to flows and shall simply refer to them in passing as forced or free convection. Some representative convectively augmented separations are shown in Figure 19 for illustrative purposes, and a somewhat larger number listed in Table 6.

In all cases the cup-mixing solute velocity differs from the flow-average velocity of the solvent because of the polarization taking place. This is shown quantitatively for ultrafiltration-induced polarization chromatography ("UPC"[69] or flow field flow fractionation[44]), in Example 9 below. It may readily be seen qualitatively in Figure 19A: here the solute velocity must be somewhere between the mean solvent velocity and zero.

The range of convectively augmented separations and the number of causative effects are both very large; some idea of this can be gained from Table 6, where some representative processes are listed. Even this short listing contains some processes which are either unusual or very complex.

Among the latter are particulate adsorption (aerosol filtration) and foam fractionation processes, which depend in part on mechanisms we have not yet considered. This is indicated by Figure 20 for aerosol filtration in a granular bed of collector particles (idealized here as spheres). Shown are the trajectories of representative aerosol particles (numbered 1 through 6) originally on the indicated fluid streamline. These pass through the granular bed until they touch a collector particle, when they are held permanently by van der Waal's forces. The basic mechanism of retardation is thus thermodynamic and closely allied to adsorption, and the equilibrium situation is one of total immobilization. However, if the particles were mathematical points moving on the gas streamlines there would be no retardation at all. The diffusional mechanisms by which the particles move to the collector surface are therefore of primary interest, and there are five of these (numbered to correspond with the particles in the figure):

1. Direct interception – Particle surface touches collector if streamline through particle center comes within one particle radius of a collector.

2. Inertial deviation – Since aerosols are more dense than the suspending gas they tend to depart from curved streamlines as shown.

3. Diffusion – Particles smaller than about 1 μm in diameter are affected strongly by Brownian motion and hence move from their original streamline by true concentration diffusion.

4. Gravity settling – This is important for particles larger than about 1 μm.

5. Electrostatic attraction – almost always occurs via charges on the collectors and induced dipoles – a nonlinear effect.

Clearly the first two of these effects are not normally included in the kinetic theory of gases. Descriptions of aerosol filtration and such allied processes as centrifugal collection in cyclones or froth flotation must be initiated at the molecular (here particulate) level. Inertial forces must be added to the true molecular mechanisms previously introduced. Similar additions may be needed for other extensions of our preceding discussion to particulate systems.

Polarization chromatography, or field flow fractionation, includes a variety of diffusionally induced polarization processes still in the developmental stage. One of these, ultrafiltration-induced polarization chromatography (UPC) is described in Example 9 below. Other promising polarization mechanisms include sweep diffusion, pressure diffusion, electrodiffusion (electrophoresis), thermal diffusion, and higher order effects such as dielectrophoresis[87] or magnetophoresis.[65] Steady counterflow modes for these same polarization processes are much more familiar: counterflow flow thermal diffusion separations in Clusius-Dickel columns, electrodecantation, and continuous countercurrent ultracentrifugation. This last process, for example, is now being tested on a very large scale for fractionation of uranium isotopes.

All two-phase chromatographic operations, and the corresponding steady counterflow separations such as distillation, appear to be thermo-

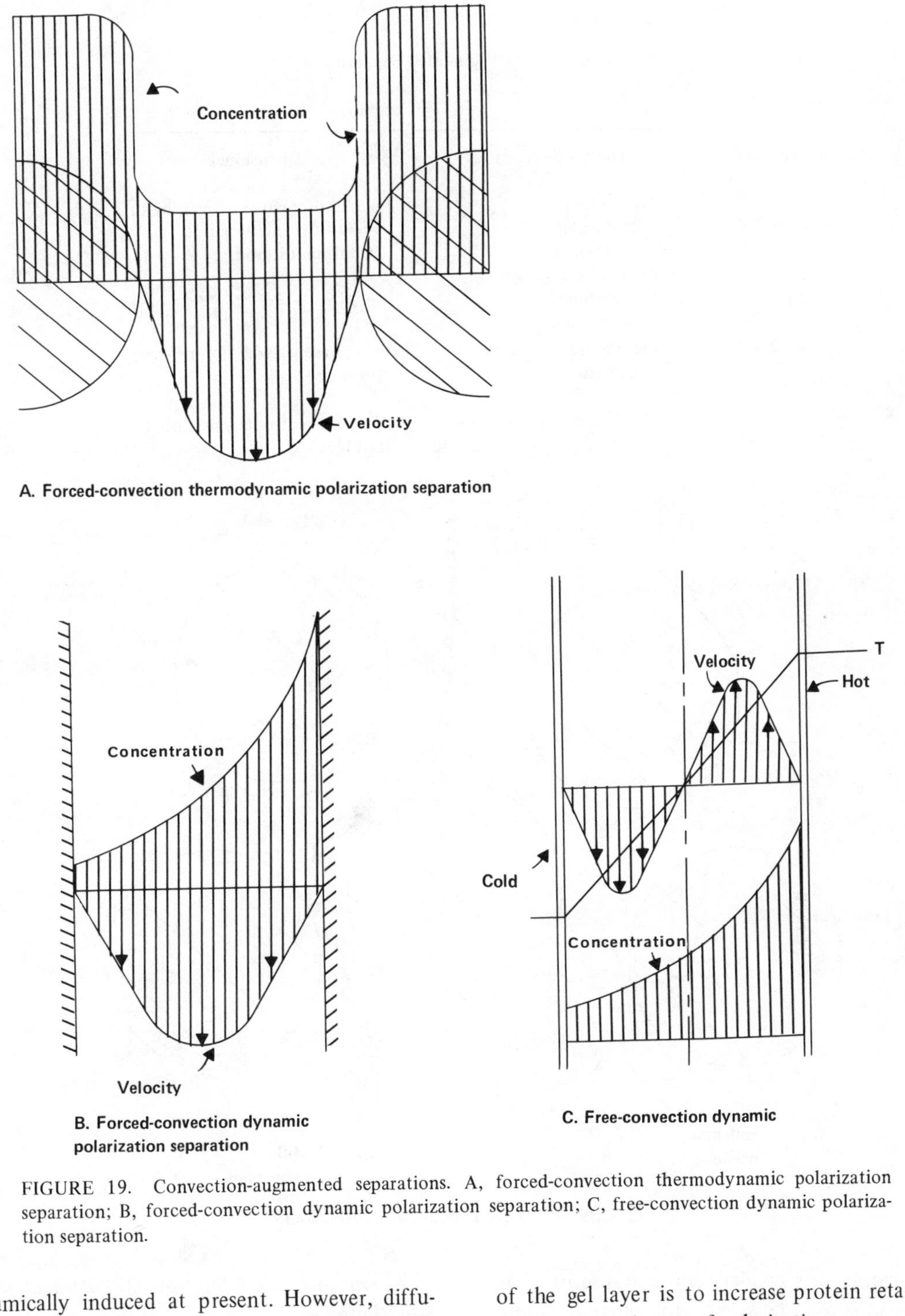

FIGURE 19. Convection-augmented separations. A, forced-convection thermodynamic polarization separation; B, forced-convection dynamic polarization separation; C, free-convection dynamic polarization separation.

dynamically induced at present. However, diffusionally induced separations of this type are possible, at least in principle, and one such possibility is suggested in Figure 21. Shown here is a variation of electropolarization chromatography ("EPC"[89]) in which the hollow fiber contains an inner gel layer permeable to protein, in addition to the outer protein-impermeable "skin." The effect of the gel layer is to increase protein retardation for any given degree of polarization.

Three-phase processes such as dialysis usually employ stationary membranes separating quite similar mobile phases. As a result, polarization is normally dependent primarily on rates of diffusion across the membrane, and is diffusion induced. Particularly interesting applications of this type

TABLE 6

Convectively Augmented Separations

Phases	Polarization: Thermodynamic	Polarization: Diffusional
1	Adsorption Molecular Particulate Foam fractionation Molecular Particulate	Polarization chromatography or Field-flow fractionation (Continuous modes)
2	Liquid-liquid extraction distillation	Two-phase polarization processes (untested)
3	Membrane-mediated fluid-fluid separations (rare)	Dialysis, electrodialysis, liquid bubbles

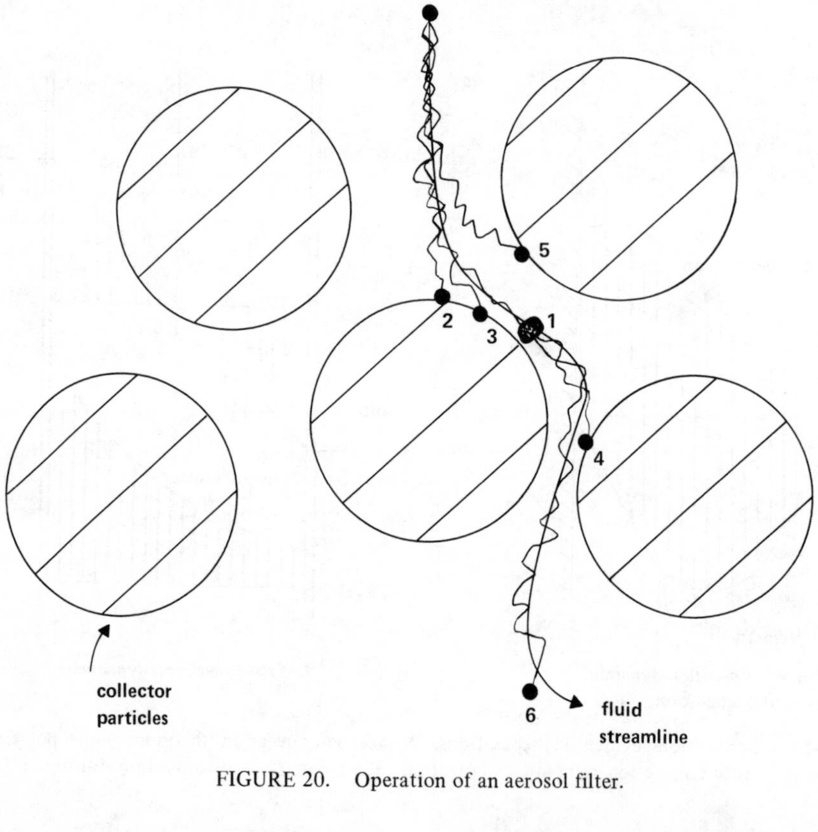

FIGURE 20. Operation of an aerosol filter.

involve carrier or secondary active transport.[27] It is also possible, however, to separate quite different immiscible phases by a membrane, and in this case the polarization is thermodynamically induced. This is desirable, for example, if the mobile phases are difficult to separate. These difficulties commonly result from small density differences or the formation of stable emulsions.

Mass-transport Modeling in Well-defined Flow Situations

We begin here by looking at two well-defined and relatively simple situations: chromatographic operation in a fixed bed of uniform spherical absorbent particles and polarization chromatography in slit flow. These have been well investigated and are useful for testing more general

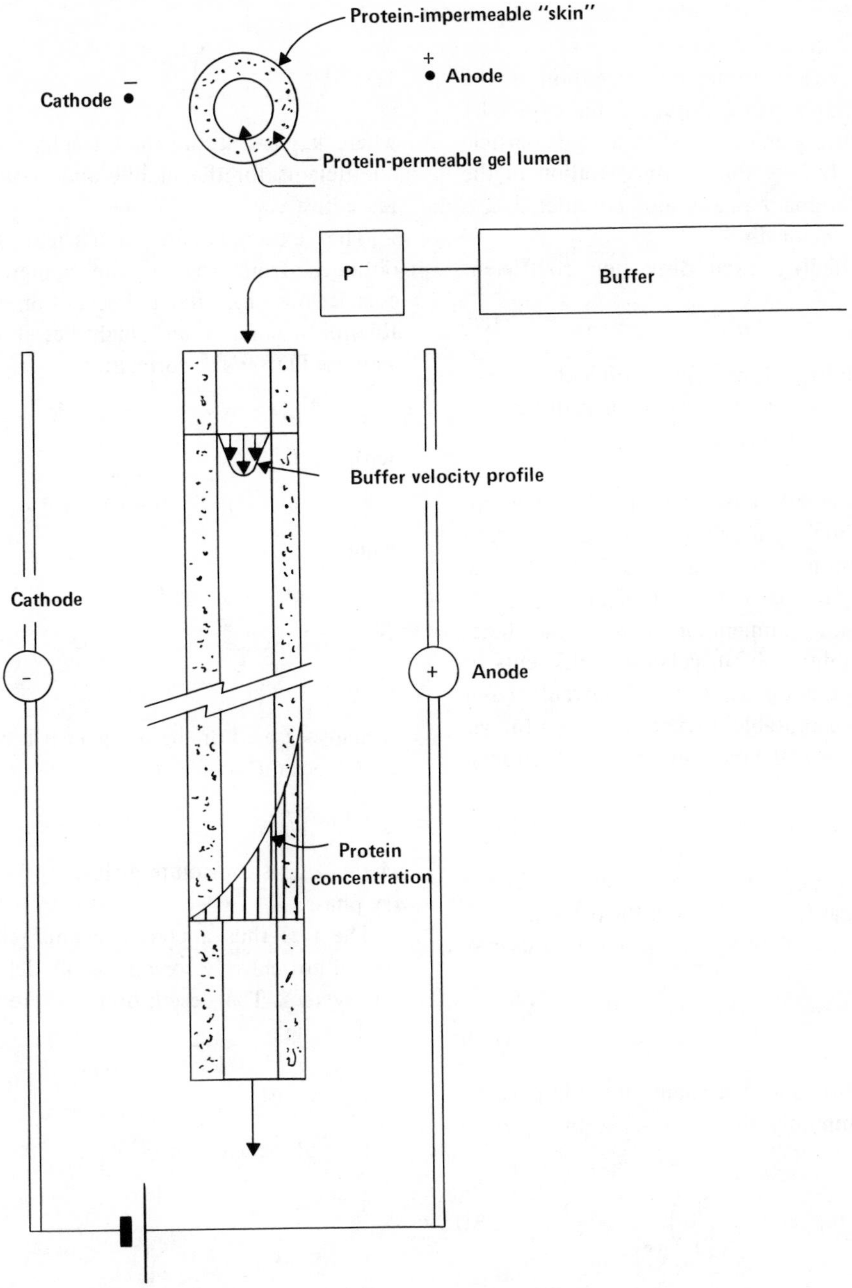

FIGURE 21. Two-phase polarization chromatography.

mass-transfer models. We shall be most interested in the average speed of the solute molecules, dispersion about the mean and the possibilities for focusing, and the importance of boundary conditions.

Example 8: Chromatography in a fixed bed of uniform spheres – It may readily be seen that the geometric scale of flow perturbations and the temporal scale of diffusional transients in the region occupied by a single packing particle are both typically small compared to those for the column as a whole. We therefore ignore these in our formal description and write a pseudo-continuum continuity equation for the column as:

$$\epsilon \frac{\partial c_i}{\partial t} + (1 - \epsilon) \frac{\partial c_{is}}{\partial t} + \epsilon \langle v \rangle \frac{\partial c_i}{\partial z} = \epsilon E \frac{\partial^2 c_i}{\partial z^2} \qquad (187)$$

where

ϵ = Fraction of column volume occupied by the mobile phase

c_i = $c_i(z,t)$ = Solute concentration in the mobile phase, assumed uniform over the region occupied by a single particle

c_{is} = $c_{is}(z,t)$ = Solute concentration in the stationary phase, also considered uniform locally

E = Effective axial dispersion coefficient

$$E \doteq e + \mathscr{D}_{im} \tag{188}$$

e = "Eddy" dispersion coefficient

$\mathscr{D}_{im}$ = Molecular effective binary diffusivity of solute i in the mobile phase

The eddy dispersion coefficient results primarily from interparticle mixing in packed beds and Taylor dispersion in channel flows. Both of these are thoroughly discussed in standard references,[196] and we will not comment on them further here. The simple addition of dispersion coefficients in Equation 188 is not exact, but it is convenient and almost always acceptable. Normally, except for gas chromatography and high-pressure liquid chromatography

$$e >> \mathscr{D}_{im} \tag{189}$$

and molecular dispersion can be ignored in the mobile phase, as it normally is in the particles.

It remains to relate c_{is} to c_i, and it is usually assumed that

$$\frac{\partial c_{is}}{\partial t} = F(c_i, c_{is}) \tag{190}$$

that is, that diffusional transients are unimportant. The most commonly used expression for Equation 190 is

$$(1 - \epsilon)\frac{\partial c_{is}}{\partial t} = (k_{tot}a)\left(c_i - \frac{c_{is}}{K_D}\right) \tag{191}$$

where

k_{tot} = Overall interfacial mass-transfer coefficient

a = Interfacial area per unit volume of bed

K_D = (c_{is}/c_i^*) = equilibrium distribution coefficient

c_i^* = Mobile-phase concentration in equilibrium with c_{is}

and

$$k_{tot} = \left(\frac{1}{k_m} + \frac{1}{K_D k_s}\right)^{-1} \tag{192}$$

where k_m and k_s are the intraphase mass-transfer coefficients for the mobile and stationary phases respectively.

The external-phase coefficient k_m can be obtained from any of the numerous available correlations for fixed beds. For low particle Reynolds number and high Péclet number one may use Pfeffer's[84] correlation

$$(k_m D_p/\mathscr{D}_{im}) = A(D_p \langle v \rangle/\mathscr{D}_{im})^{1/3} \tag{193}$$

with

$$A = 1.26\,(1 - \gamma^5)/(2 - 3\gamma + \gamma^5 - 2\gamma^6) \tag{194}$$

where

$$\gamma = (1 - \epsilon)^{1/3}$$

Note that

$$\epsilon \sim 0.38$$

in many cases. For the particles it is customary to use Glueckauf's correlation

$$k_s \sim 10\mathscr{D}_{is}/D_p \tag{195}$$

where $\mathscr{D}_{is}$ is the solute diffusivity in the stationary phase.

There is thus a complete and self-consistent, even if not entirely convincing, model available for this system. The description is made a bit clearer by defining:

θ = $v_z t/L$

L = Length of column

η = z/L

χ = c_i/c_{i0}

c_{i0} = Feed concentration

χ_s = c_{is}/c_{i0}

χ^* = c_i^*/c_{i0}

Pé = $v_z L/E$

α = $K_D(1 - \epsilon)/\epsilon$

Γ = $(k_{tot}a)(L/v_z)/(1 - \epsilon)K_D$

$$k_{tot} = \left(\frac{1}{k_e} + \frac{1}{K_D k_s}\right)^{-1}$$

k_e = External-phase concentration based mass-transfer coefficient

k_s = Solid-phase mass-transfer coefficient

We thus obtain:

$$\frac{\partial \chi}{\partial \theta} + \alpha \frac{\partial \chi^*}{\partial \theta} + \frac{\partial \chi}{\partial \eta} = \frac{1}{Pé} \frac{\partial^2 \chi}{\partial \eta^2} \quad (196)$$

$$\alpha \frac{\partial \chi^*}{\partial \theta} = \Gamma(\chi - \chi^*) \quad (197)$$

which is the most complete description normally considered (see, however, Reference 94).

We now look at the simple specific example of composition-independent K_D to get a "feel" for the characteristics of Equations 196 and 197. More specifically, we consider a step increase in feed concentration, described by:

$$\chi(0, \eta) = \chi^*(0, \eta) = 0 \qquad \eta > 0 \quad (198)$$

$$\chi(\theta, 0) = 1 \qquad \theta > 0 \quad (199)$$

The solution, in Laplace transformation with respect to θ, is, for linear systems (Γ = constant):

$$\bar{\chi}(s, \eta) = \frac{1}{s} \exp\left\{\frac{\eta Pé}{2}\left[1 - \sqrt{1 + 4s\left[s + \Gamma\left(1 + \frac{1}{\alpha}\right)\right] / Pé \left(s + \frac{\Gamma}{\alpha}\right)}\right]\right\} \quad (200)$$

No explicit inversion is available.

However, one can evaluate moments with respect to τ defined by:

$$I_n \equiv \int_{\bar{\theta}}^{\infty} [1 - \chi(\tau, 1)]\,(\tau - \bar{\theta})^n d\tau - \int_0^{\bar{\theta}} \chi(\tau, 1)(\tau - \bar{\theta})^n d\tau \quad (201)$$

where

$$\bar{\theta} = (1 + \alpha) = \bar{t}\langle v \rangle / L \quad (202)$$

$$\bar{t} = (L/\langle v \rangle)[\epsilon + (1 - \epsilon)K_D] \quad (203)$$

The mean residence time $\bar{t}$ is just the saturation time in the absence of dispersion.

The first four moments have been calculated by Knight;[63] these are

$$I_0 = 0 \quad (204)$$

$$I_1 = \bar{\theta}^2 \left[\frac{1}{Pé} + \frac{\alpha^2}{(1 + \alpha)^2 \Gamma}\right] \quad (205)$$

$$I_2 = \bar{\theta}^3 \left[\frac{4}{Pé^2} + \frac{4\alpha^2}{(1 + \alpha)^2 Pé \Gamma} + \frac{2\alpha^3}{(1 + \alpha)^2 \Gamma^2}\right] \quad (206)$$

$$I_3 = \bar{\theta}^4 \left\{\frac{30}{Pé^3} + \frac{3}{Pé^2} + \frac{6\alpha^2}{(1 + \alpha)^2}\left[\frac{6}{Pé^2 \Gamma} + \frac{1}{Pé \Gamma}\right] + \frac{6(3\alpha + 2)\alpha^3}{(1 + \alpha)^4 Pé \Gamma^2} + \frac{3\alpha^4}{(1 + \alpha)^4}\left[\frac{1}{\Gamma^2} + \frac{2}{\Gamma^3}\right]\right\} \quad (207)$$

These results show that:

1. The nondispersive saturation time is the true mean residence time, since $I_0 = 0$.

2. The dispersion about $\bar{\theta}$, represented by I_1 for saturation curves, is just the sum of those due to axial dispersion and mass-transfer resistance ($1/k_{tot}$) individually. This is shown by Equation 205 which could be written as

$$I_1 = \bar{\theta}^2 (Pé, tot)^{-1} \quad (208)$$

or

$$I_1 = \bar{\theta}^2 \frac{\alpha^2}{(1 + \alpha)^2} \Gamma_{tot} \quad (209)$$

where

$$Pé, tot = \left[\frac{1}{Pé} + \frac{\alpha^2}{(1 + \alpha)^2 \Gamma}\right]^{-1} \quad (210)$$

$$\Gamma_{tot} = \left[\frac{(1 + \alpha)^2}{\alpha^2 Pé} + \frac{1}{\Gamma}\right]^{-1} \quad (211)$$

Equation 205 has been very widely used.

3. The skewness, represented by Equation 206, the kurtosis, represented by Equation 207, and shape factors provided by the higher moments depend in a much more complex way on Pé, Γ, and α. Equations 204 through 207 are valuable for fitting any trial function for χ to the transform-space solution $\bar{\chi}$ of Equation 200.

This is done by the method of moments, i.e., by equating moments of the trial function to those of Equations 204 to 207 or their extensions. As a practical matter the higher moments give progressively less useful information and in real situations moments higher than I_2 are almost always obscured by experimental error. In separations work it is customary to ignore even I_2 and settle only for a one-parameter description of dispersion about the mean.

One can also use these relations to characterize a pulse input using the relations:

$$\chi_{\text{pulse}} = \frac{\partial}{\partial\theta}(\chi_{\text{step}})\,\Delta\theta \quad \chi(\theta, 0) = 1 \quad 0 < \theta < \Delta\theta$$

$$= 0 \quad \theta < 0 \text{ or } \theta > \Delta\theta \tag{212}$$

$$= \frac{\partial}{\partial\eta}(\chi_{\text{step}})\,\Delta\eta \quad \chi(0, \eta) = 1 \quad 0 < \eta < \Delta\eta$$

$$= 0 \quad \eta > \Delta\eta \tag{213}$$

$$(I_n)_{\text{pulse}} = (I_{n-1})_{\text{step}} \tag{214}$$

These are the most generally useful solutions.

The usual approach is to invert Equation 200 for the two limiting cases:

$Pé = \infty$:

$$\chi(\theta, \eta) = J(\Gamma\eta, \Gamma\theta/\alpha) \tag{215}$$

where

$$J(x, y) = 1 - \int_0^x e^{x'+y}\, J_0\,(\sqrt{-4x'y})dx' \tag{216}$$

For long columns ($\Gamma\eta > 2$ and $\Gamma\theta > \alpha$):

$$\chi \doteq \frac{1}{2}\left[1 + \text{erf}\,(\sqrt{\Gamma\theta/\alpha} - \sqrt{\Gamma\eta} + \underline{\sqrt{\alpha/\theta\Gamma} + \sqrt{1/\Gamma\eta}})\right] \tag{217}$$

For finite Pé use

$$\Gamma_{\text{Tot}} = \left[\frac{(1+\alpha)^2}{\alpha^2 Pé} + \frac{1}{\Gamma}\right]^{-1} \tag{218}$$

in place of Γ

$\Gamma = \infty$:

$$\chi(\theta, 1) = \frac{1}{2}\left\{1 + \text{erf}\left[\sqrt{\frac{Pé}{(1+\alpha)\theta}}\left(\frac{\theta - 1 - \alpha}{2}\right)\right] \underline{+ e^{Pé}\,\text{erfc}\left[\sqrt{\frac{Pé}{(1+\alpha)\theta}}\left(\frac{\theta + 1 + \alpha}{2}\right)\right]}\right\} \tag{219}$$

To use for finite Γ write:

$$Pé_{\text{tot}} = \left[\frac{1}{Pé} + \frac{\alpha^2}{(1+\alpha)^2\Gamma}\right]^{-1} \tag{220}$$

in place of Pé. These approximations will be exact insofar as mean residence time and standard deviation about the mean are concerned, and the underlined contributions will often be negligible.

The skewness, and the more subtle shape factors represented by the higher moments, will not be exact, but these deficiencies are not usually serious. This is shown by Figures 22 and 23.

Example 9: Polarization chromatography and Taylor diffusion – We now consider convective augmentation of polarization within a single phase, and again we concentrate our attention on the chromatographic mode of operation. For illustrative purposes we consider ultrafiltration-induced polarization chromatography (UPC) in slit flow.[44,69] One can, however, use other geometries[89] and other polarizing forces.[42] Systems of this type are becoming increasingly important, in both the chromatographic and steady countercurrent modes, and they are also useful to introduce the important subject of convection-induced dispersion or Taylor dispersion. We now attempt to describe what happens when a small solute pulse is introduced to the flow channel of Figure 24, and we confine our attention for the moment to a somewhat idealized situation: We assume steady two-dimensional laminar flow and pseudobinary diffusion. Solute motion is then described by:

$$\frac{\partial c}{\partial t} + \frac{\partial}{\partial x} cv_x + \frac{\partial}{\partial y} cv_y = \mathcal{D}\left(\frac{\partial^2 c}{\partial x^2} + \frac{\partial^2 c}{\partial y^2}\right) \tag{221}$$

Here c is the concentration of the polymeric solute under consideration, $\mathcal{D}$ is an effective binary diffusivity of this solute, and **v** is the fluid velocity. System geometry is defined in Figure 24. We next assume the cross-flow velocity to be small compared to the axial-flow velocity, and that the effects of polymer concentration on system hydrodynamics are negligible. The velocity profile is then described by

$$v_x = 6\,\bar{u}\left[\left(\frac{y}{B}\right) - \left(\frac{y}{B}\right)^2\right] \tag{222}$$

$$v_y = -v_w \tag{223}$$

Here $\bar{u}$ is the flow-average axial velocity and v_w is the velocity of the cross flow; both are considered constant. We shall consider more complex flow patterns later.

The boundary conditions on concentration are obtained from the assumption that solute cannot penetrate the walls. Thus

$$v_y c = \mathcal{D}\frac{\partial c}{\partial y} \quad \text{at } y = 0, B \tag{224}$$

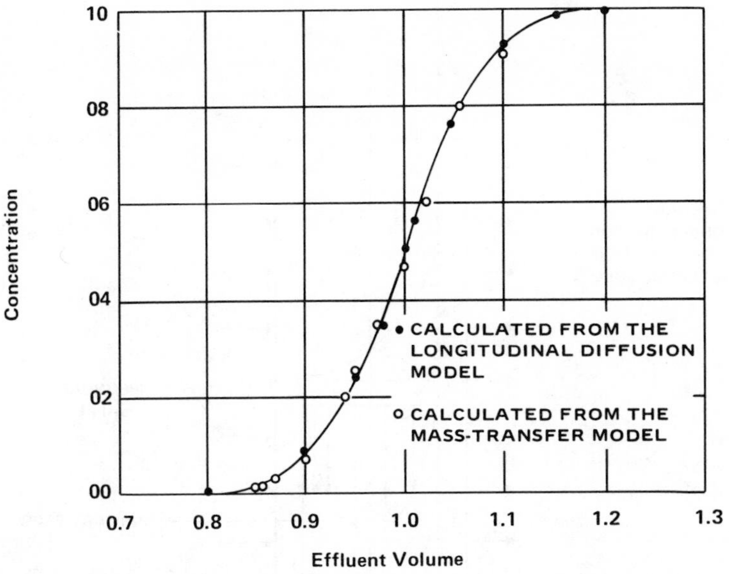

FIGURE 22. Comparison of mass-transfer models for a linear saturation process. (From Lightfoot, E. N., Sanchez-Palma, R. J., and Edwards, D. O., Chromatography and allied fixed-bed separations process, in *New Separation Techniques,* Schoen, H. M., Ed., Interscience, New York, 1962. With permission.)

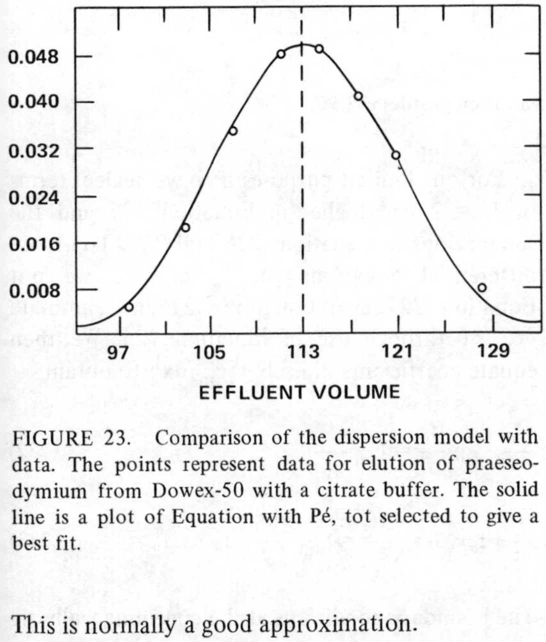

FIGURE 23. Comparison of the dispersion model with data. The points represent data for elution of praseodymium from Dowex-50 with a citrate buffer. The solid line is a plot of Equation with Pé, tot selected to give a best fit.

This is normally a good approximation.

Equation 221 can be averaged formally over the channel width with the aid of Equation 224 to obtain

$$\frac{\partial <c>}{\partial t} + \frac{\partial}{\partial x}<v_x c> = \mathcal{D}\frac{\partial^2 <c>}{\partial x^2} \tag{225}$$

where

$$<Q> \equiv \frac{1}{B}\int_0^B Q dy \tag{226}$$

Henceforth <c> will be written as c_m, the area mean concentration. It is our purpose to determine c_m as a function of position and time, and we shall do this by obtaining useful explicit approximations for $<v_x c>$ in terms of the mean velocity $\bar{u}$ and mean concentration c_m.

To do this we follow the lead of Gill and Sankarasubramanian[45] and postulate that

$$c = \sum_{k=0}^{\infty} f_k(y, t)\frac{\partial^k c_m}{\partial x^k} \tag{227}$$

Putting Equation 227 into 221 we get

$$\frac{\partial c_m}{\partial t} + <v_x f_0>\frac{\partial c_m}{\partial x} = (\mathcal{D} - <v_x f_1>)\frac{\partial^2 c_m}{\partial x^2} - \sum_{k=2}^{\infty} <v_x f_k>\frac{\partial^k c_m}{\partial x^k} \tag{228}$$

or

$$\frac{\partial c_m}{\partial t} + R\bar{u}\frac{\partial c_m}{\partial x} = (\mathcal{D} + \epsilon)\frac{\partial^2 c_m}{\partial x^2} - \sum_{k=2}^{\infty} <v_x f_k>\frac{\partial^k c_m}{\partial x^k} \tag{229}$$

where

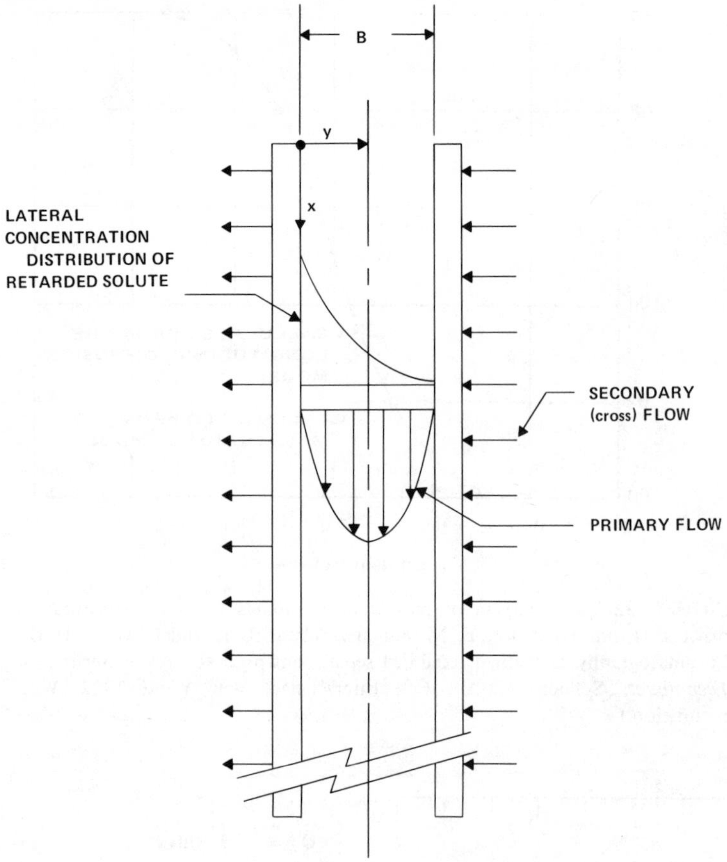

FIGURE 24. Velocity and concentration profiles in UPC.

$$R \equiv \langle v_x f_0 \rangle / \bar{u} \tag{230}$$

and

$$\epsilon = -\langle v_x f_1 \rangle \tag{231}$$

Equation 231 is convenient for our purposes because R and ϵ, from the first two terms of Equation 227, have particularly important physical significance: The retardation factor R is just the ratio of the mean convective velocity of solute to that of solvent, while ϵ is an effective axial dispersion coefficient, resulting from the equivalent of Taylor dispersion in this system. The remaining terms of the series are needed to provide detailed descriptions of pulse shape, but they are of secondary importance, particularly in long columns. Our primary objective is then to obtain predictions of R and ϵ, which are functions only of time; as for the packed-column operations just discussed, the higher moments are of secondary importance. We do not discuss them here, but Lee and Lightfoot[69] show how they may be obtained.

For our limited purposes then we neglect terms of k = 2 and higher in Equation 227 and the summations in Equations 228 and 229. To obtain differential equations for f_0 and f_1 we put Equation 227 into Equation 221 and eliminate $\partial c_m/\partial t$ through use of Equation 225. We then equate coefficients of each $\partial^k c_m/\partial x^k$ to obtain

$$\frac{\partial f_0}{\partial t} - v_w \frac{\partial f_0}{\partial y} = \mathcal{D}_{im} \frac{\partial^2 f_0}{\partial y^2} \tag{232}$$

$$\frac{\partial f_1}{\partial t} + f_0 v_x - v_w \frac{\partial f_1}{\partial y} = \mathcal{D}_{im} \frac{\partial^2 f_1}{\partial y^2} + f_0 \langle v_x f_0 \rangle \tag{233}$$

The boundary conditions at the confining walls are

$$\mathcal{D}_{im} \frac{\partial f_k}{\partial y} + v_w f_k = 0 \tag{234}$$

at

$$y = 0, B \tag{235}$$

Initial conditions depend upon the feed procedure,

but we shall assume here that

$$f_0(y, 0) = 1 \tag{236}$$

$$f_1(y, 0) = 0 \tag{237}$$

This corresponds to uniform initial distribution of the pulse across the slit.

The solutions for f_0 are

$$f_0 = f_0^{(\infty)} + f_0^{(t)}$$

where

$$f_0^{(\infty)} = \text{Pé}\, e^{-\text{Pé}\eta}/(1 - e^{-\text{Pé}}) \tag{238}$$

$$f_0^{(t)} = \sum_{n=0}^{\infty} T_{on}(\tau)\, Y_n(\eta) \tag{239}$$

$$\text{Pé} = v_w B/\mathcal{D} \tag{239a}$$

$$\tau = v_w B/\mathcal{D} \tag{239b}$$

$$\eta = y/B \tag{239c}$$

$$T_{on}(\tau) = \frac{(e^{\text{Pé}/2}(-1)^n - 1)\text{Pé}}{\left[n^2\pi^2 + \left(\frac{\text{Pé}}{2}\right)^2\right]}\, e^{-\left[\text{Pé} + \frac{4n^2\pi^2}{\text{Pé}}\right]} \tag{240}$$

$$Y_n(\eta) = \frac{e^{-\text{Pé}\eta/2}\left[n^2\pi^2 \cos n\pi\eta - \frac{n\pi\text{Pé}}{2}\sin n\pi\eta\right]}{\left[n^2\pi^2 + \left(\frac{\text{Pé}}{2}\right)^2\right]} \tag{241}$$

Note that ϕ_0 depends only upon one parameter, the Péclet number. The transient contribution normally decays rapidly enough to be of neglibible practical importance.

The expression for f_1 is in general much more complex and is best determined numerically. However, for Pé = v_w = 0, and

$$f_0 = 1 = R \tag{242}$$

then

$$\frac{\partial f_1}{\partial t} - \mathcal{D}_{im}\frac{\partial^2 f_1}{\partial y^2} = \langle v_x\rangle - v_x$$

$$= \bar{u}\left[1 - 6\left(\frac{y}{B} - \frac{y^2}{B^2}\right)\right] \tag{243}$$

This expression may be readily integrated and yields at steady state

$$\lim_{\substack{t\to\infty\\ \text{Pé}\to 0}} \{\epsilon\} = \frac{B^2 u^2}{210\mathcal{D}} \tag{244}$$

This is known as the Taylor dispersion coefficient for slit flow.

In summary, we may write the diffusion equation in pseudo-continuum form as

$$\frac{\partial c_m}{\partial t} + R\bar{u}\frac{\partial c_m}{\partial x} \doteq (\mathcal{D} + \epsilon)\frac{\partial^2 c_m}{\partial x^2} \tag{245}$$

with

$$R = \langle v_x f_0\rangle/\bar{u} = R(\tau, \text{Pé}) \tag{246}$$

$$\epsilon = -\langle v_x f_1\rangle = \epsilon(\tau, \text{Pé}) \tag{247}$$

and

$$\lim_{\tau\to\infty}\{R\} = (6/\text{Pé})\left[\coth\left(\frac{\text{Pé}}{2}\right) - \frac{2}{\text{Pé}}\right] \tag{248}$$

$$\lim_{\substack{\tau\to\infty\\ \text{Pé}\to 0}}\{\epsilon\} = \frac{B^2\bar{u}^2}{210\mathcal{D}} \tag{249}$$

Also, it may be shown that

$$\lim_{\substack{\tau\to\infty\\ \text{Pé}\to\infty}}\{\epsilon\} = \frac{72}{\text{Pé}^4}\frac{B^2\bar{u}^2}{\mathcal{D}} \tag{250}$$

which predicts very small axial dispersion for significantly high Pé.

System predicted behavior for short times and intermediate Pé, along with data of Lee and Lightfoot,[69] are shown in Figures 23 to 27.

Note that for a pulse feed

$$c_m = \frac{c_0}{\sqrt{4\pi(\mathcal{D} + \epsilon t)}}\exp\left[-(x - R\bar{u}t)^2/4(\mathcal{D} + \epsilon)t\right] \tag{251}$$

where c_0 is a normalization constant. This is the same form as for a packed bed; direct comparisons are therefore possible.

Figure 25 shows a comparison of predicted and observed values of retardation for bovine serum albumin. Agreement is seen to be generally good, but few data are yet available in the high-Péclet number region of greatest practical interest. At Pé > 20, R begins to approach the asymptotic limit of 6/Pé rather closely, and it is under these limiting conditions that maximum separability is achieved. Transient contributions to R are small and will not be discussed here. The dispersion coefficient ϵ as calculated from theory is a strong function of Péclet number as shown in Figure 26. It can be seen that retardation of solute in UPC also minimizes convective dispersion, which is a

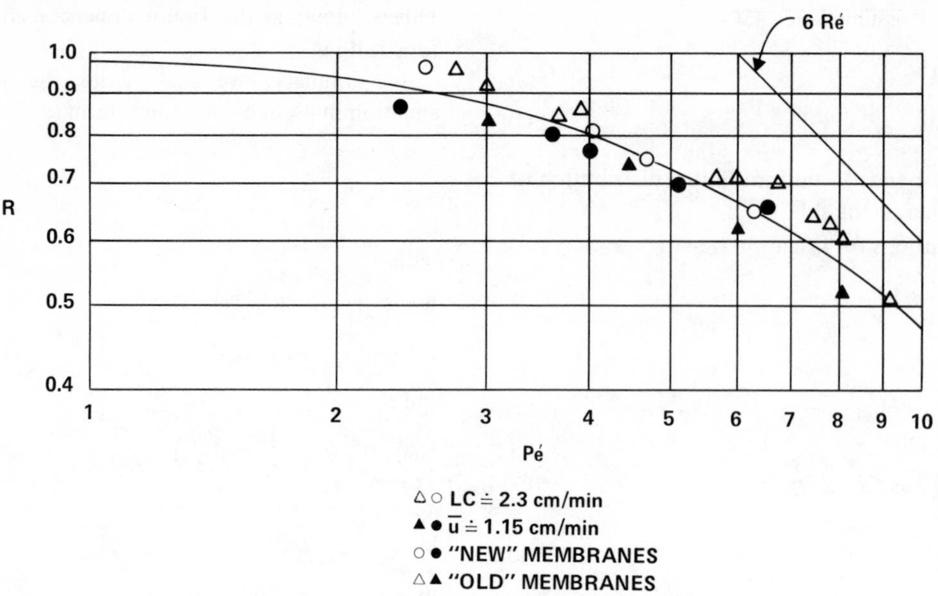

FIGURE 25. Comparison of observed retardation with prediction (B = 0.033 cm).

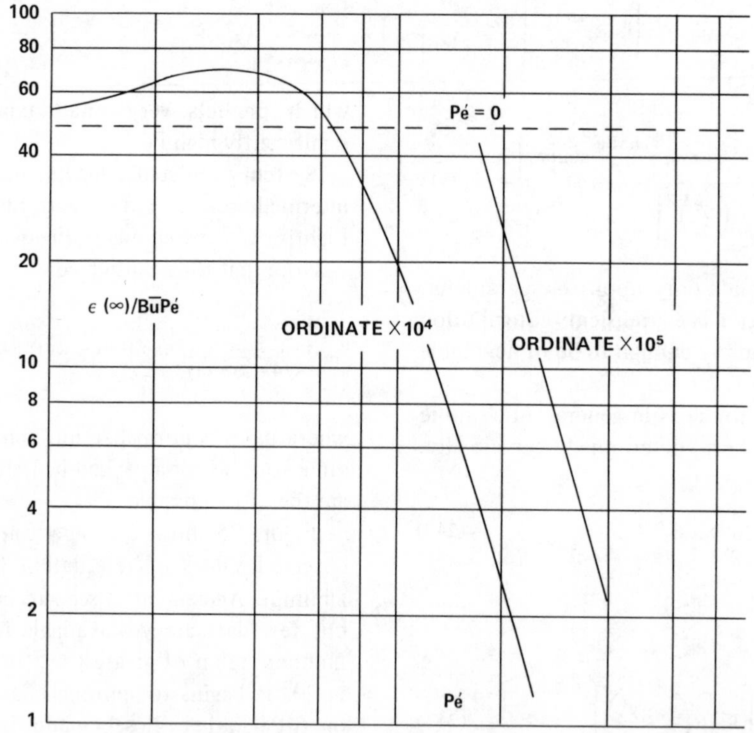

FIGURE 26. Asymptotic axial dispersion as a function of Péclet number.

highly desirable feature for any chromatographic separation. The success of the pseudo-continuum model, represented by Equation 251, is more clearly demonstrated in Figure 27. The effluent concentration profile, calculated from theory and experimentally determined system parameters

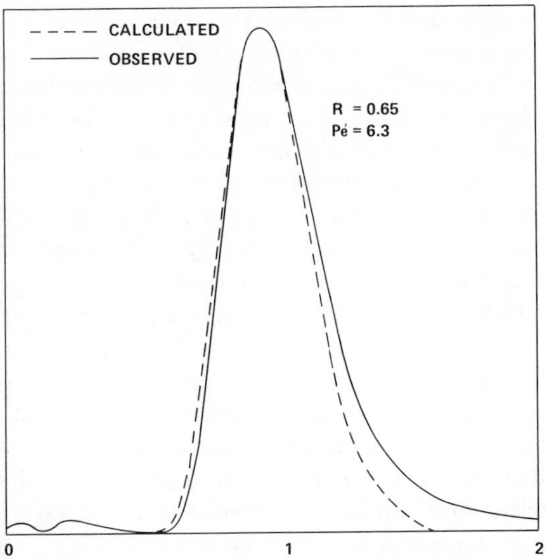

FIGURE 27. Comparison of observed and predicted effluent concentrations. BSA solution at 0.0764 ml/min; mean solute retention time $\bar{t}$ = 26.14 min; solvent retention time = 17.25 min.

(dotted curve), is in good agreement with the experimentally observed profile (solid curve).

THE MAGNITUDES OF SEPARATION PARAMETERS AND ESTIMATION OF SEPARATION POTENTIAL

The above sections provide a formal basis for describing a very wide variety of separations techniques; it now remains to use them, both for choosing between available possibilities and designing suitable processes based on those chosen. These activities are complex and depend on a wide variety of background information not easily introduced into a systematic framework. It is, however, almost always useful to proceed via three relatively well-defined stages*:

1. A preliminary general assessment of feasibility, based on the magnitudes of key separations parameters and their significance in view of existing technology
2. An estimate of separation potential based on the general characteristics of the proposed process
3. Successively more detailed descriptions of equipment performance, based on a combination of calculation and experiment

*For example see Reference 110.

In all cases it is of course desirable to minimize time and effort, and this in turn requires taking some risks; selection and design are always in the last analysis heuristic processes. With this as an apology we now discuss the above assessment stages.

Preliminary Assessment of Feasibility

Quite often the vast majority of available separations techniques can be quickly discarded on examining the expected magnitudes of key separations parameters. This is of course especially true if a reasonably suitable process exists to serve for comparison. Perhaps the single most powerful comparison is between the magnitudes of possible separative forces and the randomizing effects of Brownian motion. The utility of such a procedure is suggested by the listing of characteristic magnitudes in Table 5. Thus it is seen immediately from this table that electrophoretic forces are quite strong since a potential of only 25 mV can produce a unit change in the logarithm of chemical activity, i.e., a concentration ratio on the order of 2 to 3.

One must of course also have some appreciation of technological limitations. As a specific example, the magnetic field of 2.5×10^6 G listed in the table is about 100-fold higher than those produced by readily available magnets. Similarly, the electric field gradient of 10^4 V/cm^2 required to align a characteristic protein calls for very small spacings (of the order of magnitude of 1 μm) between electrodes if an aqueous solution is to be used as the suspending medium. This means that dielectrophoretic[87] polarization chromatography of proteins is possible but difficult to implement.

It may be useful to prepare tables showing trends of migrational velocities as a function of molecular parameters. The effect of the molecular weight is a good example. Thus one can write a convenient "close-separation" approximation for centrifugation against gravity in a binary rotating system as

$$J^{\star}_{Ar} = -c\mathcal{D}_{AB}\left[\frac{\partial x_A}{\partial r} + \frac{(c_A\bar{V}_A - \omega_A)}{c\mathcal{R}T}\frac{\partial p}{\partial r}\right] \tag{252}$$

If we specialize this for low-density gases with molecular weights M_A and M_B such that

$$|M_A - M_B| << M_A \tag{253}$$

we find

$$c\mathcal{R}T = p \tag{254}$$

$$c_A \bar{V}_A = x_A \tag{255}$$

$$\omega_A = x_A \Big/ \left[1 + x_B\left(\frac{M_B - M_A}{M_A}\right)\right] \left[1 - x_B\left(\frac{M_B - M_A}{M_A}\right)\right] x_A \tag{256}$$

$$\partial p/\partial r = \rho r \Omega^2 \tag{257}$$

$$\rho = Mp/\mathcal{R}T \text{ with } M \sim M_A \tag{258}$$

where Ω is the angular velocity of the centrifuge. Then

$$J^{\star}_{Ar} \doteq -c\mathcal{D}_{AB}\left[\frac{\partial x_A}{\partial r} + x_A(1 - x_A)(M_B - M_A)r\Omega^2/\mathcal{R}T\right] \tag{259}$$

Note that the pressure-diffusion term contains only the differences in molecular weights, not the fractional differences as for most physical separation mechanisms. This suggests that pressure diffusion (or centrifugation) is relatively more promising for heavier isotopes. This is just what is observed; centrifugation is being actively investigated for uranium enrichment, but it has never been seriously considered for the isolation of deuterium.

The dependence of the dispersive forces induced by Brownian motion on particle size can be illustrated, for example, by filtration operations where we find the hierarchy:

- Reverse osmosis
- Ultrafiltration
- Microfiltration
- Filtration (of macroscopic particles, large colloids to gravel)

In reverse osmosis Brownian effects are so strong that boundary-layer polarization can be suppressed with ease, thus facilitating solvent removal but making solute collection all but impossible. In macroscopic filtration the situation is reversed and Brownian effects are negligible: cake formation is now difficult to avoid. Micro-and ultrafiltration are intermediate in this respect.

Another good example of the interactions between dispersive and migrational forces is given by settling because of the wide range of sizes and migrational velocities covered by this process.

The smallest particles of industrial importance whose settling is not prevented by Brownian motion are aerosols, and these migrate slowly (whether in centrifugal, gravitational, or electrical fields). For this reason they are normally collected by convection through fibrous or granular beds of very small characteristic dimensions. Conversely, microbial cells in fermenters escape damage in part because they are not effectively intercepted by the impeller blades. At the other end of the settling spectrum are the coarse granular solids effectively removed by the simple primary treatment (settling) tanks of sewage treatment plants. Here the migrational velocity is comparable to the rather high transport velocity across the settler.

Convection as a dispersive force has already been described. To date there is no reliable way of predicting *a priori* the magnitude of dispersion caused by nonideal flow, except for the simple case of "Taylor dispersion" and related phenomena (e.g., polarization chromatography). Experimental techniques such as pulse or sinusoidal impulse-response methods often must be applied to assess the flow nonidealities of existing equipment. Modifications of the equipment to improve the flow pattern within will eventually follow. This is essentially the "evolutionary design" concept of Box.[12]

Estimation of Separation Potential

Once a basic separation mechanism has been at least tentatively selected, it is necessary to incorporate it into some physical structure, and the next problem is to settle as efficiently as possible on a suitable geometry and operating conditions. Clearly one wishes to find the best possible design in the shortest possible time, and also to estimate the inherent potential of any class of separator under consideration.

The entire process above is normally carried out with existing technology and results in the selection of a known quantity, e.g., an "off-the-shelf" distillation column, and this is not always unreasonable. Such a procedure is usually fast and reliable, but it may also be expensive.

Where the economics justify a substantial developmental effort, more innovative possibilities should be considered. One of the most impressive of all such developmental efforts was the search for effective isotope enrichment procedures under the Manhattan Project, and one of the key tools developed in that effort was the value function, already introduced in the second section of this chapter. We consider two examples of its use here and suggest that its utility be further investigated. Our first example deals with design at the continuum level, and our second with the arrangement of individual units in cascades.

Example 10: The separation potential of a sweep-diffusion cell – A sweep-diffusion column for isotope fractionation is shown schematically in Figures 28 and 29. A process gas, species 0, moves radially across the cylindrical separation chamber and tends to drive the isotopes, species 1 and 2, toward the periphery. The two isotopes diffuse back against this flow at slightly different rates to produce a radial separation. The radial separation in turn is multiplied by counterflow, and the counterflow is induced by downward flow of process-gas condensate on the outer chamber wall. As in many similar situations, it is possible to make a useful analysis by neglecting end effects, essentially assuming the chamber to be very long. The basis for the whole process is described by the set of Stefan-Maxwell equations, which may be written here as:

$$\nabla x_i = \sum_{\substack{j=1 \\ \neq i}}^{N} \frac{x_i x_j}{\mathcal{D}_{ij}} (v_j - v_i) \qquad (i = 1, 2, \ldots N) \tag{260}$$

where the $\mathcal{D}_{ij}$ are the binary pair diffusivities for existing temperature and total pressure. More specifically

$$\nabla x_1 = \frac{x_1 x_2}{\mathcal{D}_{12}} (v_2 - v_1) + \frac{x_0 x_1}{\mathcal{D}_{01}} (v_0 - v_1) \tag{261}$$

$$\nabla x_2 = \frac{x_2 x_1}{\mathcal{D}_{21}} (v_1 - v_2) + \frac{x_0 x_2}{\mathcal{D}_{02}} (v_0 - v_2) \tag{262}$$

We may now add these two equations, neglecting differences between $\mathcal{D}_{01}$ and $\mathcal{D}_{02}$ (both represented by $\mathcal{D}_{io}$ from now on), to obtain

$$\nabla x_1 + \nabla x_2 = -\nabla x_0 = \frac{N_0 x_I - N_I x_0}{c\mathcal{D}_{I0}} \tag{263}$$

where $x_I = x_1 + x_2$ and $\mathbf{N}_I = \mathbf{N}_1 + \mathbf{N}_2$. Equation 263 is readily rearranged to

$$\mathbf{N}_0 = -c\mathcal{D}_{I0} \nabla x_0 + x_0 (\mathbf{N}_0 + \mathbf{N}_I) \tag{264}$$

which is just Fick's law. We now take a careful look at the boundary conditions cited on the figure: uniform mole fractions of species 0 on both cylindrical surfaces. This assumed situation (which must represent some idealization) suggests that $dx_0/dz = 0$ everywhere and also that N_{0r} is independent of z. We thus find

$$N_{0z} = c_0 \, v_z(r) \tag{265}$$

$$N_{0r} = -c\mathcal{D}_{I0} \frac{dx_0}{dr} + x_0 (N_{0r} + N_{Ir}) \tag{266}$$

We next note that

$$N_{Ir} = 0 \tag{267}$$

on the basis of similar arguments. Then

$$N_{0r} (1 - x_0) = -c\mathcal{D}_{I0} \frac{dx_0}{dr} = c\mathcal{D}_{I0} \frac{d(1 - x_0)}{dr} \tag{268}$$

with

$$rN_{0r} = \text{constant} \tag{269}$$

by species continuity. This is a simple film-theory description which is readily integrated to yield

$$N_{0r} = (c\mathcal{D}_{I0}/r) \frac{\ln\left[\dfrac{1 - x_{01}}{1 - x_{0\epsilon}}\right]}{\ln[1/\epsilon]} \tag{270}$$

(where ϵ = film thickness) which is a well-known result. The behavior of the sweep gas can thus be obtained by a simple binary treatment.

To determine the segregation of isotopes produced by the sweep gas requires a considerably more subtle pseudo-binary treatment (see Reference 11, Section 18.4). Carrying out a careful order-of-magnitude analysis following Shachter et al.[100] we find:

$$\mathbf{N}_{1r} = -c\mathcal{D}\left[\frac{\gamma}{R \ln \frac{1}{\epsilon}} \ln\left(\frac{x_{01}}{x_{0\epsilon}}\right) x(1 - x) + \frac{dx}{dr}\right] \tag{271}$$

where

$x = x_1/(x_1 + x_2)$ = isotope fraction of species 1

N_r = The radial molar flux of species 1

$$\mathcal{D} = \mathcal{D}_{10} \Big/ \left[\frac{\mathcal{D}_{10}}{\mathcal{D}_{12}} - 1 + \frac{1}{x_0}\right]$$

$$\gamma = 2(\mathcal{D}_{10} - \mathcal{D}_{20})/(\mathcal{D}_{10} + \mathcal{D}_{20})$$

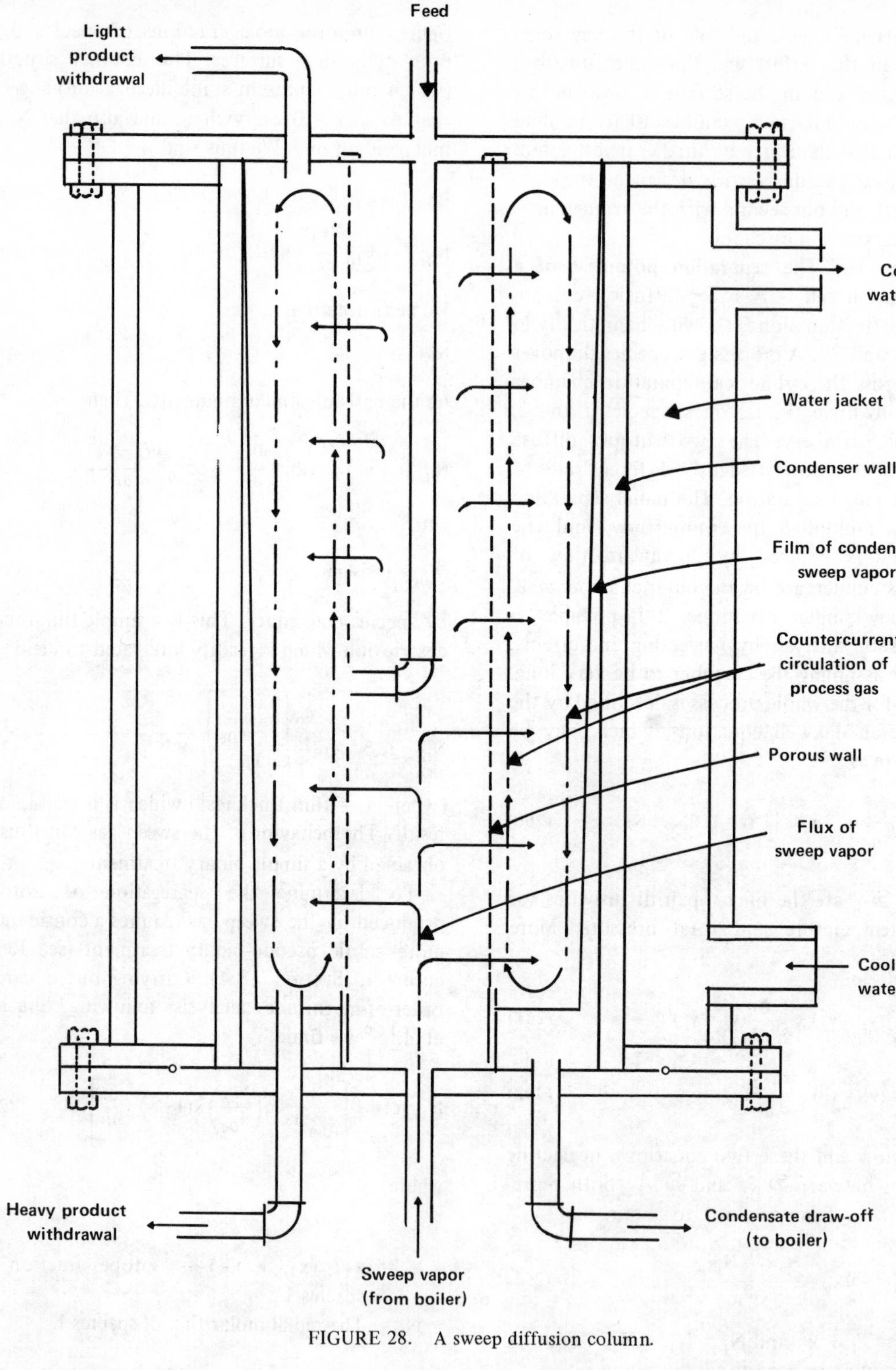

FIGURE 28. A sweep diffusion column.

x_0 = Local mole fraction of process-gas.

Returning again to the boundary conditions assumed in this problem, we find

$$N_I = 0 \text{ at } r = \epsilon R, R \tag{272}$$

and

$$N_{1r} = 0 \tag{273}$$

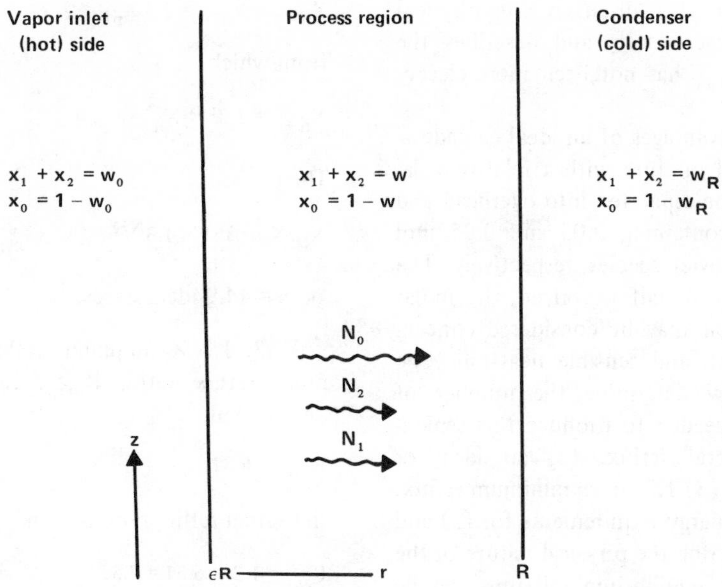

FIGURE 29. Coordinate system and nomenclature for sweep diffusion column theory.

everywhere (as stated above). Then, on a sweep-gas free basis,

$$N_{1r} = J^{\star}_{1r} \tag{274}$$

where $J^{\star}_{i}$ is the flux of species i with respect to the molar-average velocity and

$$J^{\star}_{1r} = -c\mathcal{D}\left[\frac{\gamma}{R}\,\frac{\ln(x_{01}/x_{0\epsilon})}{\ln(1/\epsilon)}\,x(1-x) + \frac{\partial x}{\partial r}\right] \tag{275}$$

The axial flux $J^{\star}_{1z}$ is as yet undetermined, and it is in fact quite difficult to obtain.

We can, however, easily estimate separation potential by recognizing that the local volumetric rate of value production is

$$R_V = -(J^{\star}_{1}\cdot\nabla x)/[x(1-x)]^2 \tag{276}$$

which for our situation yields

$$R_V[x(1-x)]^2 = c\mathcal{D}\left[\frac{\gamma}{R}\,\frac{\ln(x_{01}/x_{0\epsilon})}{\ln(1/\epsilon)}\,x(1-x)\,\frac{\partial x}{\partial r} + \left(\frac{\partial x}{\partial r}\right)^2\right]$$

$$\text{plus terms in}\left(\frac{\partial x}{\partial z}\right)^2 \tag{277}$$

The maximum local rate of value production occurs when

$$\frac{\partial R_V}{\partial(\partial x/\partial r)} = \frac{\partial R_V}{\partial(\partial x/\partial z)} = 0 \tag{278}$$

and at this maximum:

$$\frac{\partial x}{\partial z} = 0 \tag{279a}$$

$$\frac{\partial x}{\partial r} = -\frac{1}{2}\,\frac{\gamma}{R}\,\frac{\ln(x_{01}/x_{0\epsilon})}{\ln(1/\epsilon)}\,x(1-x) \tag{279b}$$

Then

$$(R_V)_{max} = \frac{1}{2}\,\frac{c\mathcal{D}}{[x(1-x)]^2}\left[\frac{\gamma}{R}\,\frac{\ln(x_{01}/x_{0\epsilon})}{\ln(1/\epsilon)}\,x(1-x)\right]^2$$

$$= \frac{1}{2}\,c\mathcal{D}\left[\frac{\gamma}{R}\,\frac{\ln(x_{01}/x_{0\epsilon})}{\ln(1/\epsilon)}\right]^2 \tag{280}$$

and

$$(\delta U) = \int_V (R_V)\,dV \tag{281}$$

This integral is readily evaluated once $x_0(r)$ has already been determined but this is unnecessary. The maximum R_V, instead of its volume average, is sufficient for estimating separation potential.

The equations for value function production of ultracentrifuges and thermal diffusion processes are very similar to Equation 277.[20,78] Equation 280 then applies to quite a wide variety of process conditions.

Moreover the potential indicated by this equation is reasonably realistic. It is shown by Olander[78] that present-day centrifuges have separative powers of about 55 to 60% of this maximum. Olander also discusses the physical significance of these results and describes the reasons why $(R_v)_{max}$ has not been more closely approached.

Example 11: Advantages of an ideal cascade – An equimolar ideal mixture with a relative volatility of 1.3 is to be separated into overhead and bottom products containing 0.05 and 0.95 mol fractions of the heavier species, respectively. The feed may be assumed half vaporized, the molar heat of vaporization may be considered concentration independent, and sensible heats may be neglected. We now determine the number of theoretical stages needed to produce this separation using (1) total reflux, (2) an ideal or no-mixing cascade, (3) 1.2 times minimum reflux. We also compare energy requirements for (2) and (3) above, and describe the physical nature of the ideal cascade. The equilibrium relations can be expressed as

$$Y_n = 1.3\, X_n \tag{282}$$

or

$$y_n = 1.3\left[\frac{x_n}{1-x_n}\right] \Big/ \left[1 + 1.3\left(\frac{x_n}{1-x_n}\right)\right] \tag{283}$$

where X_n and Y_n represent molar ratios while x_n and y_n are molar fractions. The operating lines* are

1. Total reflux: here we have

$$x_{n+1} = y_n \tag{284}$$

or

$$X_{n+1} = Y_n \tag{285}$$

from where

$$X_{n+1} = 1.3\, X_n \tag{286}$$

then

$$X_N/X_0 = 19/0.05263 = (1.3)^{N+1} = 361 \tag{287}$$

or N = 22.45 ideal stages.

2. Ideal cascade: from the "no-mixing" requirement we have

$$x_{n+1} = y_{n-1} \tag{288}$$

or

*For stagewise calculations see, for example, Reference 75.

$$X_{n+1} = Y_{n-1} = 1.3\, X_{n-1} \tag{289}$$

from which

$$X_{n+1} = 1.3^{1/2}\, X_n \tag{290}$$

Then

$$X_N/X_0 = 361 = 1.3^{N/2} \tag{291}$$

or N = 44.9 ideal stages.

3. 1.2 × minimum reflux ratio: the minimum reflux ratio, R_{min}, can be immediately determined,

$$R_{min} \doteq 6.31 \tag{292}$$

the actual reflux ratio is then

$$R_{act} = 1.2 \times 6.31 = 7.57 \tag{293}$$

The ratio of liquid stream to the vapor stream in the rectifying section is

$$(L/V)_{rect} = \frac{7.57}{8.57} = 0.883 \tag{294}$$

Stepping off plates for the rectifying section yields

$$N_{rect} = 27 \tag{295}$$

and the system symmetry requires that

$$N_{total} \doteq 2 \times 23.5 + 1 = 55 \tag{296}$$

which is substantially, larger than for the ideal cascade.

We now consider the energy requirements for our system and note: For the column operating in the conventional manner

$$V_n = V_m + \frac{1}{2}\,\text{mol} \tag{297}$$

where V_n and V_m are the vapor streams in the rectifying and stripping sections, respectively. Defining

$$V_n - L_n = P \tag{298}$$

then

$$\frac{V_n}{P} = \frac{L_n}{P} + 1 = 1 + R_{act} = 8.57 \tag{299}$$

and

$$V_m = 8.57 \times \frac{1}{2} - \frac{1}{2} = 3.785 \text{ mol} = \text{boilup rate} \tag{300}$$

Energy required,

$$Q = \tilde{\lambda} V_m = 3.785\, \tilde{\lambda} \tag{301}$$

where $\tilde{\lambda}$ is the molar heat of vaporization.

For the column designed as an ideal cascade, reboilers must be added at each stage in the exhausting section and the total boilup is that just below the feed plate. For our situation, symmetry requires that, at the feed plate,

$$L_f = V_f \tag{302}$$

since the slope of the operating line is unity. Then

$$V_{f-1} = V_f - \frac{1}{2} \tag{303}$$

$$V_f = L_f \tag{304}$$

$$V_{f-1} = L_f - \frac{1}{2} \tag{305}$$

with

$$Q = (V_{f-1})\tilde{\lambda} \tag{306}$$

which latter result is just a material balance. To complete our development we use the species material balance

$$V_{f-1}\, y_{f-1} = L_f x_F - W x_W \tag{307}$$

where x_F and x_W are the molar fractions in the feed and overhead, respectively, and W is the overhead stream; and the operating line equation

$$x_{f-1} = x_F/1.3^{1/2} \tag{308}$$

or

$$y_{f-1} = 1.3^{1/2}\, x_F \tag{309}$$

Then

$$y_{f-1} = 0.53274 \tag{310}$$

and

$$V_{f-1}\, 0.53274 = \left(V_{f-1} + \frac{1}{2}\right)\frac{1}{2} - \frac{1}{2}\, 0.05 \tag{311}$$

which yields

$$V_{f-1}\left[0.03274\right] = \frac{1}{2}\, \frac{1}{2} - 0.05 \tag{312}$$

or

$$V_{f-1} = 6.87 \tag{313}$$

We find then that

$$\frac{N_{Tot}}{N_{Tot}(\text{ideal})} \cong \frac{55}{44.9} \doteq 1.22 \tag{314}$$

and

$$\frac{Q}{Q(\text{ideal})} \cong \frac{3.79}{6.87} \doteq 0.55 \tag{315}$$

where the conventional column is operated at 1.2 times minimum reflux.

For this separation ideal operation is certainly not justified. Energy costs are high, and the reduction in number of stages is more than offset by the complexity of ideal staging. This is typical of situations where identity of upflow and downflow streams is maintained without added energy input.

However, it becomes clear that wherever the central pinched region is troublesome a "bent" operating line could be quite beneficial.[20,61] Such bent operating lines are occasionally used for difficult separations, and it appears that ideal-cascade theory gives a useful estimate of N.

Prediction of Equipment Performance

Even if the separation potential can be simply and reliably predicted, it is necessary to determine how closely any proposed design approaches this limit; it is always necessary, by some combination of calculation and experiment, to predict equipment performance quantitatively. Accuracy always carries a price, however, and it is desirable to develop a hierarchy of calculation procedures suitable for successively more precise screening of fewer process alternatives until one finally arrives at a final design. The mathematical form of the final description will of course depend upon the nature of the system modeled. It should, however, be clear from the above discussion of morphology that many useful similarities exist between apparently quite different processes. In the remainder of this section we indicate by example how the developments in mass-transport theory over the last two decades can be used to advantage for reducing computational effort and increasing conceptual understanding.

Need for a Computational Hierarchy

In most serious design problems one tends to go

over some aspects many times, at different levels of precision and reliability. Consider, for example, a successful process in which the leaching of a solid particle is important. The time required for this leaching will probably be estimated first at the level of feasibility assessment, next with sufficient precision to compare its magnitude more closely with other possible rate-limiting steps, and finally, if it is truly important, as realistically as possible. However, other less time-consuming aspects of the problem should have been passed over at earlier stages.

We consider this particular example here because of its simplicity: If the effective diffusivity is constant and the shape not too intractable we can obtain a complete description, in the form of an infinite convergent series, for a very wide variety of boundary conditions.[17]

Now at the first level of assessment it usually is satisfactory* to say that the leaching time

$$t_L \sim L^2/\mathscr{D} \qquad (316)$$

where L is a reasonably chosen diffusion distance and $\mathscr{D}$ is the effective binary diffusivity. Similar zeroth-order approximations are available for a wide variety of other situations, for example the use of the Weiss ϕ parameter for diffusion and chemical reaction.[118] These are extremely valuable and too little used.

If, however, t_L is long enough to be of serious concern, one next makes lumped-parameter estimates of leaching rate by assuming all solute mass is concentrated at one point. Often one can make simple bounding calculations which suffice for a practical situation. This procedure yields a result often very close to the lead term in the complete solution and corresponds to an elementary collocation procedure, based on a single collocation point.

In a few, but necessarily important, cases one may wish to go further. One very attractive way to develop such a hierarchy is orthogonal collocation, for which a large literature exists.[103,104,113,114] This approach appears to be very powerful, economical, and flexible, and generally well suited to our purposes.

Comparison of Competing Processes

Both chemists and engineers like to characterize complex systems in terms of simple measures: resolution, required numbers of transfer units, and so forth. Such a procedure tends to be comfortable if imprecise, and it is often quite useful. However, potentially serious approximations are almost always involved, and it is desirable to work from a solid foundation where possible. We consider here differential chromatography as a simple useful example as to how one might proceed, and how to test the simplifications made.

Initially sharp feed pulses broaden with time to produce bell-shaped concentration/distance relations looking more or less like a standard error curve. There are many ways to characterize these curves (see for example Reference 6), but normally this can be done adequately in terms of a small number of parameters:

- Mean (first moment of concentration with respect to time or position)
- Dispersion (second moment)
- Skewness (third moment)

and so forth. Very seldom do reliability of data or process goals justify more than three moments, and most often two suffice. These parameters in turn can be obtained from a variety of physical models, generally combining lumped diffusive and dispersive terms (see Lightfoot et al.[73]). At the level of the second moment, system description is almost completely insensitive to the details of the model[63] and it is conventional to use the equation

$$\frac{\partial \bar{c}_i}{\partial t} + \bar{V}_i \frac{\partial \bar{c}_i}{\partial z} = \epsilon_i \frac{\partial^2 \bar{c}_i}{\partial z^2} \qquad (317)$$

where

$\bar{c}_i$ = Cross-sectional average concentration
$\bar{V}_i$ = Velocity of the center of mass of species i
ϵ_i = Effective diffusion coefficient of species i

to describe behavior of all differential chromatographic systems. Recent interesting examples were reported by Aris,[4] Cox,[24] Sankarasubramanian and Gill,[98,99] Lee et al.,[68] and Reis et al.[89,90]

CONCLUSIONS

This paper represents an attempt to organize the description of separations processes in terms of process morphology, separation mechanisms, and magnitudes of key system parameters. Accordingly an entire section has been devoted to each of these

*Though one must be careful with internal surfaces, such as pores.

aspects. The purpose of this final section is to integrate the three into a coherent separation scheme. We must, however, say at the outset that such an integration is a formidable task and that we have so far made only a beginning.

Our progress to date is summarized schematically in Figure 30, which shows morphology, mechanisms, and magnitudes combined in a tentative way to form a three-dimensional classification matrix. It appears at time of writing that this overall classification scheme is sufficient for including most known separation techniques, but that each coordinate of the matrix must be further subdivided in ways yet to be determined. We discuss this fine structure separately for each coordinate and then show the utility of the overall scheme by putting the separations listed by King into appropriate "pigeonholes." This is done in Table 7.

A Summary of Morphology

We consider here a restricted range of morphologies which can be conveniently characterized by a single number, that portion to the left of the decimal point representing the feed descriptors and that to the right representing species "flow." The significance of these numbers is described in Table 8, and representative separations are given for most of the entries; further examples are provided in the text immediately below.

For simplicity we consider only two categories of feed, differential or batch corresponding to the number 1, and continuous, given by number 2. Clearly a much more elaborate series could be

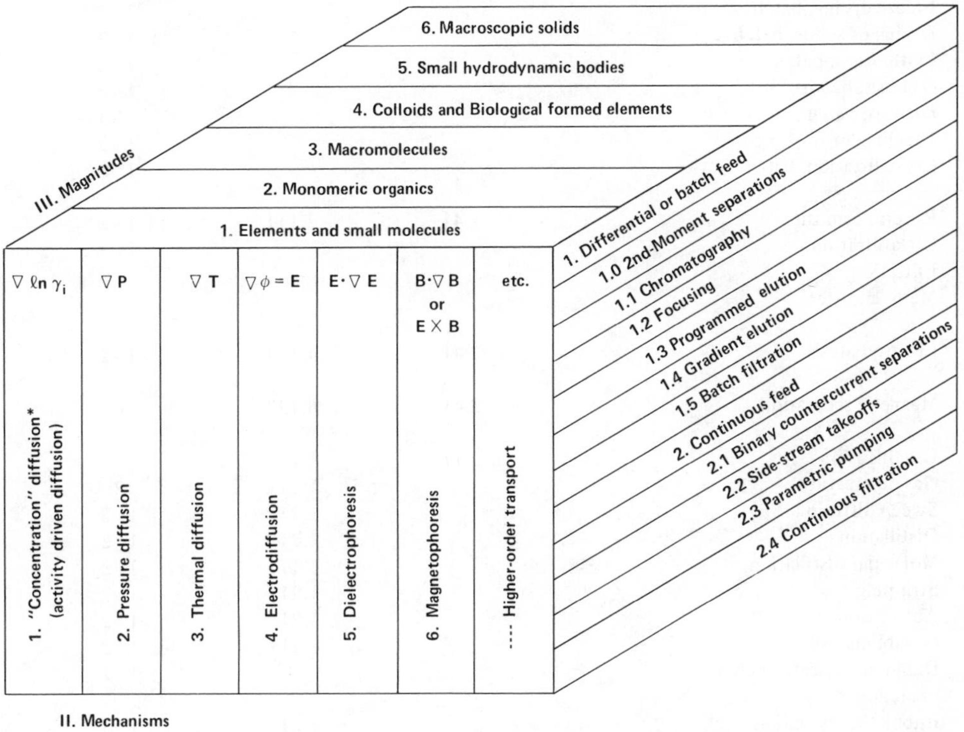

FIGURE 30. A tentative separation matrix.

*Concentration diffusion is normally taken to include both Brownian dispersion and migration induced by gradients in activity coefficients. We are primarily interested in the latter here. The distinction between these two effects will be made more systematically in future work.

TABLE 7

Classification of the Separation Processes Cited in Reference 61*

Process	Morphology	Mechanism	Magnitude
Paper chromatography	1.10	1.2	1–3
Gel filtration			3–4
Ultracentrifugation	1.10	2.1	3–4
Zonal electrophoresis	1.10	4.1	3–4
Two-dimensional electrophoresis	1.11	4.1	3–4
Mass spectrometry	1.11	6.1	1
Centrifugation	1.20	2.1	5–6
Cyclone			6
Settling			6
Electrostatic precipitation	1.21	5.1	6
Adsorption	1.40	1.2	1–3
Ion exchange			
Evaporation, batch	1.50	1.111	1–2
Zone melting			1–2
Flash expansion, batch			1–2
Freeze drying, batch			1–2
Drying of solids, batch			1–2
Clathration, batch			1–2
Osmosis, batch			1–2
Dialysis, batch			1–3
Leaching or washing			1–3
Crystallization, batch			1–6
Reverse osmosis	2.41	2.111	1–2
Ultrafiltration			3–4
Filtration			5–6
Mesh demister			6
Electrodialysis	2.41	4.111	1–2
Magnetic separation	2.41	6.122	6
Gas diffusion	2.11	1.111	1
Gas permeation		1.111	2
Sweep diffusion		1.21	1–2
Distillation		1.21	1–2
Molecular distillation		1.111	1–2
Stripping		1.21	1–2
Absorption		1.21	1–2
Desublimation		1.111	1–2
Dual-temperature exchange reaction**		–	1–2
Bubble fractionation		1.21	1–3
Extraction		1.21	1–3
Thermal diffusion – Clusius column		3.21	1–3
Flotation		2.1211	4–5
Electrolysis**	2.41	–	1

*Many of the cited processes can in fact be carried out in a variety of ways. We consider here only the most common operations.

**Higher-order phenomena.

TABLE 8

A Simplified Morphological Classification

I-1. Differential or Batch Feeds

- 1.0. No migration in x_1-direction
  - 1.00 No migration in x_2-direction: second moment separations by Brownian dispersion
- 1.1. Uniform migration in x_1
  - 1.10. No migration in x_2 : simple chromatography
  - 1.11. Uniform migration in x_2: two-dimensional chromatography; free flow electrophoresis
- 1.2. Spatial gradient in x_1
  - 1.20. No migration in x_2 : one-dimensional focusing
  - 1.21. Uniform migration in x_2: two-dimensional chromatography with focusing in one direction; free-flow electrophoresis with isoelectric focusing
  - 1.22. Spatial gradient in x_2 : two-dimensional focusing (no existing examples?)
- 1.3. Temporal gradient for x_1
  - 1.30. No migration in x_2 : programmed elution chromatography
  - 1.31. Uniform migration in x_2: two-dimensional chromatography with programmed elution in direction 1
  - 1.32. Spatial gradient in x_2: programmed elution in x_1 with focusing in x_2
  - 1.33. Temporal gradient in x_2 : two-dimensional gradient elution
- 1.4. Temporal and spatial gradients for x_1
  - 1.40. No migration in x_2 : gradient elution chromatography
  - 1.41. Uniform migration in x_2: two dimensional chromatography with gradient elution in direction 1
  - 1.42. Spatial gradient in x_2 : gradient elution in x_1 with focusing in x_2
  - 1.43. Temporal gradient in x_2: gradient elution in x_1 with programmed elution in x_2
  - 1.44. Temporal and spatial gradients in x_2: two-dimensional gradient elution
- 1.5. Spatial step change in x_1
  - 1.50. No migration in x_2: batch filtration and batch phase-change processes (evaporation, crystallization; zone melting)
  - 1.51. Uniform migration in x_2 : batch cross-flow filtration, etc.
  - 1.52. Spatial gradients in x_2 : filtration or phase transition in x_1 with focusing in x_2 (no existing examples?)
  - 1.53. Temporal gradients in x_3: filtration with crossed gradient elution (no existing examples?)
  - 1.54. Temporal and spatial gradient in x_2: filtration with cross-flow gradient elution
  - 1.55. Spatial step change in x_2 : dual filtration (no existing examples?)

I-2. Continuous Feeds

- 2.0. No migration in x_1
  - 2.00. No migration in x_2 : not feasible
- 2.1. Uniform migration in x_1
  - 2.10. No migration in x_2: all familiar binary cocurrent or countercurrent separations
  - 2.11. Uniform migration in x_2: steady two-dimensional multicomponent separations
- 2.2. Spatial gradient in x_1
  - 2.20. No migration in x_2 (possibly unstable situation)
  - 2.21. Uniform migration in x_2: sidestream take-offs; continuous focusing separations
  - 2.22. Spatial gradient in x_2 (possibly unstable)
- 2.3. Temporal gradient in x_1 : No continuous processes exist for the flow descriptors used in this table. However continuous feeds are possible for such cyclic processes as parametric pumping.

TABLE 8 (continued)

A Simplified Morphological Classification

2.4. Spatial step function in x_1
- 2.40. No migration in x_2 (unstable)
- 2.41. Uniform migration in x_2 : continuous filtration and phase-change operations
- 2.42. Spatial gradient in x_2 (?)
- 2.43. Not continuous
- 2.44. Spatial step function in x_2 (not useful ?)

used, but little appears to be gained by this at present. We characterize "flow" in terms of the species migration velocity and consider five classes:

0. Zero velocity – Characteristic behavior can be described solely in terms of Brownian dispersion.

1. Uniform velocity – Characteristic behavior depends only on differences in migration rate.

2. Spatial gradients in velocity – Characteristic behavior depends upon spatial gradients in a velocity component.

3. Temporal gradients in velocity – Characteristic behavior depends on variation of velocity components with time.

4. Spatial step changes in velocity – Characteristic behavior depends on abrupt spatial changes in velocity components.

The first digit to the right of the decimal point refers to the x_1 direction and the second to x_2. To avoid redundancy we require that the second digit never exceed the first.

This scheme requires that the number of individual feed or flow classifications never exceed ten for any coordinate (x_1, x_2, x_3,t), and this may ultimately prove insufficient. For the moment this does not appear to be a problem, and the simplicity of single-digit classifications is valuable. It may also be seen that extension to three-dimensional migration is straightforward.

Finally, inspection of even this abbreviated table shows a substantial number of possibilities that do not seem yet to have been exploited, and some of which seem promising. There are also entries in the table which are physically inadmissible or quite unlikely to prove useful, and in general it appears that abbreviated tables such as this should be carefully examined before going on to more extensive lists.

A Summary of Mechanisms

The primary headings chosen for mechanisms in Figure 30 follow directly from the generalized Stefan-Maxwell equations, and they are hardly controversial. The finer subdivisions are less definite, however, and in the last analysis these are a matter of taste. Table 9 lists the set of subdivisions which we have chosen. The headings in the tables are described briefly below.

Continuum migration has already been defined, but some of the subheadings are new. By eu-molecular we mean truly molecular systems for which the Stefan-Maxwell equations may be considered exact; this is the range usually considered in treatments of diffusional operations, but it will be convenient for us to consider macroscopic particles as well as true molecules in our general scheme. We must, however, recognize that the behavior of such giant pseudo-molecules differs from that described by the diffusion equations.

Diffusion appears to be adequately described by hydrodynamic diffusion theory up into the Stokes' flow range, but nonlinear drag forces occur at finite Reynolds numbers; e.g., settling of macroscopic particles by the equivalent of pressure diffusion. Transient (relaxation) effects also become more pronounced, for example in jigging. Ionic charge begins to become ambiguous for molecules of the molecular size of proteins, and one must begin to deal with such slippery concepts as that of zeta potential. The dividing line between molecules and particles is a fuzzy one that should be further explored.

A Summary of Magnitudes

Molecular size is also a convenient basis for describing magnitudes because so many key separation parameters are size dependent. Brownian motion becomes progressively less important, and dipolar and higher-order interactions more so, as particle size increases. As a

TABLE 9

Mechanistic Classification

1. Continuum Migration
   1.1. Eu-molecular
      1.11. Isotropic
         1.111. Steady
         1.112. Transient (relaxation phenomena)
      1.12. Anisotropic
   1.2. Pseudo-molecular
      2.11. Isotropic
         2.111. Steady
         2.112. Transient
      2.12. Anisotropic
2. Convectively Augmented Pseudo-continuum Migration (polarization induced)
   2.1. Migration vs. Brownian dispersion
   2.2. Migration vs. convection
   2.3. Opposed migrations

result some operations such as settling or magnetic induction are largely limited to macrosopic particles. In almost all cases equipment geometry, particularly key dimensions, and operating parameters such as voltage gradients are substantially affected by solute size. There are, however, other important magnitudes to consider, and these remain to be effectively organized.

A particularly important criterion is scale of operation: analytical, micropreparative, etc., up to high-tonnage production. The early mass-reduction stages of pharmaceutical isolations* have much more in common with the heavy chemicals industry than with the later stages of the isolation procedure.

Closely allied to scale are unit cost of the material being processed and specifications of product quality; one uses quite different procedures in producing protein concentrates for feed, food, and pharmaceutical applications.

Another important aspect of magnitudes is the degree of concentration required.

Finally, and by no means least important, are the magnitudes of transport and thermodynamic parameters, in particular those which are anomalous in nature. Seeking anomalies is the most difficult aspect of separations research to systematize, but it is also potentially the most rewarding. We close on this note.

ACKNOWLEDGMENT

The above-suggested approaches to description of separations processes were developed and tested during formal classroom teaching in the chemical engineering department of the University of Wisconsin and as part of research efforts by all four authors. The research of Messrs. Lee and Lightfoot was supported in large part by the National Science Foundation, under grant ENG 75/05456. Dr. Reis was supported primarily by the Calouste Gulbenkian Foundation of Portugal, and to a smaller extent by NSF. Dr. Waissbluth was supported by CONACYT of Mexico, under grant 1063, and by the Graduate School of the University of Wisconsin, Madison. These various sources of support were vital to our effort, and they are gratefully acknowledged.

*Typically large-scale filtration, extraction, or precipitation.

REFERENCES

1. **Abramowitz, M. and Stegun, I.,** Handbook of Mathematical Functions, National Bureau of Standards, 1964.
2. **Abrams, D. S. and Prausnitz, J. M.,** Statistical thermodynamics of liquid mixtures: A new expression for the excess gibbs energy of partly or completely miscible systems, *AIChE J.,* 21, 116, 1975.
3. **Anderson, N. G.,** Preparative particle separation in density gradients, *Q. Rev. Biophys.,* 1, 217, 1968.
4. **Aris, R.,** On the dispersion of a solute by diffusion, convection and exchange between phases, *Proc. R. Soc. London Ser. A,* 252, 538, 1959.
5. **Barker, P. E.,** Continuous chromatographic refining, in *Progress in Separation and Purification,* Vol. 4, Perry, E. S. and Van Oss, C. J., Eds., Interscience, New York, 1971.
6. **Bassingthwaighte, J. B.,** Blood flow and diffusion in mammalian organs, *Science,* 167, 1347, 1970.
7. **Benedict, M. et al.,** Report of Uranium Isotope Separation Review Ad Hoc Committee, Oak Ridge Operations Report ORO-694, June 2, 1972.
8. **Benedict, M. and Pigford, T. H.,** *Nuclear Chemical Engineering,* McGraw-Hill, New York, 1957.
9. **Berman, A. S.,** A Theory of Isotope Separation in a Long Countercurrent Gas Centrifuge, AEC Report K-1536, 1962.
10. **Bier, M.,** *Electrophoresis: Theory, Methods, and Application,* Vol. 1, Academic Press, Washington, D.C., 1959.

10a. **Bier, M.,** *Electrophoresis: Theory, Methods, and Application,* Vol. 2, Academic Press, Washington, D.C., 1968.

11. **Bird, R. B., Stewart, W. E., and Lightfoot, E. N.,** *Transport Phenomena,* John Wiley & Sons, New York, 1960.
12. **Box, G. E. P.,** Experimental Strategy, Technical Report No. 111, Department of Statistics, University of Wisconsin, 1967.
13. **Brenner, H.,** Monograph in preparation.
14. **Brenner, H. and Condiff, D. W.,** Transport mechanics in systems of orientable particles, *J. Colloid Interface Sci.,* 41(2), 228, 1972.
15. **Burrows, G.,** *Molecular Distillation,* Clarendon Press, Oxford, 1960.
16. **Chapman, S. and Cowling, T. G.,** *Mathematical Theory of Non-uniform Gases,* 2nd ed., Cambridge University Press, London, 1951.
17. **Carslaw, H. S. and Jaeger, J. C.,** *Conduction of Heat in Solids,* 2nd ed., Clarendon Press, Oxford, 1959.
18. **Catsimpoolas, N.,** Isoelectric focusing and isotachophoresis of proteins, *Sep. Sci.,* 8(1), 71, 1973.
19. **Cline, G. B.,** Continuous sample flow density gradient centrifugation, in *Progress in Separation and Purification,* Vol. 4, Perry, E. S. and Van Oss, J. C., Eds., Interscience, New York, 1971.
20. **Cohen, K.,** *The Theory of Isotope Separation,* McGraw-Hill, New York, 1951.
21. **Cooney, D. O.,** The Separation of Interfering Solutes by Selective Adsorption in Fixed Beds, Ph.D. thesis, University of Wisconsin, Madison, 1966.
22. **Cooney, D. O. and Lightfoot, E. N.,** Multicomponent fixed-bed sorption of interfering solutes. System behavior under asymptotic conditions, *Ind. Eng. Chem. Fundam.,* 5, 25, 1966.
23. **Cooney, D. O.,** Effect of mass transfer on stability of miscible displacement fronts in porous media, *Ind. Eng. Chem. Fundam.,* 5, 426, 1966.
24. **Cox, H. C., Hessels, J. K. C., and Tenen, J. M. G.,** On the efficiency of gel electrophoresis, *J. Chromatogr.,* 66, 19, 1972.
25. **Coxon, M. and Binder, M. J.,** Isotachophoresis theory-structure of the ionic species interface, *J. Chromatogr.,* 95, 133, 1974.
26. **Cuatrecasas, P. and Anfinsen, C.,** Affinity Chromatography, *Methods Enzymol.,* 22, 345, 1971.
27. **Cussler, E. L., Jr.,** *Multicomponent Diffusion,* Elsevier, Amsterdam, 1976.
28. **DeClerk, K., Buys, T. S., and Pretorius, V.,** A classification framework for separation science, *Sep. Sci.,* 6, 759, 1971.
29. **de Groot, S. R. and Mazur, P.,** *Non-equilibrium Thermodynamics,* North-Holland, Amsterdam, 1962.
30. **Derjaguin, B. V. and Bakanov, S. P.,** Theory of gas flow in a porous body near the knudsen region. Pseudo molecular flow, *Soviet Physics Doklady,* 2, 326, 1957, and *Discuss. Faraday Soc.,* 30, 130, 1960.
31. **DiMarzio, E. A. and Guttman, C. M.,** Separation by flow, *Macromolecules,* 3, 131, 1970.

33. **Done, J. N. and Knox, J. H.,** Practice and potential of high-speed liquid chromatography, *Process Biochem.,* 7(9), 11, 1972.
34. **Evans, R. B., III, Watson, G. M., and Mason, E. A.,** Gaseous diffusion in porous media at uniform pressure, *J. Chem. Phys.,* 35, 2076, 1961.
35. **Evans, R. B., III, Watson, G. M., and Mason, E. A.,** Gaseous diffusion in porous media. II. Effect of pressure gradients, *J. Chem. Phys.,* 36, 1894, 1962.
36. **Feynman, R. P.,** *Lectures on Physics,* Addison-Wesley, Reading, Mass., 1963.
37. **Fox, J. B.,** Continuous chromatography apparatus, *J. Chromatogr.,* 43, 48, 1969.
38. **Fredenslund, A., Jones, R. L., and Prausnitz, J. M.,** Group-contribution estimation of activity coefficients in nonideal liquid mixtures, *AIChE J.,* 21, 1086, 1975.
39. **Friedberg, F.,** Affinity chromatography and insoluble enzymes, *Chromatogr. Rev.,* 14, 12, 1971.

40. **de la Garza, A.,** A generalization of the matched abundance-ratio cascade for multicomponent isotope separation, *Chem. Eng. Sci.,* 18, 73, 1963.
41. **de la Garza, A., Garrett, G. A., and Murphy, J. E.,** Some value functions for multicomponent isotope separation, USAEC Report K-1455, July 1960 and *Chem. Eng. Sci.,* 15, 188, 1961.
42. **Giddings, J. C.,** Nonequilibrium theory of field-flow fractionation, *J. Chem. Phys.,* 49, 81, 1968.
43. **Giddings, J. C.,** *Dynamics of Chromatography,* Marcel Dekker, New York, 1965.
44. **Giddings, J. C., Yang, F. J., and Myers, M. N.,** Flow field-flow fractionation: Theoretical and experimental characterization, *Sep. Sci.,* in press.
45. **Gill, W. N. and Sankarasubramanian, R.,** Exact analysis of unsteady convection diffusion, *Proc. R. Soc. London Ser. A,* 316, 341, 1970.
46. **Glueckauf, E.,** Theory of chromatography, *Trans. Faraday Soc.,* 51, 34, 1955.
47. **Gmehling, J. and Onken, V.,** to be published in *Chem. Ing. Tech.*
47a. **Gmehling, J. and Onken, V.,** Vapor-liquid equilibrium data collection, *DECHEMA Chem. Eng. Data Series,* in press.
48. **Grushka, E., Caldwell, K. D., Myers, N. M., and Giddings, J. C.,** Field flow fractionation, *Sep. Purif. Methods,* 2, 127, 1973.
49. **Hannig, K.,** Eine Neuentwicklung der Trägerfreien Kontinuierlichen Elektrophorese, *Z. Physiol. Chem.,* 338, 211, 1964.
50. **Hannig, K.,** The application of free-flow electrophoresis to the separation of macromolecules and particles of biological importance, in *Modern Separation Methods of Macromolecules and Particles,* Gerritsen, T., Ed., Interscience, New York, 1969.
51. **Haglund, H.,** Isotachophoresis – A principle for analytical and preparative separation of substances such as proteins, peptides, nucleotides, weak acids, metals, *Sci. Tools,* 17(1), 1, 1970.
52. **Happel, J. and Brenner, H.,** *Low Reynolds Number Hydrodynamics,* Prentice-Hall, Englewood Cliffs, N.J., 1965.
53. **Helfferich, F.,** *Ion Exchange,* McGraw-Hill, New York, 1962.
54. **Hirschfelder, J. O., Curtiss, C. F., and Bird, R. B.,** *The Molecular Theory of Gases and Liquids,* John Wiley & Sons, New York, 1954.
55. **Howard, D. W., Lightfoot, E. N., and Hirschfelder, J. O.,** The hydrodynamic resolution of optical isomers, *AIChE J.,* 22, 794–798, 1976.
56. **Hwang, S-T. and Kammermeyer, K.,** *Membranes in Separations,* Interscience, New York, 1975.
57. **Kabat, E. A.,** *Structural Concepts of Immunology and Immunochemistry,* Holt, Rinehart and Winston, New York, 1968.
58. **Kanagawa, A.,** Evaluation of enrichment by centrifugal separation, UCRL-Trans-10891 July 1975, translated from **Genshiryoku Kogyo,** 20, 40, 1974.
59. **Karger, B. L., Snyder, L. R., and Horvath, C.,** *An Introduction to Separation Science,* John Wiley & Sons, New York, 1973.
60. **Kedem, O. and Katchalsky, A.,** Thermodynamic analysis of the permeability of biological membranes to non-electrolytes, *Biochim. Biophys. Acta,* 27, 229, 1958.
61. **King, C. J.,** *Separation Processes,* McGraw-Hill, New York, 1971.
62. **Kirchoff, R. H. and Hamdi, A.,** Continuous-flow dielectrophoresis, *J. Electrochem. Soc.,* 120, 1, 1973.
63. **Knight, J. R.,** Large-Scale Purification of Proteins by Gel-Permeation Chromatography, Ph.D. thesis, University of Wisconsin, Madison, 1970.
64. **Kolin, A.,** Continuous electrophoretic fractionation stabilized by electromagnetic rotation, *Proc. Natl. Acad. Sci. U.S.A.,* 46, 509, 1960.
65. **Kolin, A.,** Use of magnetic fields in new approaches to fractionation of particles and molecules in liquid columns, *Protides Biol. Fluids Proc. Colloq.,* 12, 410, 1964.
66. **Kolin, A. and Luner, S. J.,** Endless belt electrophoresis, in *Progress in Separation and Purification,* Vol. 4, Perry, E. S. and Van Oss, C. J., Eds., Interscience, New York, 1971, 93.
67. **Kozinski, A. A., Schmidt, F. P., and Lightfoot, E. N.,** Velocity profiles in porous-walled ducts, *Ind. Eng. Chem. Fundam.,* 9, 502, 1970.
68. **Lee, H. L., Reis, J. F. G., Dohner, J., and Lightfoot, E. N.,** Single-phase chromatography: Solute retardation by ultrafiltration and electrophoresis, *AIChE J.,* 20, 776, 1974.
69. **Lee, H. L. and Lightfoot, E. N.,** Preliminary report on ultrafiltration induced polarization chromatography – An analog of field flow fractionation, *Sep. Sci.,* in press.
70. **Lightfoot, E. N.,** *Transport Phenomena and Living Systems,* John Wiley & Sons, New York, 1974.
71. **Lightfoot, E. N.,** Estimation of heat and mass transfer rates, in *Lectures in Transport Phenomena,* AIChE Continuing Education Series No. 4, AIChE, New York, 1969.
72. **Lightfoot, E. N., Bassingthwaighte, J. B., and Grabowski, E. F.,** Hydrodynamic models for diffusion in microporous membranes, *Ann. Biomed. Eng.,* 4, 78, 1976.
73. **Lightfoot, E. N., Sanchez-Palma, R. J., and Edwards, D. O.,** Chromatography and allied fixed-bed separations processes, in *New Separation Techniques,* Schoen, H. M., Ed., Interscience, New York, 1962, 99.
74. **Ludviksson, V. and Lightfoot, E. N.,** The dynamics of thin liquid films in the presence of surface-tension gradients, *AIChE J.,* 17, 1166, 1971.
75. **McCabe, W. and Smith, J. C.,** *Unit Operations of Chemical Engineering,* McGraw-Hill, New York, 1967.

76. **Möller, W. J. H. M., Van Oss, G. A. J., and Overbeek, J. T. G.,** Electric conductivity and transference of alkali albuminates, *Trans. Faraday Soc.*, 57, 325, 1961.
77. **Newman, J. S.,** *Electrochemical Systems,* Prentice-Hall, Englewood Cliffs, N.J., 1973.
78. **Olander, D. R.,** Technical basis of the ultra-centrifuge, *Adv. Nucl. Sci. Technol.*, 6, 106, 1972.
79. **Ornstein, L.,** Disc electrophoresis I – Background and theory, *Ann. N.Y. Acad. Sci.*, 121, 321, 1964.
80. **Otocka, E. P.,** High speed gel permeation chromatography – Application of liquid chromatographic techniques, *J. Chromatogr.*, 76, 149, 1973.
81. **Paul, D. R.,** Membrane separation of gases using steady cyclic operation, *Ind. Eng. Chem. Process Des. Dev.*, 10, 375, 1971.
82. **Pauschmann, H.,** A vector scheme for separation processes, *Z. Anal. Chem.*, 258, 358, 1972.
83. **Pfann, W. G.,** *Zone Melting,* John Wiley & Sons, New York, 1966.
84. **Pfeffer, R.,** Heat and mass transport in multiparticle systems, *Ind. Eng. Chem. Fundam.*, 3(4), 380, 1964.
85. **Phillips, C. and Groseva, V. M.,** Separation of multicomponent hydrocarbon mixtures spreading on a water surface, *Sep. Sci.*, 10(2), 111, 1975.
86. **Philpot, J. S. L.,** Electrophoretic Separation Apparatus, British Patent 1,150,722, 1969.
87. **Pohl, H. A. and Crane, J. S.,** Dielectrophoresis of cells, *Biophys. J.*, 11, 711, 1971.
88. **Porter, M. C. and Michaels, A. S.,** Membrane ultrafiltration, Part 5, *Chem. Technol.*, p. 56, January 1972.
89. **Reis, J. F. G. and Lightfoot, E. N.,** Electropolarization chromatography, *AIChE J.*, 22, 779, 1976.
90. **Reis, J. F. G., Lightfoot, E. N., and Lee, H. L.,** Concentration profiles in free-flow electrophoresis, *AIChE J.*, 20(2), 362, 1974.
91. **Reusch, C. F. and Cussler, E. L., Jr.,** Selective membrane transport, *AIChE J.*, 19, 736, 1973.
92. **Rietema, K.,** Efficiency in separating mixtures of two constituents, *Chem. Eng. Sci.*, 7, 89, 1957.
93. **Rony, P. R.,** The extent of separation: On the unification of the field of chemical separations, *AIChE Symp. Ser.*, 68(120), 89, 1972.
94. **Rosen, J. B.,** Kinetics of a fixed bed system for solid diffusion into spherical particles, *J. Chem. Phys.*, 20, 387, 1952.
95. **Rozen, A. M.,** Theory of Isotope Separation in Columns, translation available from U.S.S.R. Office of Translation Services, (Joint Publication Research Service No. 11213; CSO: 6667-N).
96. **Rudd, D. F., Powers, G. J., and Siirola, J. J.,** *Process Synthesis,* Prentice-Hall, Englewood Cliffs, N.J., 1973.
97. **Rudd, D. F. and Watson, C. C.,** *The Strategy of Process Engineering,* John Wiley & Sons, New York, 1968.
98. **Sankarasubramanian, R. and Gill, W. N.,** Correction to unsteady convective diffusion with interphase mass transfer, *Proc. R. Soc. London Ser. A*, 341, 407, 1974.
99. **Sankarasubramanian, R. and Gill, W. N.,** Unsteady convective diffusion with interphase mass transfer, *Proc. R. Soc. London Ser. A*, 333, 115, 1973.
100. **Shachter, J., Von Halle, E., and Hoglund, R. L.,** Diffusion separation methods, in *Encyclopedia of Chemical Technology,* Vol. 7, 2nd ed., Interscience, New York, 1965, 91.
101. **Slattery, J. C.,** *Momentum, Energy, and Mass Transfer in Continua,* McGraw-Hill, New York, 1971.
102. **Staverman, J. A.,** The theory of measurement of osmotic pressure, *Recl. Trav. Chim. Pays Bas,* 70, 344, 1951.
103. **Stewart, W. E.,** Solution of transport problems by collocation methods, in *Lectures in Transport Phenomena,* AIChE Continuing Education Series No. 4, AIChE, New York, 1969.
104. **Stewart, W. E. and Sørensen, J. P.,** Transient reactor analysis by orthogonal collocation, *Fifth European Symposium on Chemical Reaction Engineering,* 1972.
105. **Sussman, M. V. and Rathore, R. N. S.,** Continuous modes of chromatography, *Chromatographia,* 8(2), 55, 1975.
106. **Sussman, M. V.,** Continuous chromatography, *Chem. Technol.*, 6(4), 260, 1976.
107. **Sussman, M. V., Astill, K. N., Rombach, R., Cerullo, A., and Chen, S. S.,** Continuous surface chromatography, *Ind. Eng. Chem. Fundam.*, 11, 181, 1972.
108. **Sweed, N. H.,** Parametric pumping, in *Progress in Separation and Purification,* Vol. 4, Perry, E. S. and Van Oss, C. J., Eds., Interscience, New York, 1971, 171.
109. **Taylor, G. I.,** Dispersion of soluble matter in solvent flowing slowly through a tube, *Proc. R. Soc. London Ser. A,* 219, 186, 1953.
110. **Thompson, R. W. and King, C. J.,** Systematic synthesis of separation schemes, *AIChE J.*, 18(5), 941, 1972.
111. **Tuthill, E. J.,** New concept for the continuous chromatographic separation of chemical species, *J. Chromatogr. Sci.*, 8, 285, 1970.
112. **Vermeulen, T., Nady, L., Krochta, J., Ravoo, E., and Darryl, H.,** Design theory and separation in preparative-scale continuous-flow annular-bed electrophoresis, *Ind. Eng. Chem. Proc. Dis. Dev.*, 10(1), 91, 1971.
113. **Villadsen, J. V.,** *Selected Approximation Methods for Chemical Engineering Problems,* Reproset, Copenhagen, 1970.
114. **Villadsen, J. V. and Stewart, W. E.,** Solution of boundary-value problems by orthogonal collocation, *Chem. Eng. Sci.*, 22, 1483, 1967.
115. **Wagener, K., Freyer, H., and Bilal, B.,** Countercurrent electrophoresis, *Sep. Sci.*, 6, 483, 1971.
116. **Wankat, P. C.,** Two-dimensional cross-flow cascades, *Sep. Sci.*, 7(3), 233, 1972.
117. **Wankat, P. C.,** Two-dimensional development in staged systems, *Sep. Sci.*, 7(4), 345, 1972.
118. **Weisz, P. B.,** Diffusion and chemical transformation, *Science,* 179, 433, 1973.

119. **Wilhelm, R. H., Rice, A., Rolks, R., and Sweed, N.,** Parametric pumping: A dynamical principle for separating fluid mixtures, *Ind. Eng. Chem. Fundam.,* 7, 337, 1968.
120. **Bracewell, R.,** *The Fourier Transform and Its Applications,* McGraw-Hill, New York, 1965.
121. **Garreau et al.,** *Comptes Rendus,* 256, 3680, 1963.
122. **Atroshenko, L. S. and Voronina, S. M.,** Diffusion in a falling film in the presence of a nonuniform magnetic field, *Int. Chem. Eng.,* 12(3), 465, 1972.
123. **Condon, E. U. and Odishaw, H.,** *Handbook of Physics,* 2nd ed., McGraw-Hill, New York, 1967.
124. **Strickland, R. D.,** Electrophoresis, *Anal. Chem.,* 46(5), 95R, 1974.
125. **Phillips, S. C.,** *An Introduction to Crystallography,* Longmans, New York, 1949.

INTERACTION OF FLUID DYNAMICS, INTERFACIAL PHENOMENA, AND MASS TRANSFER IN EXTRACTION PROCESSES

K. Schügerl, H. G. Blaschke, U. Brunke, and R. Streicher

TABLE OF CONTENTS

INTRODUCTION

The mass transfer across the interface of two liquids plays an important role in extraction processes and in heterogeneous reactions for which the reaction partners are originally in two immiscible liquids. The exchange rate and/or the rate of the mass-transfer-limited chemical reaction is determined by the interfacial area of the systems and by the mass transfer coefficient.

According to the extended two-film theory the overall resistance of the mass transfer consists of the individual resistances of the two phases and the interface. Other models, like the penetration model, preserve this division of the overall resistance into three components.

Because of the insufficient accuracy of the measuring techniques which are applied to the investigation of mass exchange processes, one usually makes overall statements on the resistance of mass exchange. A separation of the individual resistances is carried out theoretically by the use of different mathematical models. The validity of the assumptions made in these models is still only partially experimentally proven.

The aim of the present paper is to investigate the properties of these partial resistances by means of new powerful measuring techniques and advanced mathematical models. The paper considers the mass transfer in two different systems:

- in two-phase film flow, and
- in single droplets.

In the second section the models are developed for these systems; in the third section the principles of the new measuring techniques are explained; and in the fourth section the experimental setup and the measurements are described for the film-flow investigations. The experimental setups and the measurements with single droplets are discussed in the fifth section. Finally, an outlook is given in the sixth section for possible new results to be achieved by improved measuring techniques.

MATHEMATICAL MODELS OF HYDRODYNAMICS AND MASS TRANSFER

Two-phase Film Flow

Velocity Profiles in Stationary Two-phase Laminar Flow in Horizontal Cylindrical Channels

The flow of one-phase thin liquid films was considered by V. G. Levich in his book.[1] Two-phase liquid films in horizontal channels have been recently investigated.[2–4] The hydrodynamics of such a flow system can be described by the Navier-Stokes equations, but up to now no general and exact solution of these equations for laminar two-phase flow in tubes has been available. E. Schadow[3] has developed a solution which is restricted to the case of equal pressure drop in both phases. Based on the results of Schadow a general and exact solution was developed by Brunke.[5]

Consider the two-phase film flow in cylindrical z (longitudinal), r (radial), and φ (azimuthal) coordinates: The lighter Phase 1 fills the upper half ($0 \leqslant \varphi \leqslant \pi$) and the heavier Phase 2 the lower half ($\pi < \varphi \leqslant 2\pi$) of the channel: The interface is at $\varphi = \pi$; μ_1 and μ_2 are the dynamic viscosities of the Phases 1 and 2, p_1 and p_2 are the pressures in these phases, and V_{zi} the velocity component of Phase i in direction of z.

Only fully developed stationary two-phase flow will be considered. The fluids are assumed to be incompressible, so that the following differential equations describe the two-phase flow:

$$-\mu_1\left(\frac{\partial^2 v_{z,1}}{\partial r^2}+\frac{1}{r}\frac{\partial v_{z,1}}{\partial r}+\frac{1}{r^2}\frac{\partial^2 v_{z,1}}{\partial \varphi^2}\right)+\frac{dp_1}{dz}=0 \quad (1)$$

$$-\mu_2\left(\frac{\partial^2 v_{z,2}}{\partial r^2}+\frac{1}{r}\frac{\partial v_{z,2}}{\partial r}+\frac{1}{r^2}\frac{\partial^2 v_{z,2}}{\partial \varphi^2}\right)+\frac{dp_2}{dz}=0 \quad (2)$$

It is assumed that the pressure drop in Phase 2 has a k*-fold value of the pressure drop in Phase 1

$$\left(\frac{dp_2}{dz}\right)=k^*\left(\frac{dp_1}{dz}\right) \quad (3)$$

From this, Equation 1 and 2 become

$$-\mu_1\left(\frac{\partial^2 v_{z,1}}{\partial r^2}+\frac{1}{r}\frac{\partial v_{z,1}}{\partial r}+\frac{1}{r^2}\frac{\partial^2 v_{z,1}}{\partial \varphi^2}\right)+\frac{dp_1}{dz}=0 \quad (4)$$

$$-\mu_2\left(\frac{\partial^2 v_{z,2}}{\partial r^2}+\frac{1}{r}\frac{\partial v_{z,2}}{\partial r}+\frac{1}{r^2}\frac{\partial^2 v_{z,2}}{\partial \varphi^2}\right)+k\left(\frac{dp_1}{dz}\right)=0 \quad (5)$$

The following boundary conditions have to be considered:

1. The velocity at the wall is zero.

$$v_{z,1}(R,\varphi)=v_{z,2}(R,\varphi)=0 \quad (6)$$

2. At the interface the sheer stresses and the velocities are equal.

$$\mu_1\frac{\partial v_{z,1}}{\partial \varphi}=\mu_2\frac{\partial v_{z,2}}{\partial \varphi} \qquad \varphi=0,\pi,2\pi \quad (7)$$

$$v_{z,1}(r,0)=v_{z,2}(r,2\pi) \quad (8)$$

$$v_{z,1}(r,\pi)=v_{z,2}(r,\pi) \quad (9)$$

The solution of Brunke[5] is based on the solution of Schadow[2] for the partial, inhomogeneous differential equations of second order:

$$v_{z,1}(r,\varphi)=A_1\left[1-\left(\frac{r}{R}\right)^2+B\left(1-\left(\frac{r}{R}\right)^2\cos 2\varphi\right)+B\sum_{n=0}^{\infty}E_n\left(\frac{r}{R}\right)^n\sin n\varphi\right] \quad (10)$$

$$v_{z,2}(r,\varphi)=A_2\left[1-\left(\frac{r}{R}\right)^2-B\left(1-\left(\frac{r}{R}\right)^2\cos 2\varphi\right)+B\sum_{n=0}^{\infty}E_n\left(\frac{r}{R}\right)^n\sin n\varphi\right] \quad (11)$$

The equations are satisfied if there is

$$A_1=-\frac{R^2}{4\mu_1}\left(\frac{dp_1}{dz}\right) \quad (12)$$

$$A_2=-\frac{R^2}{4\mu_2}k\left(\frac{dp_1}{dz}\right) \quad (13)$$

The assumptions for A_1 and A_2 are obtained by substitution of Equations 10 and 11 into Equations 1 and 2. The boundary condition (Equation 6) requires:

$$(\cos 2\varphi-1)=\sum_{n=0}^{\infty}E_n\sin n\varphi \qquad 0\leqslant\varphi\leqslant\pi$$

$$(-\cos 2\varphi+1)=\sum_{n=0}^{\infty}E_n\sin n\varphi \qquad \pi\leqslant\varphi\leqslant 2\pi \quad (14)$$

The coefficients are determined by Fourier analysis:

$$E_{2n}=0$$

$$E_{2n+1}=\frac{16}{\pi(2n+3)(2n+1)(2n-1)} \quad (15)$$

From the other boundary conditions the following equations can be obtained:

$$B=\frac{k^*\mu_1-\mu_2}{k^*\mu_1+\mu_2}$$

$$b=\frac{\mu_2}{\mu_1}$$

$$B=\frac{k^*-b}{k^*+b} \quad (16)$$

Hence, the solution of the differential equation is

$$v_{z,1}(r,\varphi)=\frac{R^2}{4\mu_1}\left(-\frac{dp_1}{dz}\right)\left[1-\left(\frac{r}{R}\right)^2+\frac{k^*-b}{k^*+b}\left(1-\left(\frac{r}{R}\right)^2\cos 2\varphi+\frac{16}{\pi}\sum_{n=0}^{\infty}\left(\frac{r}{R}\right)^{2n+1}\frac{\sin(2n+1)\varphi}{(2n+3)(2n+1)(2n-1)}\right)\right] \quad (17)$$

$$v_{z,2}(r,\varphi)=\frac{R^2}{4\mu_2}k\left(-\frac{dp_1}{dz}\right)\left[1-\left(\frac{r}{R}\right)^2-\frac{k^*-b}{k^*+b}\left(1-\left(\frac{r}{R}\right)^2\cos 2\varphi-\frac{16}{\pi}\sum_{n=0}^{\infty}\left(\frac{r}{R}\right)^{2n+1}\frac{\sin(2n+1)\varphi}{(2n+3)(2n+1)(2n-1)}\right)\right] \quad (18)$$

The pressure drop cannot easily be determined in this equation. Because of this the volumetric flow is used.

$$Q_1=\int_0^R\int_0^\pi v_{z,1}(r,\varphi)\,r\,dr\,d\varphi \quad (19)$$

$$Q_2 = \int_0^R \int_\pi^{2\pi} v_{z,\,2(r,\,\varphi)}\, r\, dr\, d\varphi \tag{20}$$

The velocities determined in Equations 17 and 18 are inserted in Equations 19 and 20. By integration the volumetric flow Q_1 and Q_2 may be obtained as function of the pressure drop gradient $\frac{dp_1}{dz}$

$$Q_1 = \frac{R^4}{4\mu_1}\left(\frac{dp_1}{dz}\right)\left[\frac{\pi}{4} + \frac{k^* - b}{k^* + b}\left(\frac{\pi}{2} + \frac{32}{\pi}\sum_{n=0}^{\infty} \frac{1}{(2n+3)^2\,(2n+1)^2\,(2n-1)}\right)\right] \tag{21}$$

$$Q_2 = \frac{R^4}{4\mu_2}\left(\frac{dp_1}{dz}\right) k \left[\frac{\pi}{4} - \frac{k^* - b}{k^* + b}\left(\frac{\pi}{2} + \frac{32}{\pi}\sum_{n=0}^{\infty} \frac{1}{(2n+3)^2\,(2n+1)^2\,(2n-1)}\right)\right] \tag{22}$$

Substituting Equation 21 in Equation 17, and Equation 22 in Equation 18, gives:

$$v_{z,\,1(r,\,\varphi)} = \frac{Q_1\left[1 - \left(\frac{r}{R}\right)^2 + \frac{k^* - b}{k^* + b}\left(1 - \left(\frac{r}{R}\right)^2 \cos 2\varphi + \frac{16}{\pi}\sum_{n=0}^{\infty}\left(\frac{r}{R}\right)^{2n+1} \frac{\sin(2n+1)\,\varphi}{(2n+3)\,(2n+1)\,(2n-1)}\right)\right]}{R^2\left[\frac{\pi}{4} + \frac{k^* - b}{k^* + b}\left\{\frac{\pi}{2} + \left(\frac{32}{\pi}\sum_{n=0}^{\infty} \frac{1}{(2n+3)^2\,(2n+1)^2\,(2n-1)}\right)\right\}\right]} \tag{23}$$

$$v_{z,\,2(r,\,\varphi)} = \frac{Q_2\left[1 - \left(\frac{r}{R}\right)^2 - \frac{k^* - b}{k^* + b}\left(1 - \left(\frac{r}{R}\right)^2 \cos 2\varphi - \frac{16}{\pi}\sum_{n=0}^{\infty}\left(\frac{r}{R}\right)^{2n+1} \frac{\sin(2n+1)\,\varphi}{(2n+3)\,(2n+1)\,(2n-1)}\right)\right]}{R^2\left[\frac{\pi}{4} - \frac{k^* - b}{k^* + b}\left\{\frac{\pi}{2} + \left(\frac{32}{\pi}\sum_{n=0}^{\infty} \frac{1}{(2n+3)^2\,(2n+1)^2\,(2n-1)}\right)\right\}\right]} \tag{24}$$

k^* can be determined from Equations 21 and 22:

$$\frac{Q_1}{Q_2} = \frac{\mu_2}{\mu_1}\frac{1}{k^*}\;\frac{\left[\frac{\pi}{4} + \frac{k^* - b}{k^* + b}\left(\frac{\pi}{2} + \frac{32}{\pi}\sum_{n=0}^{\infty} \frac{1}{(2n+3)^2\,(2n+1)^2\,(2n-1)}\right)\right]}{\left[\frac{\pi}{4} - \frac{k^* - b}{k^* + b}\left(\frac{\pi}{2} + \frac{32}{\pi}\sum_{n=0}^{\infty} \frac{1}{(2n+1)^2\,(2n+3)^2\,(2n-1)}\right)\right]} \tag{25}$$

Equation 25 cannot be solved to directly give k^*. The value of k^* can only be obtained for given μ_1, μ_2, Q_1, and Q_2 by iteration.

Mass Transfer in Stationary Two-phase Laminar Flow in a Horizontal Cylindrical Channel

The general mass balance equation can be reduced, if following assumptions are made:

1. The system is in steady state

$$\frac{\partial c}{\partial t} = 0$$

in the cylinder and there is fully developed laminar flow of both of the phases, i.e., Equation 25 can be applied.

2. The flow is considered in Cartesian coordinates. The interface is in the x-z-plane, where z is the flow direction. The diffusional mass transfer occurs in direction y, across the interface (perpendicular to the interface) and along the flow direction z. It is assumed that the components of the velocity vector in direction x and y disappear and that no concentration change of the solute prevails in direction x. Hence

$$w\frac{\partial c}{\partial z} = D\left(\frac{\partial^2 c}{\partial y^2} + \frac{\partial^2 c}{\partial z^2}\right) \tag{26}$$

where w is the flow velocity in longitudinal direction.

Algebraic solutions of Equation 26 were developed for four different cases by Yamir and Taitel.[53] Pietsch developed a numerical solution and showed that for flow rates $\geqslant$1 cm/s and for molecular diffusivities $D < 10^{-4}$ cm²/s the longitudinal dispersion can be neglected, i.e.,

$$D\frac{\partial^2 c}{\partial z^2} \simeq 0$$

Hence Equation 26 can be reduced further to Equation 27:

$$w(y)\frac{\partial c}{\partial z} = D\frac{\partial^2 c}{\partial y} \tag{27}$$

where w(y) is the nonuniform velocity.

Existing Solutions of Equation 27

The solution of Equation 27, by assuming a constant flow rate

$w(y) = V_m = \text{const.}$

is given by:

$$k(z) = \left(\frac{V_m D}{\pi z}\right)^{1/2} \tag{28}$$

where k(z) is the mass transfer coefficient.

Beck and Bakker[54] investigated gas-liquid systems and solved the mass balance equation Equation 27 by means of a Laplace operator method by assuming linear velocity profile at the interface. Byers and King,[55] Tang and Himmelblau,[56] and Apelblatt and Katchalsky[57] offered algebraic solutions for laminar flow with parabolic velocity profiles of the two phases between parallel plates of infinite extension. Furthermore, they assumed that diffusional mass transfer occurs only in a thin layer near the interface. In the bulk flow, at greater distances from the interface, the initial concentration is preserved.

Schadow[3] developed an algebraic solution for finite systems with linear velocity profiles. Mass transfer across the interface of gas and liquid phases for laminar falling films with parabolic velocity profiles were investigated by Zogg,[58] Rotem and Neilson,[59] Bojadjev,[60] and Yamir and Taitel.[61] They assumed that the concentration of the solute in the gas phase remains constant.

Numerical solutions were developed by Batschelet and Grün[62] and Pietsch.[2] In his book, Crank offers a numerical solution (by means of the Crank-Nicholson method) for a similar problem.[63]

Numerical Solution of Equation 27 with the True Velocity Profiles of the Two Phases

Only Brunke[33] gives a solution of Equation 27 for the true velocity profiles of the two phases. This solution is now described. The first problem that had to be solved was that the velocity distribution w(y) is complex and the initial concentration of the solute in the phases is not uniform. To solve Equation 27, taking into account the true velocity profile and the true initial concentration of the solute in the phases, the partial differential equation was approximated by a system of difference equations. Since the velocity w(y) and the initial concentration $c_0(y)$ vary only along y, the system is cut along z in thin sheets parallel to the x-y plane, and every sheet is described along y: y_{i-1}, y_i, y_{i+1}, etc. h is the interval of equidistant grid points y_i. By this procedure the partial differential equation is converted into a system of ordinary differential equations. By the use of the Taylor series one obtains:[33]

$$\frac{\partial^2 c}{\partial y^2} = \frac{c_{i-1} - 2c_i + c_{(i+1)}}{h^2} \tag{29}$$

with an error:

$$F_{(h)} = -\frac{1}{12} h^2 \frac{\partial^4 c}{\partial y^4} - \frac{1}{360} h^4 \frac{\partial^6 c}{\partial y^6} - \ldots\ldots$$

which is less than 1% for 10 grid points. Near to the interface where strong variations of the solute concentration prevail the interval was reduced to $\frac{h}{n}$.

At the junction point of the intervals h and $\frac{h}{n}$ we have an asymmetrical second derivative:

$$\frac{\partial^2 c}{\partial y^2} = \frac{c_{i-1} - (1+n)\, c_i + n\, c_{i+1}}{\frac{h^2}{2}\left(1 + \frac{1}{n}\right)} - \frac{h^3}{3}\left(1 - \frac{1}{n^2}\right)\frac{\partial^3 c}{\partial y^3} + \ldots\ldots$$

with an error:

$$F_{(h)} = -\frac{h\left(1 - \frac{1}{n^2}\right)}{3\left(1 + \frac{1}{n}\right)}\frac{\partial^3 c}{\partial y^3} - \frac{h^2\left(1 + \frac{1}{n^3}\right)}{12\left(1 + \frac{1}{n}\right)}\frac{\partial^4 c}{\partial y^4} - \ldots\ldots$$

The (measured and/or calculated) velocity profiles were linearized in the intervals h and/or h/n for their application to the mass transfer equation (Equation 17). This equation is put into dimensionless form:

$$\frac{\partial c}{\partial z^*} = \frac{L}{R} \frac{1}{Pe^*} \frac{\partial^2 c}{\partial y^{*2}} \tag{30}$$

where

$y^* = \frac{y}{R}$

$z^* = \frac{z}{L}$

$\frac{D}{w \cdot R} = \frac{1}{Pe^*}$

Pe^* = modified Peclet number

In the following we omit the asterisks of the symbols y* and z*.

For the grid point i the approximation Equation 29 is put into Equation 30. Hence we obtain the ordinary differential equations:

$$\frac{dc_i}{dz} = \frac{L}{R \cdot Pe_i \cdot h^2}\left(c_{i-1} - 2c_i + c_{i+1}\right) \tag{31}$$

With

$$g_i = \frac{L}{R \cdot Pe_i \cdot h^2} \tag{32}$$

we obtain

$$\frac{dc_i}{dz} = g_i\,(c_{i-1} - 2c_i + c_{i+1}) \tag{32}$$

At the wall ($y = \pm 1$, $i = 1, n$) the following boundary conditions prevail, since the solute can not diffuse across the channel wall:

$$\frac{\partial c}{\partial y} = 0$$

$$y + 1 \quad \frac{\partial c}{\partial y} \sim \frac{c_1 - c_0}{h} = 0 \rightarrow c_0 = c_1$$

$$y - 1 \quad \frac{\partial c}{\partial y} \sim \frac{c_{n+1} - c_n}{h} = 0 \rightarrow c_{n+1} = c_n$$

The initial conditions are for $z = z_0$, $c_i = c_{0i}$. By that we obtain the following system of linear differential equations first order for $1 \leqslant i \leqslant n$:

$$\frac{dc_1}{dz} + g_1\,(c_1 - c_2) = 0$$

$$\frac{dc_i}{dz} + g_i\,(-c_{i-1} + 2c_i - c_{i+1}) = 0 \tag{33a}$$

$$\frac{dc_n}{dz} + g_n\,(-c_{n-1} + c_n) = 0$$

that is

$$\vec{c}' + \begin{bmatrix} g_1 & -g_1 & 0 \;\cdots & 0 & 0 & 0 \\ -g_2 & 2g_2 & -g_2 \;\cdots & 0 & 0 & 0 \\ \cdot & \cdot & \cdot & \cdot & \cdot & \cdot \\ \cdot & \cdot & \cdot & \cdot & \cdot & \cdot \\ \cdot & \cdot & \cdot & \cdot & \cdot & \cdot \\ \cdot & \cdot & \cdot & \cdot & \cdot & \cdot \\ \cdot & \cdot & \cdot & \cdot & \cdot & \cdot \\ \cdot & \cdot & \cdot & \cdot & \cdot & \cdot \\ 0 & 0 & 0 \;\cdots & -g_{n-1} & 2g_{n-1} & -g_{n-1} \\ 0 & 0 & 0 \;\cdots & 0 & -g_n & g_n \end{bmatrix} \begin{bmatrix} c_1 \\ c_2 \\ \cdot \\ \cdot \\ \cdot \\ \cdot \\ \cdot \\ \cdot \\ c_{n-1} \\ c_n \end{bmatrix} = \begin{bmatrix} 0 \\ 0 \\ \cdot \\ \cdot \\ \cdot \\ \cdot \\ \cdot \\ \cdot \\ 0 \\ 0 \end{bmatrix} \tag{33b}$$

or

$$\vec{c}' + G \cdot \vec{c} = \vec{0} \tag{33c}$$

where $\vec{c}$ means a vector and G is the matrix (Equation 33b). Since the coefficients are constant, the solution is given by:[64]

$$\vec{c} = \vec{b}\,e^{\lambda z} \tag{34}$$

Since $\vec{c}' = \lambda \cdot c$, putting Equation 34 into Equation 33c we obtain Equation 35:

$$(G - \lambda E) \cdot \vec{c} = 0 \tag{35}$$

where E is the unit matrix. The condition for nontrivial solution of c is given by

$$\det|G - \lambda E| = 0 \tag{36}$$

By that, the system of differential equations becomes an eigenvalue problem. The characteristic equation of the matrix becomes the characteristic equation of the system of differential equations. If the coefficient-determinant disappears we have n nontrivial solutions for c for the homogeneous system of equations. The characteristic determinant is given by

$$\begin{vmatrix} g_1 - \lambda & -g_1 & 0 & \cdots & 0 & 0 & 0 \\ -g_2 & 2g_2 - \lambda & -g_2 & \cdots & 0 & 0 & 0 \\ \cdot & \cdot & \cdot & & \cdot & \cdot & \cdot \\ \cdot & \cdot & \cdot & & \cdot & \cdot & \cdot \\ \cdot & \cdot & \cdot & & \cdot & \cdot & \cdot \\ 0 & 0 & 0 & & -g_{n-1} & 2g_{n-1} - \lambda & -g_{n-1} \\ 0 & 0 & 0 & & & -g_{n-1} & g_n - \lambda \end{vmatrix} = 0 \tag{37}$$

The parameter λ is a polynomial equation of nth order in λ, which is the characteristic polynomial equation of the matrix. It is the algebraic equation of degree n and has exact n real or complex roots $\lambda_1, \lambda_2 \ldots \lambda_n$. The present matrix has only elements in the mean and the two adjacent diagonals.

$$\begin{bmatrix} (\lambda - a_1) & b_1 & & & \\ b_2 & (\lambda - a_2) & b_2 & & \\ & b_3 & (\lambda - a_3) & b_3 & \\ & \cdot\cdot & & \cdot\cdot & \cdot\cdot \\ & & & b_n & (\lambda - a_n) \end{bmatrix} \quad (38a)$$

$$f_{i+1} = (\lambda - a_{i+1})\cdot f_i - b_{i+1}\cdot b_i \cdot f_{i-1} \quad (38b)$$

with $f_0 = 1, f_1 = \lambda - a_1$.

By putting the calculated eigenvalues into the matrix G one obtains the eigenvectors $\vec{a_i}$, which give together the modal matrix A. The solution is given by following equation:

$$\vec{c} = b_1 \cdot \vec{a_1} \cdot e^{\lambda_1 z} + b_2 \cdot \vec{a_2} \cdot e^{\lambda_2 z} + \ldots + b_n \cdot \vec{a_n} \cdot e^{\lambda_n z} \quad (39)$$

The system has to be fitted to the initial conditions at z = 0

$$\vec{c}_{(0)} = \vec{c}_0$$

By that we obtain

$$b_1 \cdot \vec{a_1} + b_2 \cdot \vec{a_2} + \ldots + b_n \cdot \vec{a_n} = \vec{c_0} \quad (40a)$$

or

$$A \cdot \vec{b} = c_0 \quad (40b)$$

where A modal matrix with the eigen vectors $\vec{a_i}$ and

$\vec{b} = (b_1, b_2 \ldots b_n)$ a vector

The vector $\vec{b}$ is calculated by

$$\vec{b} = A^{-1} \cdot \vec{c_0} \quad (40c)$$

The calculation was carried out by library programs for matrix operation by means of 20 grid points.[33]

It can be shown that this two-dimensional solution of the mass-transfer equation can be applied to cylindrical channels, if the measurements are carried out in the yz-plane at x = 0 (in the center). The error in the concentrations of the solute in this yz-plane (perpendicular to the interface) is always less than 2.36%.[33]

Droplets

Hydrodynamics of Droplets

Motion of liquid drops in fluid media is considered in detail in Chapter VIII of the book by Levich.[1] Two cases can be distinguished for $Re \ll 1$:

1. Pure systems
2. Systems with surface-active substances

Pure systems already have been considered by Rybczynski[5] and Hadamard,[6] who developed the well-known relation for the relative drop velocity U:

$$U = \frac{2(\rho_1 - \rho_2)\, ga^2}{3\mu_2} \, \frac{\mu_2 + \mu_1}{2\mu_2 + 3\mu} \quad (41)$$

Here are

ρ_1 and ρ_2	=	The density of droplet and continuous phases
g	=	Acceleration of gravity
a	=	Radius of the spherical droplet
μ_1, μ_2	=	Dynamic viscosity of the droplet and continuous phases

The behavior of small droplets in the presence of surface-active substances was also considered by Levich.[1] These substances are adsorbed at the interface between the two liquids. Because of the movement of the interface, Rybczynski and Hadamard[5,6] consider that the interface is continuously renewed on the upstream side of the droplet. The liquid motion carries the molecules of surface-active substances on the surface of the drop towards the rear of the drop. The resulting accumulation of surface-active substances lowers the surface tension in the rear part of the drop. The force caused by this gradient of surface tension retards the surface motion, thereby inhibiting the further accumulation of surface-active substances in the rear portion of the drop.

Depending on the rate-determining step (adsorption, bulk diffusion, or surface diffusion) different relative velocities were evaluated:

$$U = 3\, U_0 \frac{\mu_2 + \mu_1 + \gamma_1}{2\mu_2 + 3\mu_1 + 3\gamma_1} \quad (42a)$$

for adsorption as rate-determining step. Here are

$$U_0 = \frac{2}{9}\, \frac{(\rho_1 - \rho_1)ga^2}{\mu_2} \qquad \text{the Stokes velocity}$$

$$\gamma_1 = \frac{2\Gamma_0}{3\alpha a} \frac{\partial \sigma}{\partial \Gamma} \qquad \text{retardation coefficient}$$

$$\alpha = \frac{\partial P}{\partial \Gamma} - \frac{\partial Q}{\partial \Gamma}$$

Γ_0 = Equilibrium surface concentration of surface-active substances at the interface

Γ = Local surface concentration of surface-active substances at the interface

σ = Interfacial tension

$P(\Gamma)$ and/or $Q(\Gamma)$ = Number of molecules desorbed and/or adsorbed per unit area per unit time

$$U = 3\,U_0 \frac{\mu_2 + \mu_1 + \gamma_2}{2\mu_2 + 3\mu_1 + 3\gamma_2} \tag{42b}$$

for diffusion to the surface as rate-determining step with

$$\gamma_2 = \frac{2\,RT\,\Gamma_0^{\,2}\delta}{3\,Da\,c_0}$$

δ = Average thickness of diffusion layer

c_0 = Concentration of surface-active substances in the bulk

D = Molecular diffusion coefficient of surface-active molecules

and

$$U = 3\,U_0 \frac{\mu_2 + \mu_1 + \gamma_3}{2\mu_2 + 3\mu_1 + 3\gamma_3} \tag{42c}$$

for surface diffusion as rate-determining step with

$$\gamma_3 = \frac{2a\,\Gamma_0}{3\,D_s}\left|\frac{\partial\sigma}{\partial\Gamma}\right|$$

D_s = Coefficient of surface diffusion

This theory originated by Frumkin and Levich has been criticized on two points. First, the flow patterns are symmetric about the equatorial plane, while the observed patterns are asymmetric with a slowly circulating region at the rear; and second, the transition of the interface from the freely circulating state to the more or less rigid state is too gradual.[28] An alternative mechanism was proposed by Boussinesqu,[29] who introduced an interfacial viscosity. The functional form of their resulting relations is the same as in the Frumkin-Levich theory; therefore they suffer from the same deficiences as the Frumkin-Levich theory. An improved theory, which considers an inelastic film covering a portion of the droplet, was developed by Savic,[30] Griffith,[31] and Davis and Acrivos.[28] Surface-active material, adsorbed from the bulk fluid, is transported by convection to the stagnant cup, whose extent is limited by the maximum surface concentration which the film can sustain without collapse. A combination of the Frumkin-Levich model with this stagnant-cup model was given by Saville.[32] He examined two systems for large Peclet numbers: (1) almost freely circulating interface and (2) an almost rigid interface. For the first case he obtained:

$$U \simeq 3\,U_0 \frac{1}{\dfrac{2+3x}{1+x} - 0.606\,\dfrac{(\beta\Gamma_\infty/\rho\nu U)\,[2\gamma^2\,U/aD\,(1+x)]^{0.5}}{(1+x)(1+0.528)\,2\gamma^2\,U/aD\,(1+x)^{0.5}}} \tag{43a}$$

where

$$\beta = \frac{\partial\sigma}{\partial\Gamma}$$

$$\gamma = \frac{\partial\Gamma}{\partial C}$$

$$\nu = \frac{\mu}{\rho}$$

Γ_∞ = Reference solute concentration at the interface

$X = \mu_1/\mu_2$

For the second case he found:

$$U \simeq U_0 \frac{1}{1 + 0.229\,(\rho\nu\,U/\sigma_\infty)\left(\frac{3}{2}\right)^{4/3} \frac{a}{\gamma}\,Pe^{-2/3}\,\frac{\sigma_\infty}{\beta\Gamma_\infty}} \tag{43b}$$

with

$$\left|(\rho\nu\,U/\sigma_\infty)\left(\frac{3}{2}\right)^{4/3} \frac{a}{\gamma}\,Pe^{-2/3}\,\frac{\sigma_\infty}{\beta\Gamma_\infty}\right| \to 0$$

where

σ_∞ = Reference interfacial tension

$Pe = \frac{2\,a\,U}{D}$ Peclet number

For higher Reynolds numbers no analytical solution is known. For liquid droplets in liquid media the drag of spherical droplets falling at their terminal velocities was evaluated for the range 1 <

Re < 50 numerically by Hamielec et al.[8] The calculated drag coefficient C_{DT} was plotted as function of the Reynolds number and fitted by following function:

$$C_{DT} = \frac{26.5}{Re^{0.75}}\left[\frac{(1.3 + x)^2 - 0.5}{(1.3 + x)(2 + x)}\right] \quad (44)$$

The drag coefficient of the Hadamard-Rybczynski system (Re = 1.0) is given by:

$$C_{DT} = \frac{8}{Re}\left[\frac{3x + 2}{x + 1}\right]$$

where $Re = \frac{2a\,U}{\nu}$, droplet Reynolds number.

Mass Transfer Between the Droplet and the Continuous Phase

The mass transfer rate can be controlled either by the mass transfer resistance in the continuous phase or in the discontinuous phase. Which resistance dominates depends on the ratio of the diffusion coefficient of the solute in the two phases D_1/D_2 and on the equilibrium distribution of the solute A between the two phases $H = \left.\frac{C_{A1}}{C_{A2}}\right)_{equil}$. The resistance is mainly in the phase 1, if

$$\frac{D_1}{D_2} \ll 1 \text{ and } H < 1$$

mainly in the phase 2, if

$$\frac{D_1}{D_2} \gg 1 \text{ and } H > 1$$

and in both of the phases, if

$$\frac{D_1}{D_2} \approx 1 \text{ and } H \approx 1$$

According to Brauer[9] and Schmidt-Traub,[10] the criterion $(H(D_1/D_2)^{1/2}$ is decisive for the dominance of the resistances. Only for

$$0.03 < H(D_1/D_2)^{1/2} < 30$$

should both of the resistances be considered.

For $H(D_1/D_2)^{1/2} < 0.03$, only the resistance in the droplet phase must be considered, and for $H(D_1/D_2)^{1/2} > 30$ only the resistance in the continuous phase must be taken into account.

Brounshtein and Fishbein[13] have shown that the mass-transfer process between the drop and the dense phase is non-steady-state when the dispersed phase resistance is controlling. Therefore the non-steady-state differential equation of mass transfer of the solute A has to be applied.[9,10,14,15] The mass balance of A in the droplet phase is given:

$$\frac{\partial C_{A1}}{\partial t} + u_{r,1}\frac{\partial C_{A1}}{\partial r} + \frac{u_{\theta,1}}{r}\frac{\partial C_{A1}}{\partial \theta} = D_1\left[\frac{\partial^2 C_{A1}}{\partial r^2} + \frac{2}{r}\frac{\partial C_{A1}}{\partial r} + \frac{1}{r^2 \sin\theta}\frac{\partial}{\partial \theta}\left(\sin\theta\frac{\partial C_{A1}}{\partial \theta}\right)\right] \quad (45a)$$

Here are

C_{A1} = Concentration of the solute A in the droplet phase
r = Radial coordinate
θ = Angular coordinate measured counterclockwise from the point of incidence of the flow
$u_{r,1}$ = Radial velocity along r
$u_{\theta,1}$ = Tangential velocity along ϕ

The mass balance of A in the continuous phase is given by:

$$\frac{\partial C_{A2}}{\partial t} + u_{r,2}\frac{\partial C_{A2}}{\partial r} + \frac{u_{\theta,2}}{r}\frac{\partial C_{A2}}{\partial \theta} = D_2\left[\frac{\partial^2 C_{A2}}{\partial r^2} + \frac{2}{r}\frac{\partial C_{A2}}{\partial r} + \frac{1}{r^2 \sin\theta}\frac{\partial}{\partial \theta}\left(\sin\theta\frac{\partial C_{A2}}{\partial \theta}\right)\right] \quad (45b)$$

Here are C_{A2} concentration of solute A and $u_{r,2}$ the corresponding velocities in the continuous phase. The initial conditions are for t = 0,

$$C_{A1} = C_{A10} \quad (45c)$$

for every r,

$$C_{A2} = C_{A2\infty}$$

and the boundary conditions:

for $\theta = 0$,

$$\frac{\partial C_{A1}}{\partial \theta} = 0$$

$$\frac{\partial C_{A2}}{\partial \theta} = 0$$

for r = 0,

$$\theta = \frac{\pi}{2}$$

$$\frac{\partial C_{A1}}{\partial r} = 0$$

for r = ∞,

$$C_{A2} = C_{A2_\infty} = \text{constant} \tag{45d}$$

Equilibrium prevails at the interface:

at r = a

$$(C_{A1})_{r=a} = H(C_{A2})_{r=a}$$

and the solute is transferred across the interface by pure diffusion:

at r = a,

$$D_1 = \left(\frac{\partial C_{A1}}{\partial r}\right)_{r=a} = D_2\left(\frac{\partial C_{A2}}{\partial r}\right)_{r=a}$$

An analytical solution of Equation 45 is possible, if one considers only short contact times. In this case the distribution of the solute concentration in the droplet does not depend on the flow and the convective terms in Equation 45 disappear.

The solution for this case is given by Brauer:[9]

$$\xi_1 = 1 - \frac{6}{\sqrt{\pi}}\,\frac{1}{1 + H(D_1/D_2)^{1/2}} \cdot Fo^{1/2} \tag{46}$$

where

$$\xi_1 = \frac{C_{A1} - H \cdot C_{A2}}{C_{A10} - HC_{A2}}$$

dimensionless concentration and

$$Fo = \frac{tD_1}{a^2}$$

droplet Fourier number (dimensionless time).

An analytical solution for the general case is not known. The following discussion considers special cases when one of the mass-transfer resistances can be neglected.

Resistance is Considered Only in the Continuous Phase

If the resistance in the discontinuous phase can be neglected one has only to consider the equation describing the continuous phase. The resistance of the continuous phase was considered for Re≪1 by Levich.[1] He found that the diffusional flux to the surface of the drop is:

$$j_2 = \frac{D_2(C_{A2\infty} - (C_{A2})_{r=a}}{\delta} \tag{47}$$

where

$$C_{A2} = C_{A2\,\infty} \text{ for } r \to \infty$$

$$C_{A2} = (C_{A2})_{r=a} \text{ at } r = a$$

and δ is the thickness of the diffusion layer:

$$\delta = \sqrt{\frac{\pi}{3}}\left(\frac{aD}{\nu_o}\right)^{1/2}\sqrt{\frac{2 + \cos\theta}{(1 + \cos\theta)^2}}$$

where ν_0 is the magnitude of the velocity at the drop's equator

$$\nu_o = \frac{\mu_2}{2}\,\frac{U}{\mu_2 + \mu_1}$$

Numerous relations are known for rigid drops which have the form

$$Sh_2 = \text{const. } Re_2^{1/2}\, Sc_2^{1/3} \tag{48}$$

Heertjes and De Nie[27] gave an excellent review of these equations.

The equations developed for nonrigid drops have the form:[27]

$$Sh_2 = \text{const. } Re_2^{1/2}\, Sc_2^{1/2} \tag{49}$$

For high Reynolds numbers the mass-transfer resistance external to a spherical drop was evaluated numerically by Weber[11] using the thin-concentration boundary-layer assumption and the interfacial velocity given by Harper and Moore.[12] His results can be put into the following form

$$Sh_2 = \frac{2}{\sqrt{\pi}}\left[1 - \frac{1}{Re_2^{1/2}}(2.89 + B)\right]^{1/2} Pe_2^{1/2} \tag{50}$$

where the Sherwood, Reynolds, and Peclet numbers are based on the properties of the external phase:

$$Sh_2 = \frac{k^*_2\, d}{D_2}$$

$$Re_2 = \frac{d\,U\rho_2}{\mu_2}$$

$$Pe_2 = \frac{dU}{D_2}$$

where k^*_2 is the mass-transfer coefficient in the continuous phase and the constant B is a function of $x = \frac{\mu_1}{\mu_2}$ and $y = \frac{\rho_1}{\rho_2}$. For $x \leqslant 2$ and $0 < y \leqslant 4$ following approximate form applies:

$$Sh_2 = \frac{2}{\sqrt{\pi}} \left[1 - \frac{1}{Re_2{}^{1/2}} (2.89 + 2.15\, x^{0.64}) \right]^{1/2} Pe_2{}^{1/2} \tag{51}$$

with an error less than 5% in $Sh_2/Pe_2{}^{1/2}$.

Resistance is Considered Only in the Discontinuous Phase

If the resistance in the continuous phase can be neglected one only has to consider the equation describing the droplet phase. Instead of using the distribution of the solute concentration in the droplet, a mean concentration C_{A1} is applied in Equation 46 and for short contact times it reduces to

$$\xi_1 = 1 - \frac{6}{\sqrt{\pi}} \cdot Fo_1{}^{1/2} \tag{52}$$

Therefore, the mean concentration depends only on the Fourier number. For droplets at rest, the mass transport inside of the droplet occurs only by radial diffusion. For this case, the following solution is given:[14,16,17]

$$E_m = \frac{C_{A10} - \overline{C_{A1}}}{C_{A10} - (C_{A1})_{r=a}} = 1 - \frac{6}{\pi} \sum_{n=1}^{\infty} \frac{1}{n^2} \exp\left(\frac{-n^2 D_1 \pi^2 t}{a^2} \right) \tag{53}$$

where E_m is the degree of extraction, and

C_{A1} = C_{A10} at $t = 0$
$\overline{C_{A1}}$ = mean concentration of A at t
n = integer

By introducing the dimensionless groups (see Equation 46), one obtains from Equation 53

$$\overline{\xi_1} = \frac{6}{\pi} \sum_{n=1}^{\infty} \frac{1}{n^2} \exp(-n^2\, Fo_1) \tag{54}$$

with

$$\overline{\xi_1} = 1 - E_m = \frac{\overline{C_{A1}} - HC_{A2\infty}}{C_{A10} - HC_{A2\infty}}$$

In pure systems and for $Re < 1$ inside of the droplet, laminar circulation prevails. Kronig and Brink[18] introduced the convective terms of Hadamard[7] and Rybczynski[6] into the equation and assumed that mass transfer between the fluid elements occurs only perpendicular to the streamlines and that it is pure diffusion. The influence of diffusion on the velocity distribution was neglected. This gives

$$\overline{\xi_1} = \frac{3}{8} \sum_{n=1}^{\infty} B_n{}^2 \exp(-\lambda_n\, 16\, Fo_1) \tag{55}$$

where λ_n and B_n are eigenvalues of the series expansion. Their numerical values were given by Heertjes et al.[19]

Proceeding from Equation 52, Handlos and Baron developed a solution for $Re > 1$.[20] They assumed that a concentration equalization between two streamlines occurs by means of turbulent mixing within a characteristic circulation time. The mass transfer occurs mainly by convection. Therefore the mean concentration does not depend on D_1. Only when the Fourier number is introduced does the mean concentration depend on D_1. By introducing the product $Re_1\, Sc_1 = Pe_1$, with

$Sc_1 = \frac{\nu_1}{D_1}$ Schmidt number

in the droplet phase

$Pe_1 = \frac{U\, 2a}{D_1}$ Peclet number

one obtains

$$\overline{\xi_1} = \sum_{n=1}^{\infty} 2\, B_n{}^2 \exp\left(-\lambda_n \frac{1}{64(1+x)} Fo_1\, Pe_1\right) \tag{56}$$

Handlos and Baron[20] considered only the first term of the series (Equation 56) with $2\, B_1{}^2 = 1$ and $\lambda_1 = 2.88$. The latter value was corrected to $\lambda_1 = 2.866$ by Skelland and Wellek.[21] Orlander pointed out that this assumption is only true for long contact times. For short contact times he proposed the approximation with $2B_1{}^2 = 0.64$ and $\lambda_1 = 2.80$.[22]

In Figure 1, the mean concentrations $\overline{\xi_1}$ are plotted as function of Fo_1 according to the models of Brauer (analytical – Equation 52),

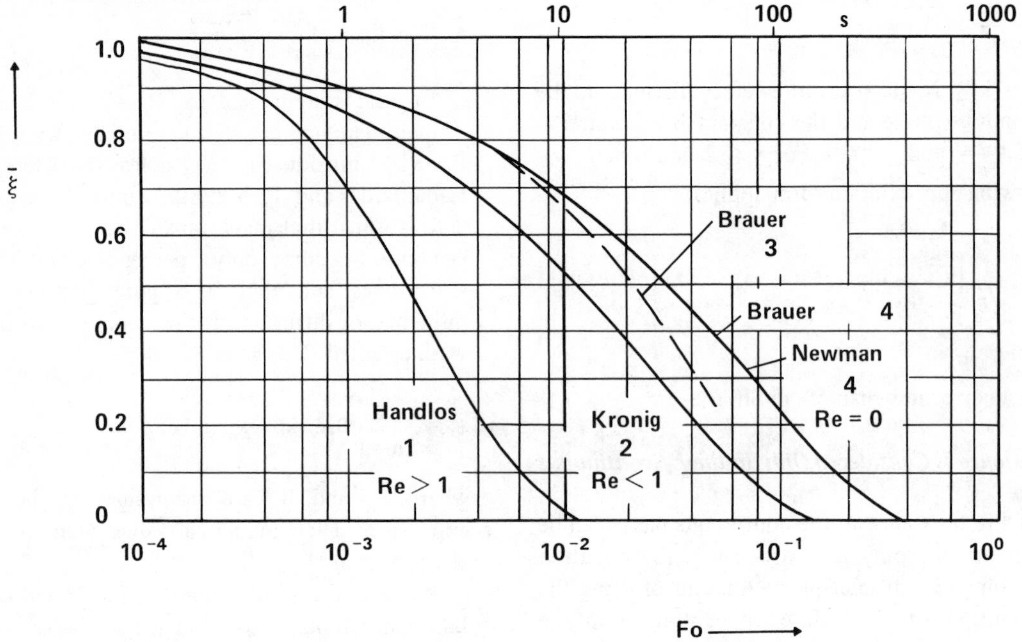

FIGURE 1. Dimensionless concentration of the solute $\bar{\xi}$ as function of the dimensionless time, Fo, for different Reynolds numbers with mass-transfer resistance only in the droplet phase (1, calculated by Equation 56 of Handlos and Baron;[20] 2, calculated by Equation 55 of Kronig and Brink;[18] 3, calculated by Equation 52 of Brauer;[9] 4, calculated by Brauer (numerical)[9] and by Equation 53 of Newman[16] with 20 terms).

Brauer (numerical – Equation 9), Newman (Equation 53), Kronig (Equation 55), and Handlos (Equation 56) for 2a = 0.31 cm, U = 7.0 cm/s and $D_1 = 2.19 \times 10^{-5}$ cm^2/s.

A comparison of the numerical results of Brauer with the results calculated by Equation 53 of Newman indicates that it is necessary to consider 20 terms in Equation 53 to obtain satisfactory results.[9]

Resistances of Both Phases are Considered

If the resistances of both phases influence the mass-transfer rate, it is necessary to consider the equations describing both of the phases. Equation 45 is used by considering the initial, boundary, and coupling conditions. Only a numerical solution is known which is restricted to $0 \leqslant Re \leqslant 1$.[9,10] For Re > 1 it is assumed that the mass transfer is a quasi-stationary process, and that the mass-transfer coefficient in the continuous phase is constant and can be calculated by the equations of the steady-state mass transfer. By this assumption it is possible to decouple the differential equations of the two phases. In this case only the solution of the balance equation in the droplet phase is needed. The constant resistance in the continuous phase appears only as a boundary condition. This resistance is defined by means of a Biot number:

$$Bi = \frac{k^*_2 \, 2a}{D_2}$$

where k^*_2 is the partial mass-transfer coefficient in the continuous phase.

If the resistance in the droplet phase dominates, the Bi number approaches infinity. In the other limiting case with a dominating resistence in the continuous phase Bi → 0. For systems at rest (Re ≅ 0), the quasi-stationary treatment of Gröber[23,24] for nonstationary heat transfer can also be applied for non-stationary mass transfer:[14]

$$\xi_1 = 6 \sum_{n=1}^{\infty} B_n \exp(-\lambda_n^2 \, Fo_1) \qquad (57)$$

The eigenvalues B_n and λ_n are given in Reference 24. Some results calculated by Equation 57 are plotted in Figure 2. The eigenvalues of the model of Kronig and Brink[18] were calculated for creeping motion (Re < 1) by Elzinga and Banchero[25] as function of the Biot number. Using these eigenvalues for different Bi numbers and the Equation 55 of Kronig and Brink one obtains

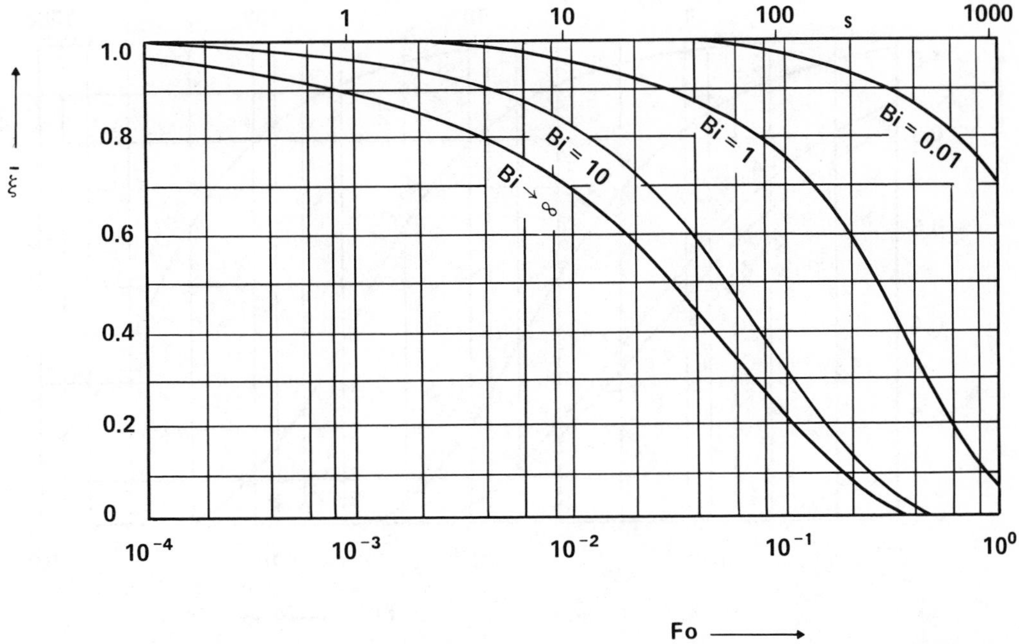

FIGURE 2. $\bar{\xi}$ as function of Fo with mass-transfer resistance in both of the phases. Calculated according to Gröber.[23,24]

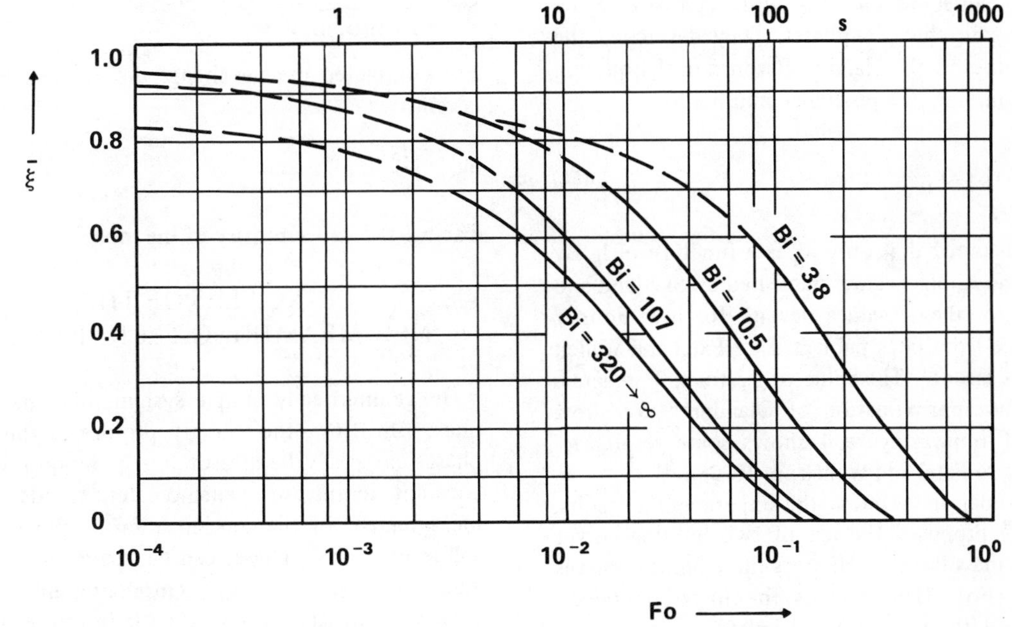

FIGURE 3. $\bar{\xi}$ as function of Fo with mass-transfer resistance in both of the phases for Re < 1. Calculated according to Elzinga and Banchero.[25]

Figure 3. One can recognize that for small Biot and Fourier numbers the concentration in the drop is too large. This can be attributed to the nonadequate approximation of only four terms in Equation 55 by Elzinga and Banchero. This equation can only be used for large Fourier numbers.

Skelland and Wellek[21] extended the Handlos-

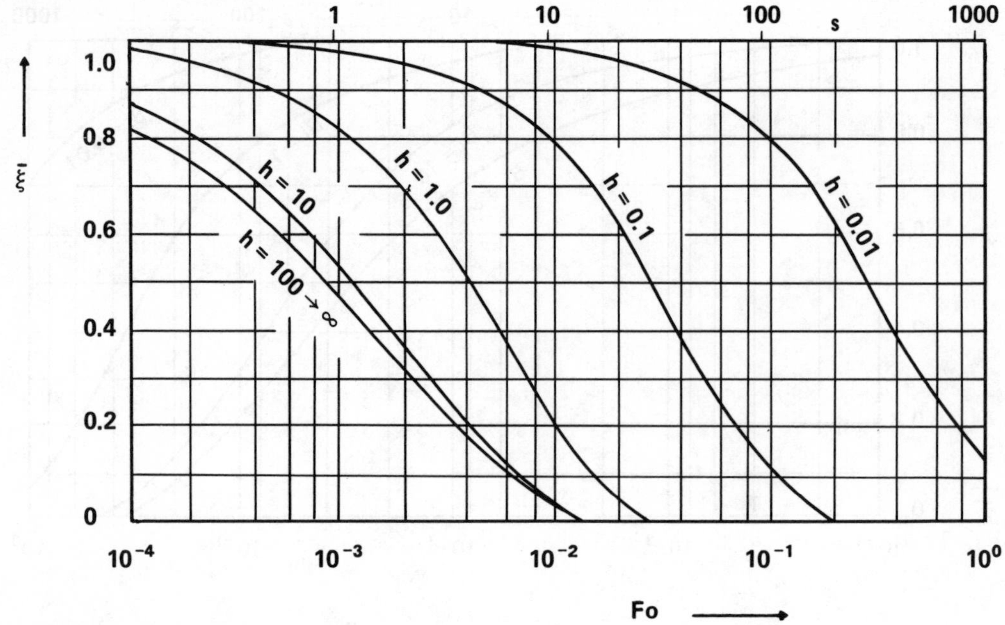

FIGURE 4. $\bar{\xi}$ as function of Fo with mass-transfer resistance in both of the phases for Re > 1. Calculated according to Patel and Wellek.[26]

Baron model to systems with comparable resistances in the two phases. They developed the eigenvalues of the Handlos-Baron model Equation 56 as function of a resistance number h:

$$h = 512\,(1 + x)\,\frac{k^*_2}{U \cdot H} \tag{58}$$

They assumed that only λ_n is a function of h. By using the λ_n eigenvalues published by Skelland and Wellek,[21] the $\bar{\xi}$ values deviate for low Fourier numbers from ones published by Patel and Wellek 2 years later.[26] The value of $\bar{\xi}_1$ for $h \to \infty$ agrees with the approximation of Olander[22] for short contact times. Figure 4 shows some results according to Patel and Wellek for Re > 1.[26]

In order to examine the experimental results, Brauer[9] proposed the use of two limiting curves for the mass transfer. He gives these limiting curves as $Sh_1(Fo)$. Here Sh_1 is the mean Sherwood number with regard to the droplet:

$$Sh_1 = \frac{k_1\,2a}{D_1}$$

where k_1 overall the mass-transfer coefficient with regard to the droplet phase.

The lower limiting curve is given for pure diffusion mass transfer by

$$Sh_1 = \frac{4}{1 + H(D_1/D_2)^{1/2}}\,Fo_1^{-1/2} \tag{59}$$

For completed mass exchange the simple relation is valid:

$$Sh_1 = \frac{2/3}{Fo_1} \tag{60}$$

Table 1 shows a summary of the models.

PRINCIPLES OF THE NEW MEASURING TECHNIQUES

In geometrically simple systems like the two-phase film flow, the velocity profiles in the two phases can easily be measured, e.g., by means of a constant temperature anemometer.[3,5] Also, the measurement of the concentration profiles of the solute in the two phases can be carried out easily, e.g., by means of gas chromatography.[2,3,5] However, the conditions near the interfaces (e.g., within an interfacial zone with a thickness of a few micrometers cannot be investigated yet because of the lack of suitable measuring technique.

Sampling near the interface disturbs the system. Optical techniques have the advantage of providing information without disturbing the system. However, optical methods are not suited to give information in regions within several micrometers

TABLE 1

Summary of the Models

	Mass transfer resistance in the continuous phase	Mass transfer resistance in the droplet phase	Mass transfer resistances in both phases: Numerical	Mass transfer resistances in both phases: Quasistationary
$Re = 0$		Newman[16] Brauer[9] $\zeta = f(Fo)$	Brauer[9] $\zeta = f(H(D_1/D_2)^{1/2}, Fo)$	Gröber[23] $\zeta = f(Bi, Fo)$
$Re \leqslant 1$	Levich[1] $j = f(D_2/U, \mu_1, \mu_2)$ Heertjes (review)[27] $Sh = f(Re, Sc)$	Kronig and Brink[18] $\zeta = f(Fo)$; $Re = 1$ Schmidt-Traub[10] $\zeta = f(Pe, Fo)$	Schmidt-Traub[10] $\zeta = f(H(D_1/D_2)^{1/2} Pe, Fo)$	Elzinga and Banchero[25] $\zeta = f(Bi, Fo)$ $Re = 1$
$Re > 1$	Heertjes (review)[27] $Sh = f(Re, Sc)$ Weber[11] $Sh = f(Re, Pe)$	Handlos and Baron[20] $\zeta = f(Pe, Fo)$		Skelland and Wellek[14] Patel and Wellek[26] $\zeta = f(h, Fo)$ $h = 512(1 + x)\frac{k^{*2}}{U \cdot H}$

from the interface.[34,35] In the range of 100 μm, the technique of an analytical ultracentrifuge can be used.[37] Very close to the interface, in a zone with a mean thickness of about 1 μm, until now only a modified scintillation technique has been applied.[4,36] In this chapter the principles of this technique will be explained.

On the other hand, to prove the validity of the models developed for droplets, it would be necessary to measure the instantaneous concentrations of the solute in the droplet during the exchange process without disturbing the droplet, (for example, by touching it with a sampling tube).

Most investigators have applied the well-known method of Colburn and Welsh and investigated droplets which were rising or falling in a column.[44-50] The measurement of the solute concentration was carried out after the separation of the phases. By changing the length of the test section, it was possible to correct for end effects. However, because the mass-transfer rate is a complex function of the time and/or the length of the test section, this correction is not satisfactory if high precision measurements are required – especially if the time dependence of the mass-transfer rate is to be evaluated.

The application of radioactive γ emitters to measure the instantaneous concentration of the solute does not solve this problem either, because it is not possible to localize the emitted signals of γ emitters as either inside or outside of the droplet. Since the investigation of the influence of the fluid-dynamic behavior of the droplet on the mass-transfer rate could not be achieved, with known experimental methods, new experimental methods have been developed.[38-43] In contrast to the photographic methods,[51,51a,52] which are based on the measurement of the change of the droplet volume and therefore are applied mainly for the investigation of steady-state mass transfer,[51] the new methods allow highly precise estimates of very small concentration differences. Therefore, true differential measurements are possible.

For application of these new methods, the following problems had to be solved:

1. Formation of droplets under well defined conditions
2. Observation of the droplet for any desired period of time without influencing its fluid-dynamic behavior
3. Precise, contactless and inertial-less measurement of the concentration of the solute in the droplet

The most difficult task was to satisfy the third

demand. Therefore, this problem should be considered in some detail.

To solve this problem a modified liquid scintillation technique was applied. This technique has been developed for the detection of low-energy β-emitters.[65] The detection is based on the luminescence of suitable organic compounds in suitable liquids (organic solvents). Luminescence, the emission of light with a characteristic spectrum, following the absorption of radiation normally of higher energy than the emission, is a property associated with conjugated and aromatic organic molecules. The absorption spectra of these molecules contain a sequence of absorption bands in the visible and ultraviolet regions. These are attributed to transitions into singlet π electronic excited states. The energy of the emitted particles is absorbed by suitable solvent molecules and transferred to the organic scintillator molecules, which transform the excitation energy into luminescent emission. These photons can be detected by photomultipliers and suitable electronic devices. The mechanism of the energy transfer in the solution strongly influences the sensitivity and the resolution of the measurements with regard to the local concentration distribution of the solute. Therefore it is discussed briefly.

The energy transfer from the solvent molecules to the scintillator molecules can occur in different ways[65,66]

1. By nonradiant transfer
   a. resonance processes
   b. energy diffusion, mass diffusion, or
2. by radiant transfer

In the present investigations radiant transfer does not play a role, because of the chosen solvent (toluene) and the range of the scintillation concentration (4 g/l).[66]

Process 1a. cannot play a role, because resonance processes only occur within a distance of 10^{-8} cm. For the scintillation concentrations of the applied technique, the resonance processes had to overcome distances of 10^{-6} cm. Therefore the main energy transfer occurs according to the mechanism 1b., where the mass diffusion, i.e., the energy transfer from the excited solvent molecule directly to a scintillator molecule by molecular impact, is only responsible for 10% of the transferred energy. The main part of the energy is transferred by energy diffusion over some solvent molecules. The range of this transport is very small, because the lifetime of the excited molecules is restricted to 10^{-9} to 10^{-13} sec.[67]

After the energy diffusion to the scintillator molecules, the light emission occurs in a range 3600 to 3700 Å. Sometimes it is necessary to apply a "secondary" scintillator, which better fits the spectral sensitivity of the photocathode of the photomultiplier in the range between 4300 and 5000 Å. The application of a secondary scintillator increases the counting yield, i.e., the sensitivity of the method, but decreases the resolution of the measurements.

The counting yield is diminished by polar solutes which are present in the liquid. These compounds disturb the energy transfer from the solvent molecules to the scintillator by converting one part of the energy into heat instead of into light. This is the so-called chemical quenching effect. If the relation between the counting yield and the concentration of the quencher is determined experimentally, the unknown concentration of the quencher can be determined by counting the scintillation events.

Method A (Figure 5) – If one applies an organic solvent (e.g., toluene) droplet which is labeled with tritium or C^{14} and therefore marked here by *, and which also contains scintillators (Sz), then the concentration of the solute x with polar groups can be measured in this phase by contactless photomultipliers. The β-rays excite the solvent molecules and the latter transfer this electronic excitation energy to the scintillator molecules which emit light. In the presence of solutes with polar groups the share of the radiationless transition increases at the expense of the light emission. The scintillation is partly quenched. The intensity of the light emission and its pulse height distribution changes.

The number of photons in light pulses depends on the energy of the β-rays. At a mean energy of tritium β-rays of 5.7 KeV, about 57 photons are produced as an average. The higher the energy of the β-rays, the higher the number of photons in light pulses, i.e., the pulse height increases. The chemical quenching process diminishes the pulse height and shifts the pulse height distribution to a lower energy range (Figure 6). Since a definite relation prevails between the decrease of the intensity of light emission (and the shift of the pulse height distribution to lower energies) and the concentration of the solute, it is possible to

Method A

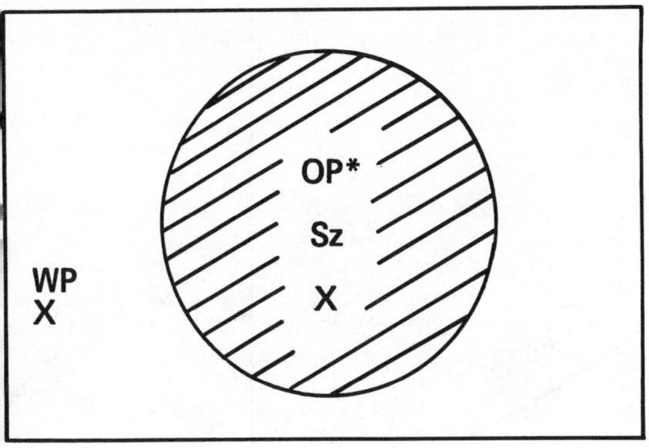

Method B

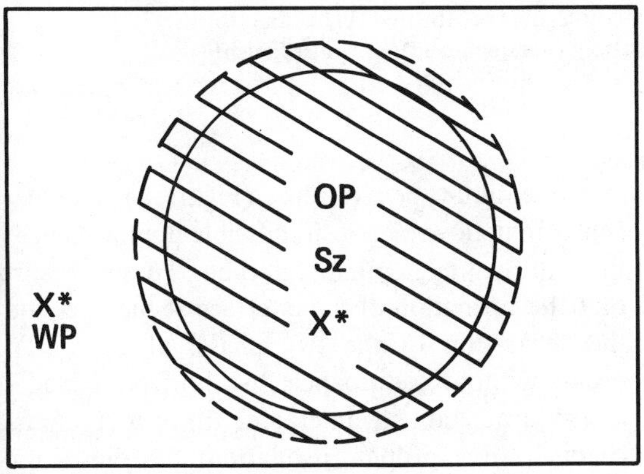

FIGURE 5. Explanation of the principle of the measurement of the solute concentration by modified scintillation technique I: OP = organic solvent phase; WP = water phase; x = solute; Sz = liquid scintillator; * = β-emitter; //// = control volume of the measurement.

estimate the instantaneous concentration of the solute within the droplet by measuring the intensity of the light emission. Also, it is possible to estimate the instantaneous mass transfer from the change of the intensity of the light emission.

If one divides the pulse height distribution of the emitted light into two ranges by means of energy discriminators, and forms the ratio of the counting rates of these two channels (channel ratio method of Birks), one can also evaluate a relation between this channel ratio and the concentration of the solute. This method can also be used to measure the instantaneous concentration of the solute within the droplet.

The two methods, i.e., the "counting rate" and the "channel ratio" methods, can be simultaneously applied, if one counts the pulses in two channels which cover the whole pulse height distribution. The sum of the counting rates of the two channels represents the "counting rate" method and their ratio the "channel ratio" method. The "channel ratio" method yields absolute concentrations. However, the result depends on the spacial distribution of the solute in the droplet. The "counting rate" method yields relative concentrations, but the result does not depend on the spacial distribution of the solute in the droplet.

Because at the beginning of the mass exchange the solute is uniformly distributed in the droplet, the "channel ratio" method can be used to estimate the absolute starting concentrations of the solute. The course of the concentration-time function is estimated then by the "counting rate" method. It is important to point out that *by Method A one only detects the solute molecules which are inside of the droplet.*

Method B (Figure 6) – If one applies to a nonlabeled solvent phase (O.P.) droplet a tritium or C^{14}-labeled solute x and scintillators (Sz), then the solvent and the scintillator molecules are excited by the β-rays again. Because of the self-quenching of the solute an experimental correction for the light emission is necessary. By applying this quenching correction the instantaneous concentration of the solute can be estimated again by means of the light emission of the scintillators.

By Method B one detects solute molecules which are within the droplet and in a thin film of the continuous phase at the interface with a mean thickness of 0.50 μm for tritium and 60 μm for C^{14}.

Method C (Figure 7) – If one locally separates the labeled phase from the scintillators in such a way that tritium water is dissolved in the lower water phase and the scintillator exists only in the upper solvent phase (because of its insolubility in water) then an excitation of the solvent and the scintillator molecules, and by that the light emission, only occurs at the interface in a thin film of the solvent phase with a mean thickness of 0.66 μm. This light emission is partially quenched by the polar solute molecules x which are present at the interface in this thin film. Therefore this method allows the estimation of the instantaneous concentration of the solute at the interface on the side of the solvent phase by means of the measurement of the light emission.

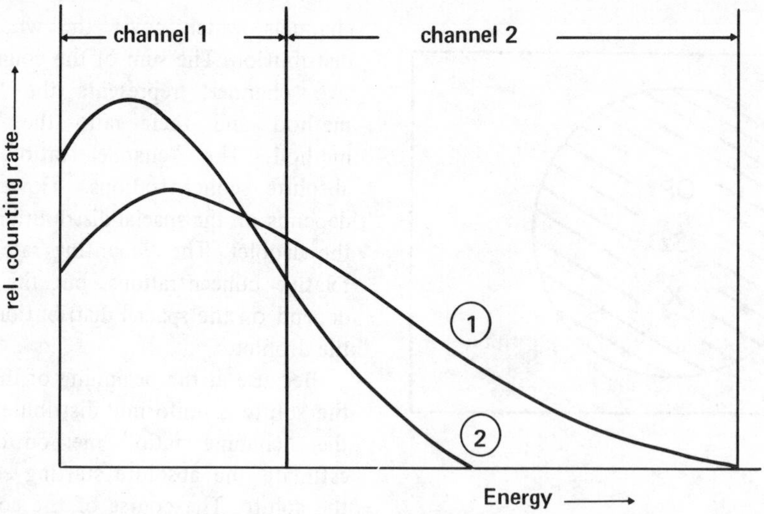

FIGURE 6. Shift of the energy distribution of the emitted light due to chemical quench: 1, pulse height distribution (nonquenched); 2, pulse height distribution (quenched).

Method D (Figure 7) – The combination of Methods A and C would allow estimation of the concentration of the solute at the interface as well as in the solvent phase, if one could use double labeling by C^{14} and tritium. However, because of the optical quench (due to the light scattering and reflexion in the test section), a clear separation of the pulse height distributions of tritium and C^{14} is not possible. Thus, Method D is not practical.

Method E (Figure 7) – This difficulty of the double labeling can be avoided if one uses an external standard (ES) together with Method C. The external standard is a closed γ-source, consisting, e.g., of Ra^{226} with an energy of 0.19 MeV. This source is transferred into the test section during the measurement for a short period of time. Hence, γ-rays are produced which have energy distribution quite similar to the one of weak β-emitters. The light emission of the scintillators due to these Compton electrons (γ-rays) can be used to estimate the concentration of the solute in the solvent phase. The combination of Method C with an external standard allows the simultaneous measurement of the concentration of the solute in the bulk solvent phase and at the interface.

TWO-PHASE FILM FLOW

Experimental Setup and Measurements[4,5,33]

The mass-transfer apparatus is similar to the so-called film-type extractor (Figure 8). Laminar concurrent flow of two immiscible liquids prevails in a horizontal, cylindrical tube. To make sure that the formation of the interface at the inlet and the separation of the two phases at the outlet occurs without disturbance, two horizontal blades are mounted at the inlet and the outlet of the channel. By proper regulation of the static pressures of the two liquids, the interface can be kept constant in the axis of the channel. Therefore the interface divides the cylindrical flow channel into two equal parts, each having the same cross section.

The flow channel was made of boron glass because of its good transmission properties for the light emitted by the scintillator. To achieve a contact angle of 90° and a plane interface of the liquids, the inside of the flow channel was coated by an organic silicon compound. The apparatus has the following advantages:

1. The contact area has a constant and definite value.
2. The hydrodynamics can be described by the Navier-Stokes equations.
3. The relative flow velocities can easily be varied.

The mass transfer tube is mounted in a heat-and light-insulated box which is kept at constant temperature (Figure 9). The two liquids are

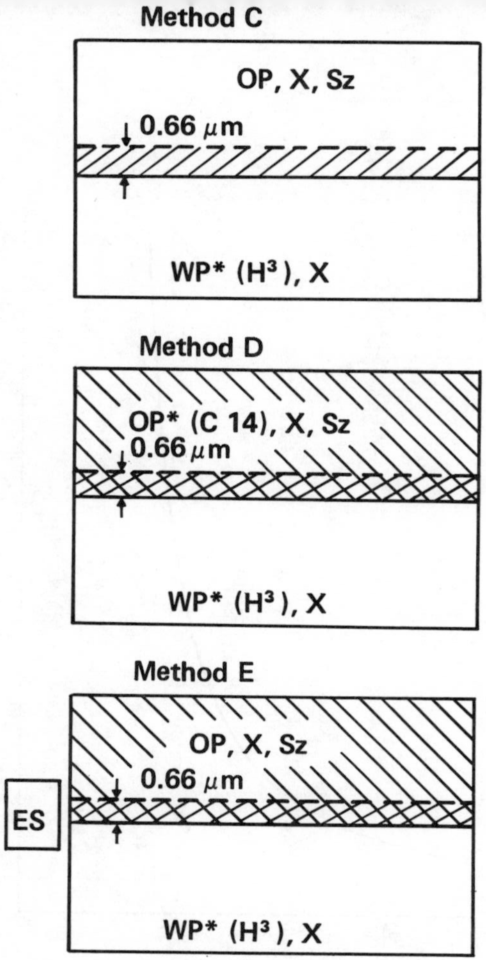

FIGURE 7. Explanation to the principle of the measurements of the solute concentration by modified scintillation technique II: OP* (C^{14}) = organic solvent phase labeled with C^{14}; WP* (H^3) = tritium water; ES = external standard; for other symbols see Figure 5.

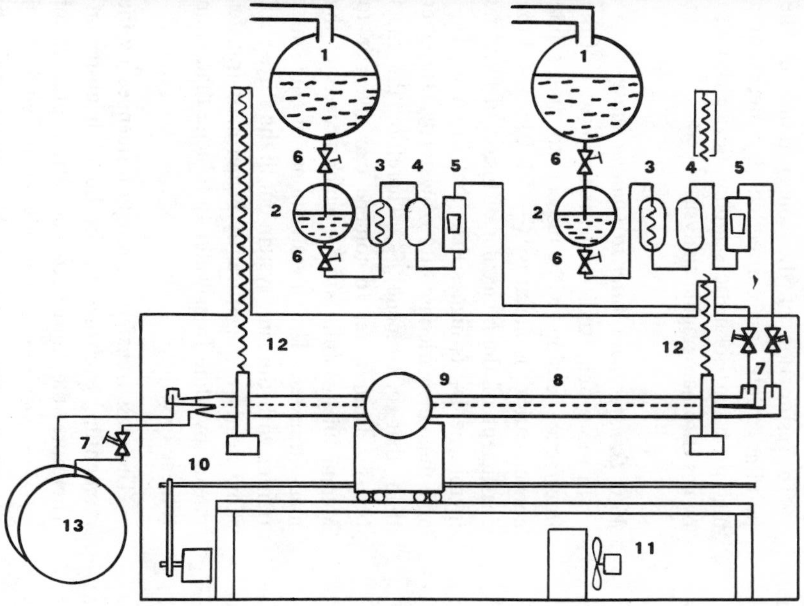

FIGURE 8. Experimental set up for two-phase film flow measurements (1, liquid storage; 2, liquid level control; 3, heat exchanger; 4, saturator; 5, flow meter; 6, on-off valve; 7, metering valve; 8, flow channel; 9, movable detector; 10, screw jack and driving motor; 11, air cooler and blower; 12, vibration absorber; 13, liquid collector).

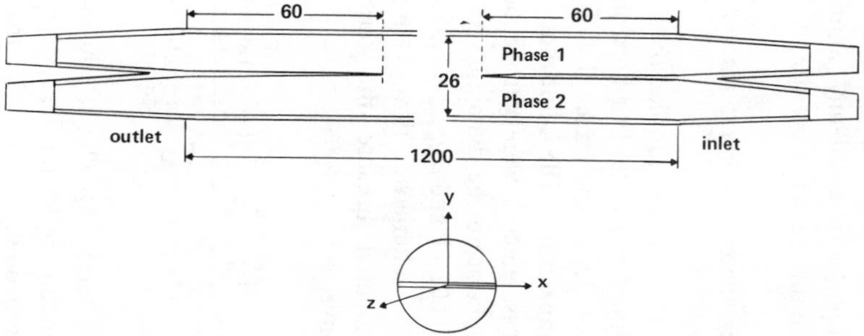

FIGURE 9. Channel for the two-phase film flow measurements.

supplied from glass vessels. The whole flow system consists of glass without any ground-glass couplings to avoid any source of contamination with surface-active agents.

Experimental Determination of the Velocity Profiles[5]

The velocity profiles of the two-phase flow of toluene and water in a horizontal, cylindrical tube have been determined by means of a constant temperature DISA-hot-film anemometer. The measurements were carried out at 18°C. At this temperature the dynamic viscosities are: $\mu_{toluene} = 0.605$ cP and $\mu_{water} = 1.053$ cP, hence b = 1.74. The volumetric flow ration Q_1/Q_2 can be computed because the series in Equation 25 converges:

$$\frac{Q_1}{Q_2} = \frac{b\left(\frac{\pi}{4} + \frac{k^* - b}{k^* + b}\right)\left(\frac{\pi}{2} - 1.0796\right)}{k^*\left(\frac{\pi}{4} - \frac{k^* - b}{k^* + b}\right)\left(\frac{\pi}{2} - 1.0796\right)} \tag{61}$$

The ratio Q_1/Q_2 is shown in Figure 10 as function of k* for the system toluene-water. For a given flow ratio, Q_1/Q_2, the value of k* can be determined graphically and inserted into Equations 23 and 24. The ratio of Q_1/Q_2 for the experiment was varied from 0.452 to 2.743. Figure 11 shows a comparison of the experimental and theoretical profiles; the agreement is reasonable.

Experimental Determination of the Concentration Profiles

The estimation of the concentration of the pyridine solute was carried out by means of a high-precision isokinetic sampling device and also by gas chromatographic analysis.[33]

Mass Transfer from Water to Toluene Phase

In the system studied, the first derivative of the interfacial tension with respect to the solute concentration is negative $(\frac{\partial \sigma}{\partial C} < 0)$. Also, the coefficient of the molecular diffusion of pyridine in toluene D_T is higher than that in water, D_W and the kinematic viscosity of water ν_W is higher than that of toluene ν_T. Therefore the mass transfer from water to toluene can give rise to Marangoni instabilities[68,69] which accelerate the mass transfer. The investigations of the mass tranfer with the same system but in the stirred cell show clearly the significantly higher mass transfer rate of pyridine from water to toluene than from toluene to water.[70]

The mass transfer is strongly influenced by the momentum exchange in the liquid inlet region. Therefore the initial concentration profiles of pyridine were experimentally estimated beyond the inlet region, where the laminar velocity profiles in both the phases was fully developed. These profiles were used as initial conditions for the theoretical calculations previously discussed.

Figure 12 shows initial concentration profiles at

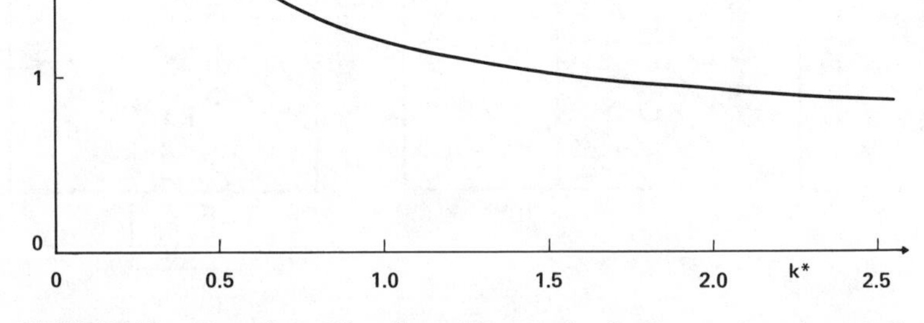

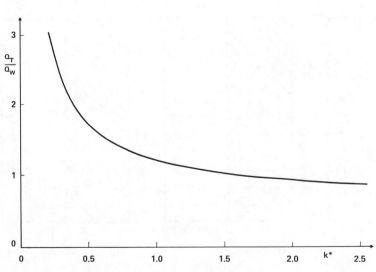

FIGURE 10. Two-phase film flow. Flow ratio Q_T/Q_W as function of the pressure drop ratio k*.

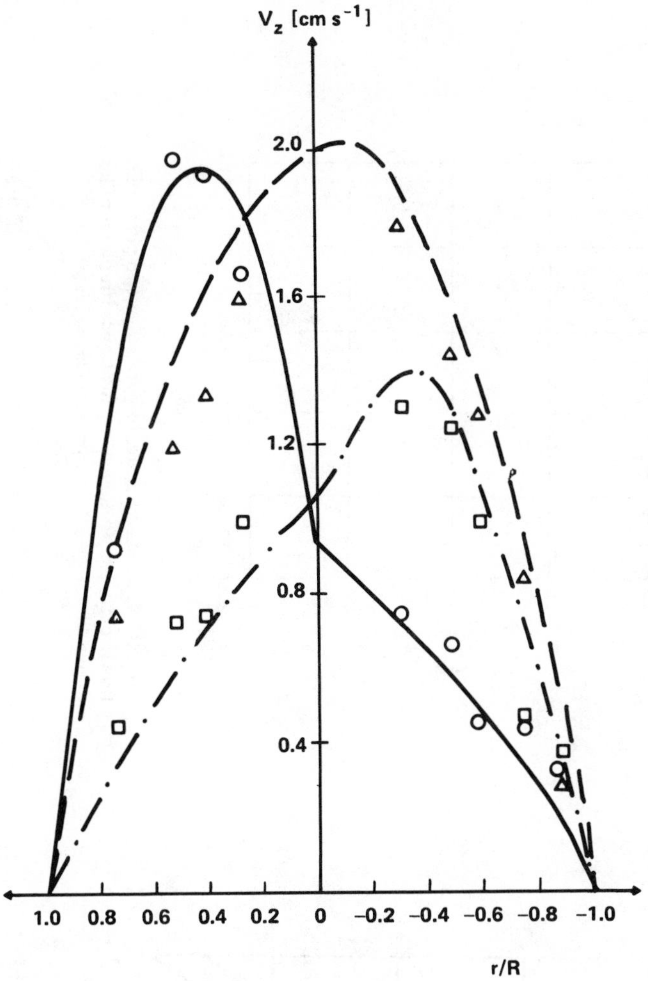

Symbol theoretical	Symbol experimental	Q_T (cm^3/s)	Q_W (cm^3/s)	(Q_T/Q_W)
———	○	2.96	1.08	2.74
– – – –	△	2.75	2.95	0.933
–•–•–•	□	1.25	2.30	0.452

FIGURE 11. Two-phase film flow. Comparison of theoretical and experimental velocity profiles; $\varphi_1 = \frac{\pi}{2}$, $\varphi_2 = \frac{3}{2}\pi$; T = 18°C; diameter of channel d = 27 mm.

20 cm distance from the edge of the inlet blade of the channel for two different Q_T/Q_W ratios and for an initial pyridine concentration in the water phase of 0.244 mol/1. Despite the higher water flow rate of run 2, the interfacial concentration of pyridine is higher for run 1 than for run 2. This is probably due to differences in the ages of the interfaces. For run 1, the contact time of the water phase is higher (τ_W = 19 sec) than for run 2 (τ_W = 12 sec); therefore the instabilities have more time to develop.

Figure 13 shows concentration profiles of pyridine measured at a distance of 80 cm from the edge of the inlet blade for different Q_T/Q_W ratios. By linear extrapolation of y = O the interfacial solute concentrations C_{Ti} and C_{Wi} were evaluated.

Run	Q_T [cm^3/s]	Q_W [cm^3/s]	k_1
1	0.133	0.138	0.963
2	0.105	0.217	0.483

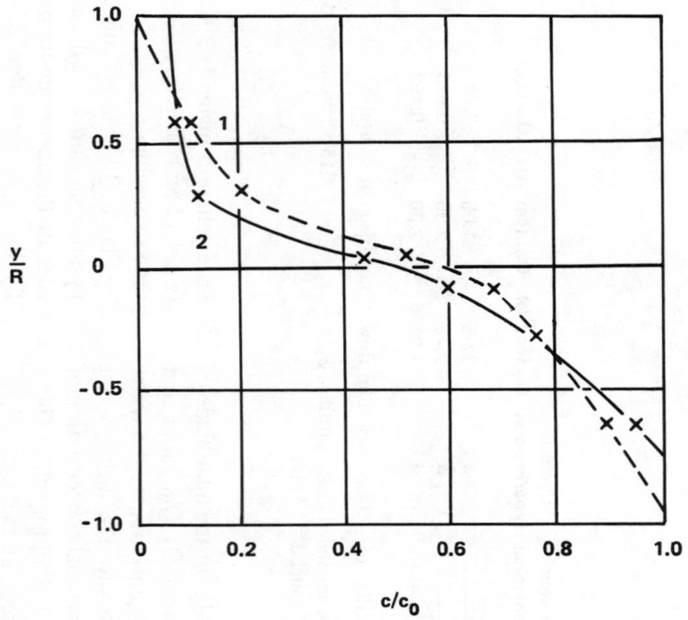

FIGURE 12. Mass transfer of pyridine in two-phase film flow from water to toluene phase. Concentration profiles of pyridine at the inlet (z = 20 cm). Interface at $\frac{y}{R} = 0$. Toluene phase $0 < \frac{y}{R} < 1$. Water phase $-1 < \frac{y}{R} < 0$.

Run	Q_T [cm^3/s]	Q_W [cm^3/s]	k_1
1	0.133	0.137	1.04
2	0.105	0.217	0.484
3	0.093	0.25	0.372

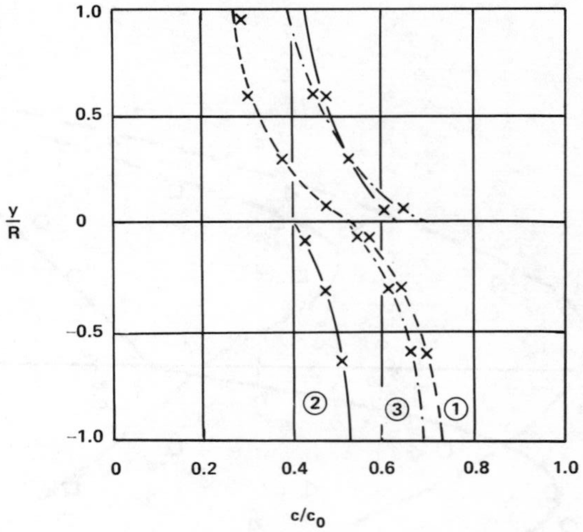

FIGURE 13. Mass transfer of pyridine in two-phase film flow from water to toluene phase. Concentration profiles of pyridine at z = 80 cm (for symbols see Figure 12).

For $K_1 \cong 1$, their ratio $G_i = \frac{CT_i}{CW_i}$ is nearly unity. This value differs significantly from the ratio of the equilibrium concentration: $G_{equil} = \frac{C_T}{C_W}$ equil which is in the range of 1.92[70] to 1.89[71]. With increasing Q_W (decreasing K_1) G_i increases to 1.65 (for K_1 = 0.484) and approaches the equilibrium value. With decreasing toluene flow rate G_i diminishes to 1.35 (for K_1 = 0.372).

The highest mass transfer rate was achieved for K_1 = 0.484, for which G_i is also the highest and nearest to the equilibrium value G_{equil}. Since these measurements were strongly influenced by interfacial instabilities, which enhance the mass transfer,[68] conditions were sought to avoid their occurence.

According to the experiments[68] and to the theory of Sternling and Scriven,[69] interfacial instabilities occur if the ratios of the molecular diffusivities and the kinematic viscosities are given by

$$\frac{D_1}{D_2} > 1 \text{ and } \frac{\nu_1}{\nu_2} < 1$$

and stability prevails for

$$\frac{D_1}{D_2} > 1 \text{ and } \frac{\nu_1}{\nu_2} \geqslant 1$$

if the solute is transferred from the phase 2 (water) to phase 1 (toluene).

To avoid the occurence of instabilities, a suitable amount of additive (a non-water-soluble oligomer (1.36 g Polyisopotylen®/1 toluene) was dissolved in the toluene phase to achieve the conditions of the stability, namely $\frac{\nu_1}{\nu_2} \geqslant 1$. (This system had the kinematic viscosity ratio ν_1/ν_2 = 1.1 in contrast to the pure system with ν_1/ν_2 = 0.68.)

Figure 14 shows the initial concentration profiles under such conditions.

A comparison of Figures 12 (for K_1 = 0.484) and 14 (for z = 20 cm and K_1 = 0.476) indicates that at z = 20 cm (and for the same K_1) the concentration profiles are nearly identical. Neither the difference in the molecular diffusion coefficients of the solute in the toluene phase nor the difference in the stabilities of the interfaces influences the concentration profiles. This lack of a stability effect can be explained by the contact time of the water phase (τ_W = 12 s), which is too short to develop the interfacial instabilites. With increasing distance from the edge of the inlet blade the instabilities gradually develop and therefore the concentration profiles in systems without and with interfacial instability become more and more different. At a distance of z = 80 cm, the difference between these profiles is very significant (compare Figure 13 for K_1 = 0.484 with Figure 14 for z = 80 cm and K_1 = 0,476). The mass transfer rate is much smaller in the stable system. Furthermore, the ratio of the interfacial concentrations of the solute is very low (G_i = 1.15) as compared to the corresponding unstable system (G_i = 1.65).

The longitudinal and transversal concentration profiles of Polyisopotylen were uniform in the toluene phase. Therefore, one can assume that the presence of this substance does not influence the concentration profiles of the solute significantly. One can conclude that the interfacial instability promotes the mass transfer and the approach of the interfacial solute concentrations to their equilibrium values.

Mass Transfer from the Toluene to Water Phase

This system is stable, since for mass transfer from 1 (toluene) to 2 (water) the ratios of D and ν are

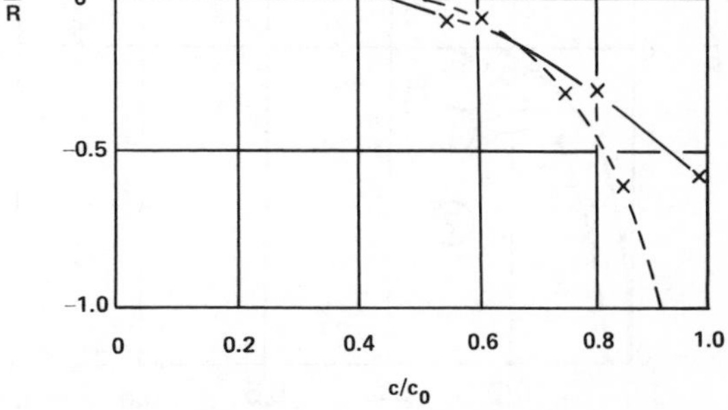

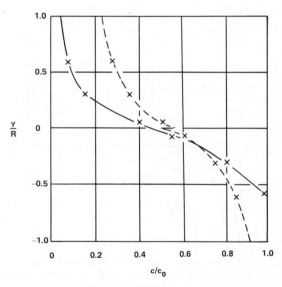

FIGURE 14. Mass transfer of pyridine in two-phase film flow from water to toluene phase. The toluene phase contains additive to suppress the interfacial instabilities. Concentration profiles of pyridine at z = 20 and 80 cm. Q_T = 0.10 cm³/s, Q_W = 0.21 cm³/s, K_1 = 0.476. For other symbols see Figure 12.

$$\frac{D_2}{D_1} < 1 \text{ and } \frac{\nu_2}{\nu_1} > 1$$

In Figure 15 the measured initial concentration profiles are plotted for $K_1 = 1.04$ and 2.39 and for initial solute concentration in toluene of 0.234 mol/1. The ratio of the flow rates influences the profiles again. For higher toluene flow rate (higher K_1) the mass-transfer rate is higher.

This can possibly be explained by the higher degree of interfacial turbulence due to higher momentum transfer rate during the formation of the interface. For higher K_1, the strong change of the velocity gradients at the interface (Figure 18) is probably responsible for this interfacial turbulence. This difference is also preserved for greater distances from the edge of the inlet blade (Figures 16 and 17). The corresponding fully developed velocity profiles are shown in Figure 18.

For mass transfer from toluene into water, one would expect a higher transfer rate for (1) than for (2) due to the (absolute) velocity gradients in the phases. The velocity gradients at the interface are strongly negative in both of the phases: Negative velocity gradients hinder the mass transfer (see following section). Therefore the higher mass-transfer rate in system (1) can not be explained by the absolute velocity profiles in the phases, but by the change of the velocity gradient at the interface.

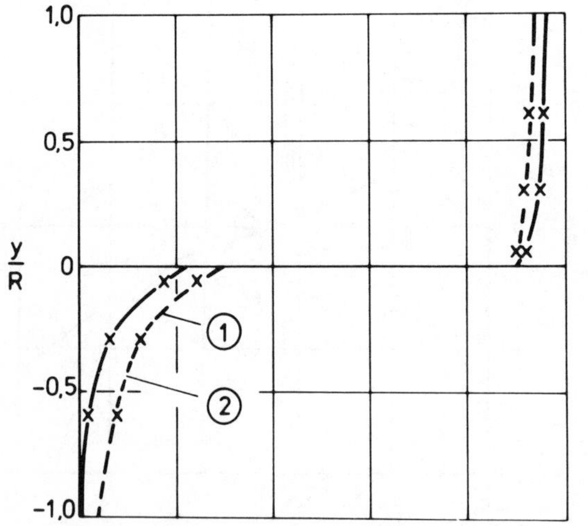

FIGURE 15. Mass transfer of pyridine in two-phase film flow from toluene to water phase. Concentration profiles of pyridine at the inlet (z = 20 cm). For additional symbols see Figure 12 .

To understand the solute concentrations profiles in the phases, one should consider the pyridine concentration at the interface in equilib-

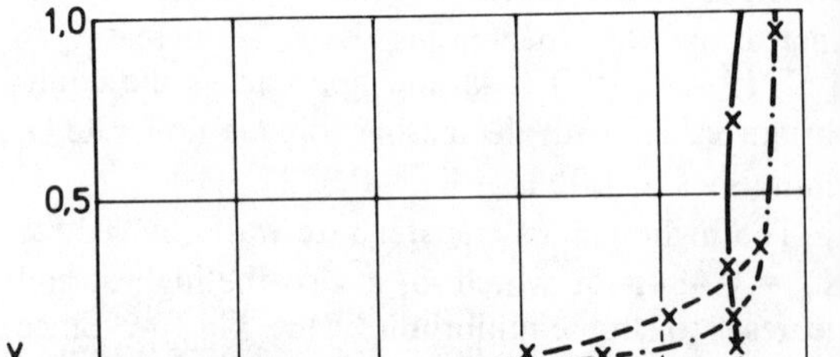

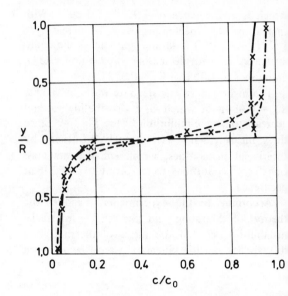

FIGURE 16. Mass transfer of pyridine in two-phase film flow from toluene to water phase. Concentration profiles of pyridine at z = 80 cm. $Q_T = 0.10$ cm³/s, $Q_W = 0.096$ cm³/s, $K_1 = 1.04$ (——— measured; ––– calculated; —•—•— fitted to the concentration profile in the water phase). For other symbols see Figure 12.

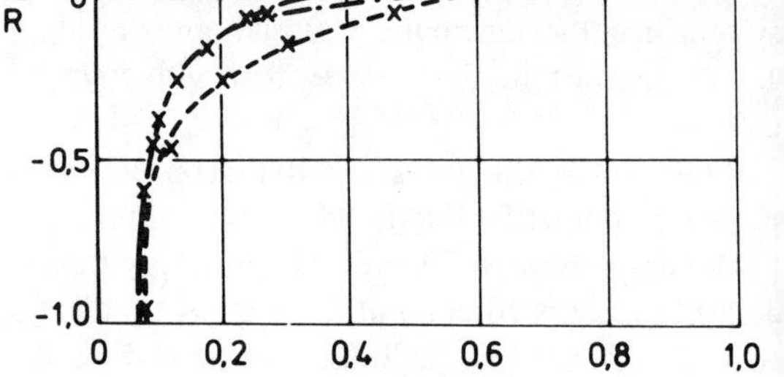

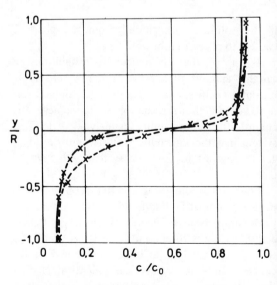

FIGURE 17. Mass transfer of pyridine in two-phase film flow from toluene to water phase. Concentration profiles of pyridine at z = 80 cm. $Q_T = 0.17$ cm³/s, $Q_W = 0.07$ cm³/s, $K_1 = 2.39$ (——— measured; ––– calculated; —•—•— fitted to the concentration profile in the water phase). For other symbols see Figure 12.

Run	Q_T [cm^3/s]	Q_W [cm^3/s]	k_1
1	0.10	0.096	1.04
2	0.17	0.071	2.39

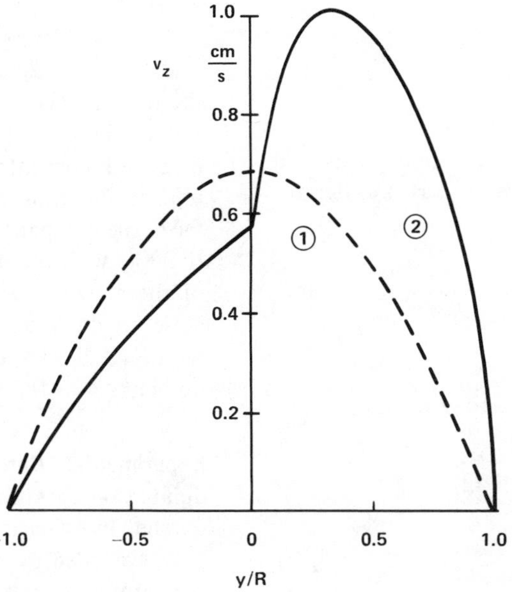

FIGURE 18. Two-phase film flow. Flow rate profiles in the toluene and water phases.

rium, Γ_{eq}. It can be calculated by the Gibbs relation:

$$\Gamma_{eq} = \frac{1}{RT} C \frac{\partial \sigma}{\partial C}$$

The equilibrium interfacial concentration of pyridine is much higher than its bulk concentration. Therefore, an enrichment of pyridine at the interface occurs. If the mass-transfer resistance in the water phase is much higher than that in the toluene phase one would expect a uniform concentration profile in the toluene phase and a steep gradient in the water phase near the interface. The enrichment of the pyridine in the toluene would change these profiles. The concentration of pyridine in the toluene phase would have a slight increase near the interface and its concentration in the water phase near the interface would fall. This behavior can be clearly recognized from Figures 16 and 17. The measured concentrations of pyridine in the toluene phase at the interface are higher and the measured concentration profiles in the water phase are steeper than the ones calculated by the diffusion model.

If one assumes that the mass-transfer resistance of the phases can be calculated by their diffusion coefficients, it is possible to estimate the interfacial resistance by means of fitting the calculated concentration profiles to the measured ones. The best fit diffusion coefficient is considered as the effective diffusion coefficient of the water phase – interface system.

Consider the overall resistance $1/K_{o.a.}$ as the sum of the partial resistance of the two phases and the interface

$$\frac{1}{K_{o.a.}} = \frac{1}{k_T} + \frac{G_i}{k_w} + \frac{1}{k_i} \tag{62}$$

where $1/k_T$, $1/k_w$ and $1/k_i$ are the mass-transfer resistances of toluene water, and the interface.

According to the present measurements

$$\frac{1}{k_T} << \frac{G_i}{k_w} + \frac{1}{k_i}$$

hence

$$\frac{1}{K_{o.a.}} \simeq \frac{1}{k_{w\,eff}} = \frac{G_i}{k_w} + \frac{1}{k_i}$$

and

$$k_i \simeq \frac{k_{w\,eff}}{1 - G_i(k_{w\,eff}/k_w)} = \frac{k_{w\,eff}}{1 - G_iK_2}$$

where

$$K_2 = \frac{k_{w\,eff}}{k_w}$$

Assuming the validity of the two-film theory and that the resistance of the water phase – interface system is given by

$$k^{-1}_{w\,eff} = \frac{h \cdot R}{D_{w\,eff}} \tag{63}$$

one obtains for k_i:

$$k_i = \frac{D_{w\,eff}/hR}{1 - G_iK_2} \tag{64}$$

if one assumes that

$$K_2 = \frac{k_{w\,eff}}{k_w} \simeq \frac{D_{w\,eff}}{D_w} \tag{65}$$

By fitting the calculated concentration profiles in the water phase to the measured one (Figures 16 and 17) one obtains

$1/k_i = 6.77 \times 10^4$ sec/cm $(K_1 = 1.04)$

$1/k_i = 4.33 \times 10^4$ sec/cm $(K_1 = 2.39)$

for the interfacial resistances.

The order of magnitude of these resistances is in good agreement with those evaluated by Chandrasekhar and Hoelscher[37] for acetic acid transport from toluene to water by ultracentrifuge, which are in the range of 1.9 to 6.3 $\times$ 10^4 sec/cm. The agreement with the results of Harada et al.,[89] who found interfacial resistances of $1/k_i = 0.8 - 3 \times 10^3$ sec/cm (*n*-valeric acid) and $1/k_i = 0.4 - 1.5 \times 10^3$ sec/cm (*n*-butyric acid) is less satisfactory.

For the estimation of k_i only the measured concentration profile in the water phase was used. The fitting of the calculated concentration profiles to the measured ones in the toluene phase is not possible, because the solute concentration increases in direction of the mass transfer (Figures 16 and 17). Therefore no fitting was carried out, but the concentration profiles were calculated by the mass balance and the measured velocity profile. Since the calculated solute concentrations are much lower near the interface than the measured ones, they must be higher than the measured ones at greater distances from the interface.

The consideration of the interfacial resistance leads to the calculated concentration profiles in the toluene phase as they are shown in Figures 16 and 17. By the extrapolation of the calculated and measured concentration profiles to y = 0 one obtains the concentration C_T close to the interface. The comparison of the calculated concentration C_T with the measured one allows estimation of the activity coefficient of pyridine in toluene close to the interface. For both of the systems with $K_1 = 1.04$ and 2.39 the same coefficient was obtained: $a_T = 0.56$.

Experimental Determination of the Interfacial Solute Concentration

The interfacial concentrations have already been evaluated by extrapolation of the concentration profiles to y = 0. This estimation is not a very satisfactory one; therefore, the interfacial concentration was also measured at the interface by Method C discussed in an earlier section. The combination of this method with the external standard method E) allowed the simultaneous measurement of the concentration of the solute in the solvent bulk phase and at the interface.

The experimental setup is shown in Figure 8. The mass-transfer channel (Figure 9) is mounted in a heat- and light-insulated box which is kept at constant temperature (4°C). The whole flow system consists of glass without any ground-glass couplings to avoid any source of contamination with surface-active agents. The flow system was cleaned with hydrofluoric acid and rinsed with distilled water before the measurements. All liquids were purified with great care to avoid any contamination.

By proper regulation of the static pressures of the two liquids their interface can be kept constant in the axis of the channel. To avoid ripple formation on the interface the whole apparatus was made vibration-free by means of damping elements. Also, high relative velocities of the phases can cause ripple formation: therefore, only velocities were applied which would not cause such disturbances.

The water phase, which was saturated with toluene, contained tritium with a specific activity of 10 mCi/l. The toluene phase, which was saturated by water, contained 5 g/l of the scintillator (2,5-diphenyloxazole, PPO). Pyridine is of analytical grade and the scintillator of scintillation grade. As external standard, a γ-source (20 μCi Ra^{226} encapsulated in PTFE), was used. It could be brought near the sample and then be transported back into a lead-shielded box by a simple pneumatic device. By this intermittent operation, the measurements with tritium were not disturbed by the γ-emission.

The Compton electrons produced in the liquids may cause Cerenkov radiation. The amount of energy exceeding the kinetic energy at the velocity of light is emitted as photons; this occurs without first exciting the scintillator. Because of this fact the Cerenkov radiation can also appear in the water phase. However, by proper adjustment of both the amplifier and the lower discriminator of the pulse height analyzer, only scintillation events due to Compton electrons are counted. In selecting the proper discriminator setting the interference with tritium pulses was avoided.

The experiments for the calibration of the channel ratio versus concentration of the quencher were carried out under geometric conditions similar to the mass-transfer investigations, i.e., the vials used had the same diameter as the mass-transfer channel and were filled half with water and half with toluene. In addition to this, the vials were longer than the diameter of the photomultipliers of the detector to allow the counting of photons with an angle of incidence equal to the angle of total reflection. All these conditions had to be considered so that the calibration curve obtained by vials could be applied to the investigations carried out by the mass-transfer channel.

The calibration measurements were carried out in the water-toluene-pyridine system in equilibrium. To estimate the error of the application of these calibration data to a two-phase flow with mass transfer across the interface, different model calculations were carried out. Other calibration curves were determined for the relation of the relative counting rate of tritium to the concentration of pyridine and for the counting rate of tritium dissolved in the toluene phase.

The average error of the estimation of the interface solute concentration is less that 6%.

Mass Transfer from the Water to the Toluene Phase

The concentration of the solute (pyridine) was estimated in the toluene bulk phase, and at the interface of the toluene phase in a thin layer with average thickness 0.66 μm simultaneously, by Method E in a longitudinal direction by moving the detector (two photomultipliers in coincidence circuit, see Figure 19) along the channel (Figure 8). Figure 20 shows the results for the pyridine transfer from water to toluene. The bulk phase concentration increases in a similar way for Runs 1 to 3. The interfacial concentration C_i has different behavior depending on the relative flow velocities. If the mean flow velocity of water is much greater than toluene flow velocity, the interfacial concentration is considerably higher than in the case of equal flow velocities.

This result can be explained by considering the convective mass transfer. An acceleration and/or deceleration of mass transfer by convective transport processes can only take place if there is a positive and/or negative velocity gradient in the phase, from which the solute is transferred to the other one. Figure 21 shows velocity profiles for Runs 1 to 4.

In Runs 1 to 3 the velocity gradient of toluene becomes more and more negative so that the mass-transfer rate decreases; this results in a higher interfacial concentration. For Run 4, the velocity gradient is strongly positive. Due to this, the interfacial concentration is very low. Also these results seem to prove the existence of a mass-transfer resistance at the interface. Only by this assumption can these variations in the interfacial concentrations be explained.

In the absence of an additional resistance at the interface, the concentration of the solute at the toluene interface can be calculated by means of the partition coefficient. The initial concentration of pyridine in water is 0.31 g mol/l, so that the interfacial concentration at the toluene side should have values of about 0.5 g mol/l, since the change of the pyridine concentration in the water bulk phase is small. For all runs the interfacial concentration C_{Ti} of pyridine is considerably lower (Figure 20) than that calculated by the partition coefficient. This interfacial resistance can also be examined by computing mass-transfer coefficients. Figure 22 shows these coefficients for Run 1 (corresponding to Figure 20). The coefficients for the water phase are computed assuming equilibrium at the interface. The flow rates of toluene

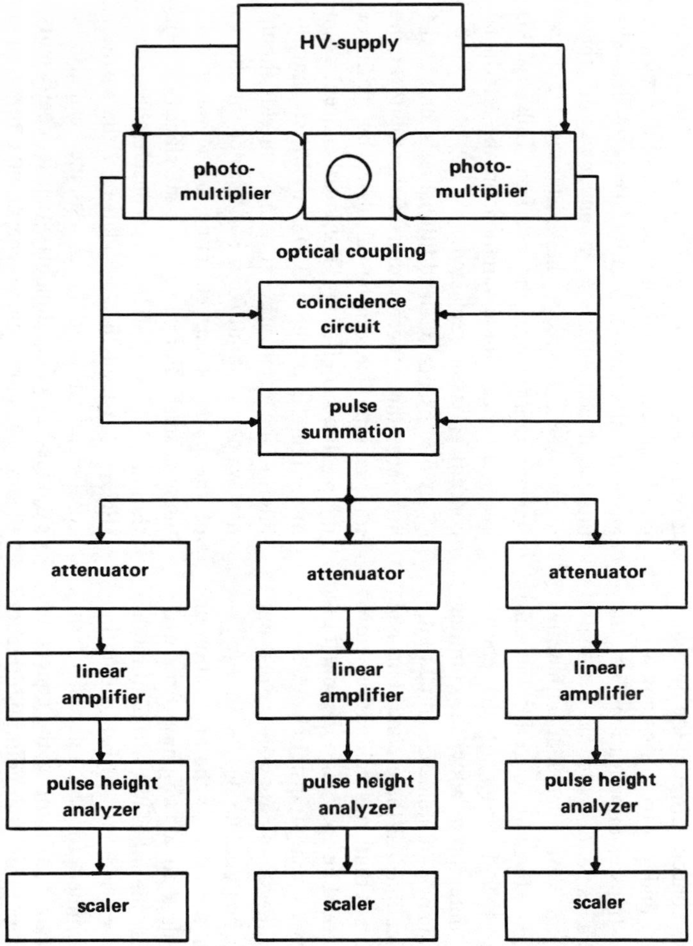

FIGURE 19. Block diagram of the liquid scintillation counter three-channel pulse-height analyzer. The (photomultiplier + optical coupling) detector is moved along the channel.

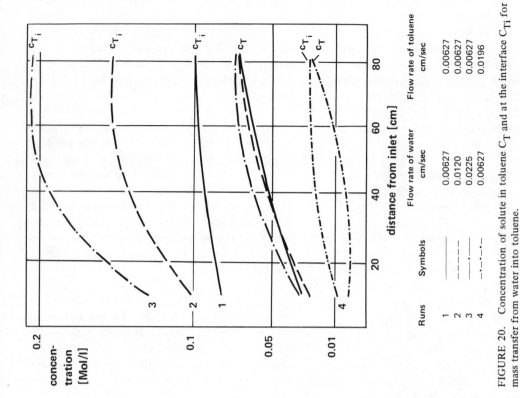

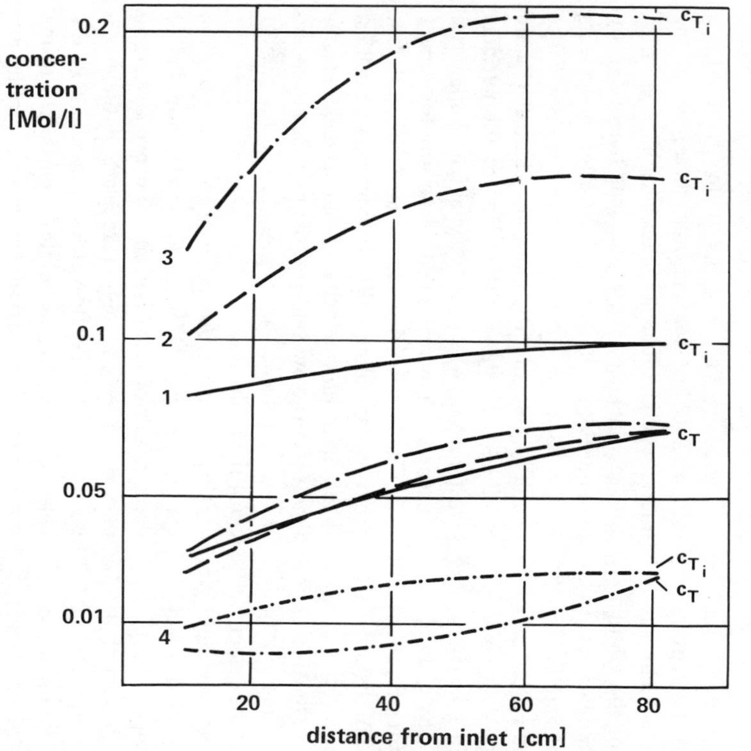

Runs	Symbols	Flow rate of water cm/sec	Flow rate of toluene cm/sec
1	———————	0.00627	0.00627
2	– – – – –	0.0120	0.00627
3	——·——	0.0225	0.00627
4	–·–·–·–	0.00627	0.0196

FIGURE 20. Concentration of solute in toluene C_T and at the interface C_{Ti} for mass transfer from water into toluene.

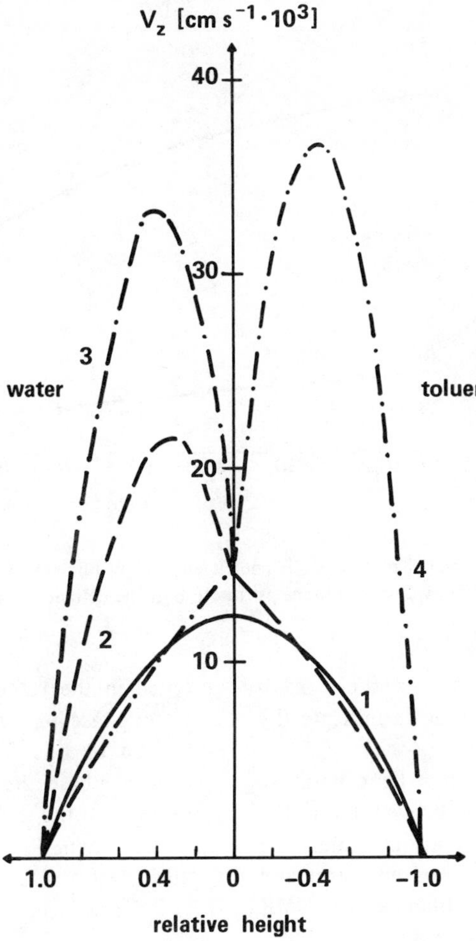

Runs	Symbols	Flow rate of water cm/sec	Flow rate of toluene cm/sec
1	————	0.00627	0.00627
2	– – – – –	0.0120	0.00627
3	•———•	0.0225	0.00627
4	–•–•–•–	0.00627	0.0196

FIGURE 21. Calculated velocity profiles for two-phase flow in a horizontal cylindrical tube.

and water are nearly equal, as are the velocity profiles (Figure 21).

In this case the diffusion coefficients alone determine the value of the mass-transfer coefficients. The diffusivity of pyridine in water is 0.59×10^{-5} cm^2/s and in toluene 1.78×10^{-5} cm^2/s. According to the penetration theory, mass-transfer coefficients can be calculated from the diffusivities. For the case described above the mass-transfer coefficients should differ by a factor 1.7. However, Figure 22 shows that the coefficients differ by a factor greater than four. This result can only be explained by assuming an additional resistance at the interface in accordance with the results discussed previously and with the experimental measurements of Chandrasekhar and Hoelscher.[37] The interfacial resistance increases with increasing distance from the edge of the entrance blade from 3.10^4 sec/cm to 6.10^4 sec/cm. Besides this direct experimental evidence, Shimbashi et al.,[72] Sinfelt et al.,[94] Harada et al.[89] and Nitsch[73,74] came to the same conclusion,

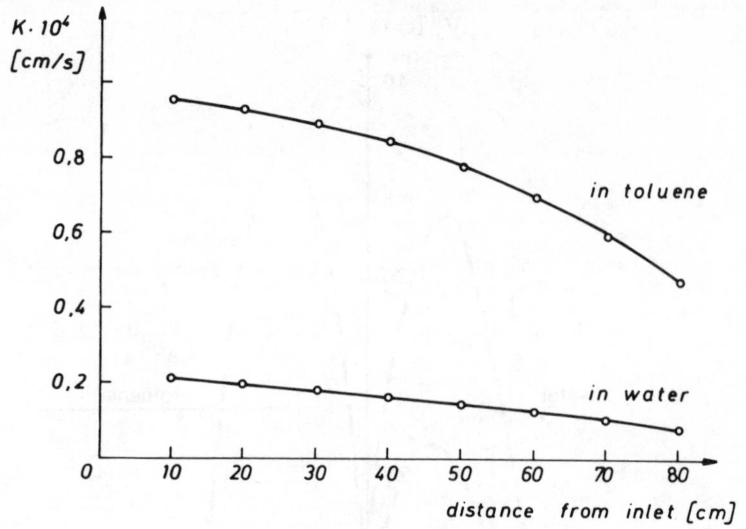

FIGURE 22. Partial mass-transfer coefficients of pyridine in the two phases for mass transfer from water to toluene as function of the distance from inlet.

based on the careful analysis of their mass-exchange measurements, which again indicate the existence of interfacial resistance.

This interfacial resistance may be caused by hydrogen bonds which must be broken before the transfer from water to toluene is possible. The existence of hydrogen bonds between water and pyridine has been proved by Blaschke by NMR measurements[4] and by Brun and Gaufres.[75]

Mass Transfer from the Toluene to the Water Phase

Figure 23 shows the results for the transfer of pyridine from toluene to water. In this case, the concentrations at the interface C_{Ti} again are higher than the bulk phase concentrations C_T of pyridine in the toluene phase; this is in accordance with the previous discussion and the experimental results of Chandrasekhar and Hoelscher.[37] This difference ($\Delta C_T = C_{Ti} - C_T$) is higher for $K_1 = 0.53$ than for $K_1 = 0.083$ and remains nearly constant along the channel (Figure 23).

Since $K_1 < 1$, the velocity gradient in the receiving water phase at the interface is negative and is positive in the transferring toluene phase. Therefore the mass transfer from the toluene bulk phase to the interface is accelerated and the transfer from the interface to the water bulk phase is decelerated. By the interfacial resistance, and by this combined mass-transfer acceleration – deceleration effect, the concentration profile is flattened in the toluene phase and steepened in the water phase near the interface (Figures 16 and 17).

Due to this flat concentration profile in the toluene phase the influence of the enrichment of pyridine at the interface becomes visible.

More experimental work is necessary to obtain quantitative results on this behavior of the solute at the interface.

MASS TRANSFER ON SINGLE DROPLETS

Several mass-transfer investigations were carried out with single droplets. An excellent review of these results is given by Heertjes and De Nie.[27] As already discussed, the main drawback of these investigations is that the concentration of the solute could not be measured in free drops during the exchange process, but only after the exchange process was finished and the phases were separated. The new modified scintillation method allows the measurement of the instantaneous concentration and mass transfer rate of the solute with high precision by means of two photomultipliers.

Experimental Setup and Measurements

The experimental setup consisted of the test section with a droplet formation device, water supply, detector with a three-channel liquid spectrometer, data accumulator, and some additional

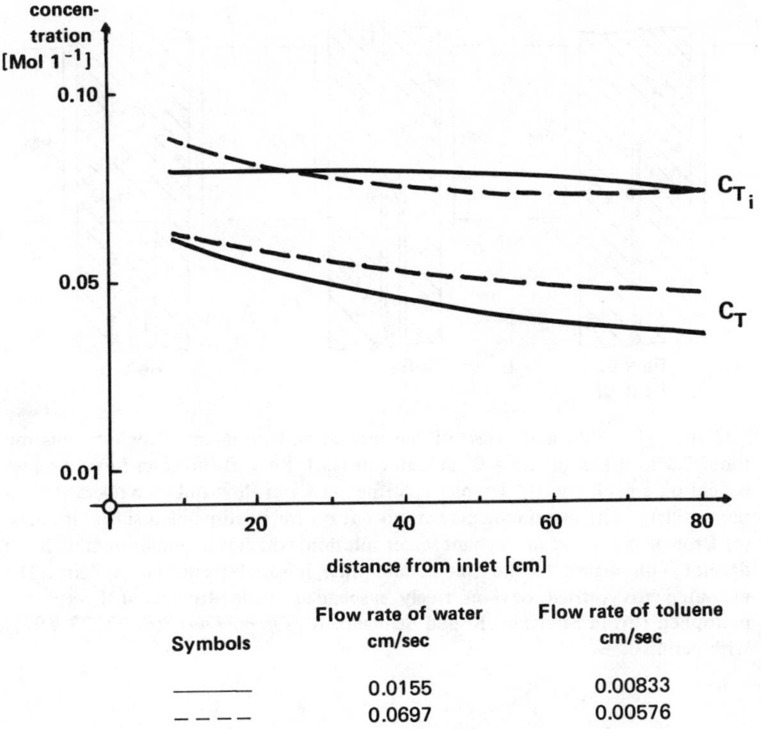

FIGURE 23. Concentration of solute in toluene C_T and at the interface C_{Ti} for mass transfer of pyridine from toluene to water.

equipment to prepare the radioactive liquid mixtures and to calibrate them.[43] The estimation of the relation between the concentration of the solute and the counting rate and/or channel ratio was carried out in the test section itself since the geometry of the system strongly influences the counting yield and the pulse height distribution of the emitted light. Because of the unfavorable geometry of the test section, in comparison with the optimized 4π geometry of standard scintillation equipment, relatively low counting yields of

$\eta = 14.6 \pm 0.9\%$ (for H^3)

and

$\eta = 28.0 \pm 0.5\%$ (for C^{14})

were achieved. In standard scintillation equipments the corresponding yields are

$\eta = 63\%$ (for H^3)

$\eta = 98\%$ (for C^{14})

These low yields could be compensated for by using relatively high specific activities of the solute and/or solvent (62 μCi/ml). This specific activity corresponds to 0.9 μCi/droplet for a droplet of 15 μl volume. By this a high time resolution and signal to noise ratio could be achieved. However, it is not possible to increase the time resolution and the signal to noise ratio by increasing the specific activity any further.

At very high pulse rates ($> 10^6$ pulse/min) a noncontrollable part of the pulse is lost because of the limited time resolution of the applied spectrometer.

The error of the concentration measurements is controlled by the statistics of the radioactive disintegration. The highest error appears at low concentration of the solute in the case of Method B and at high concentration of the solute in the case of Method A. By combining these two methods and by increasing the integration time of the pulse counting, the error can be kept below a given level.

According to the aim of the measurements, different test sections were used (Figure 24).[43]

In the test section *a* the droplet is fixed at the tip of a capillary during the exchange process. The

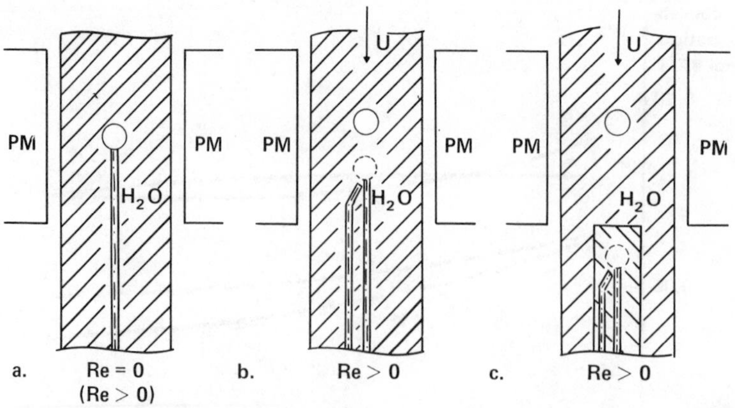

FIGURE 24. Schematic view of the measuring equipment. Droplet formation time: 0.5 to 2 sec. (a) Re = 0 (in water in rest), Re > 0 (in water flow), droplet is held on a capillary. (b) Droplet is formed in water flow and then released from the capillary. The measurements carried out on freely suspended single droplets. (c) Droplet is formed in stagnant water solution, which is in equilibrium with the droplet with regard to the solute, and then released from the capillary. The measurements carried out on freely suspended single droplets. PM = photomultiplier. (From Streicher, R. and Schügerl, K., *Chem. Eng. Sci.*, 32, 23, 1977. With permission.)

water is at rest (Re = 0), or it moves, i.e., Re> 0. In the test section *b* the droplet is formed during a time interval of 0.5 to 2 sec at the tip of a fine steel capillary again by a precision droplet formation device with variable droplet formation rate. In most cases the droplet formation rate of 2.8 μl/sec was used. The droplet volume is controlled using a timer. As soon as a droplet of desired volume is formed, it is released from the tip by a liquid thrust. The droplet rises to the position where it stays freely suspended for the rest of the measurements. The mass-transfer process was investigated in this freely suspended state of the droplet.

In the test section *c* the droplet was formed either in a stagnant water solution which was in equilibrium with the droplet or in stagnant water at the tip of the fine steel capillary. After the droplet was released from the capillary by a thrust, it rose to the position where it was investigated in a freely suspended state. To achieve this state, the parabolic velocity profile of the laminar flow in the cylindrical test section was changed by a system of wire gauze layers and a nozzle (Figure 25).

Figure 26 shows typical velocity profiles measured in test section at the position of the freely suspended droplet. This test section was installed in a closed-water cycle, in which the water was purified in five stages and reused.[43]

The test section with the flow system was mounted in a heat- and light-insulated box which was kept at constant temperature. The light pulses emitted by the scintillators were counted by two photomultipliers to increase the signal to noise ratio and processed by a three-channel spectrometer (the Tricarb 3003 made by Packard Instruments, Downers Grove, Ill.) (Figure 19). The pulse rates of the two channels were stored for the successive time sequences in a multichannel analyzer (Series 900 made by Packard Instruments) and processed by a computer. The duration of the measurements varied between 10 and 20 min. The pulse rates of each channel were integrated over the time interval of 1 sec during the first 100 sec of each run; later on, at low concentrations, the mean pulse rates were determined over greater time intervals to secure precise concentration data with a maximum relative error of 5.7%.[43]

The selected systems, water and toluene phases with acetic acid and/or dioxane solute, are typical representatives for two different substance classes, one with the mass-transfer resistance solely on the toluene side (for acetic acid) and the other with equal mass-transfer resistances on both of the sides (for dioxane) (Figures 27 to 29) on the interface.

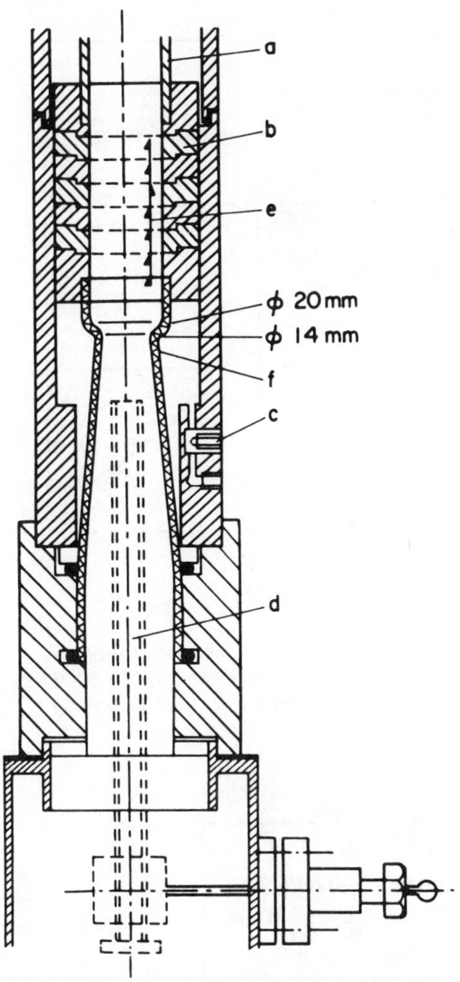

FIGURE 25. Test section (without detector). Wire-gauze nozzle system (a, gas tube; b, teflon clamps; c, air relief valve; d, droplet formation tube; e, seven wire-gauze layers; f, nozzle). (From Otto, W., Streicher, R., and Schügerl, K., *Chem. Eng. Sci.*, 28, 1777, 1973. With permission.)

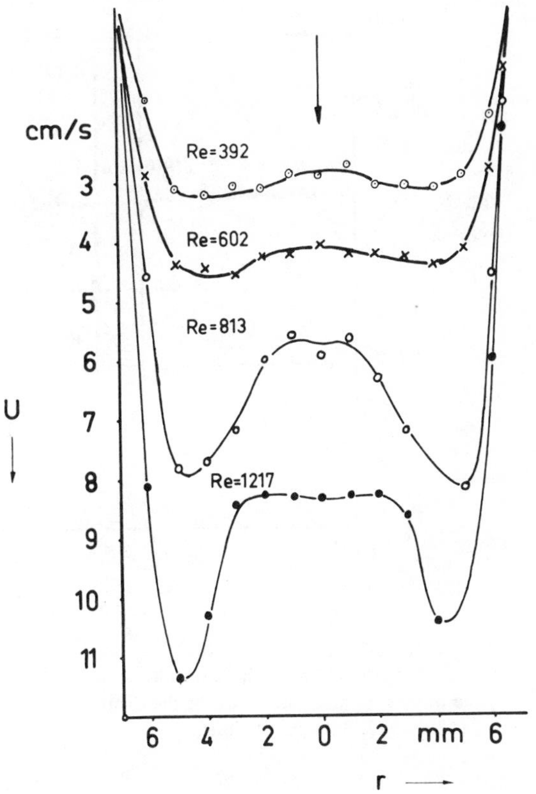

FIGURE 26. Measured velocity profiles in the test section at different Reynolds numbers.

Comparison of the Experimental Results with the Models for Pure Systems

Low Droplet Reynolds Numbers ($Re \simeq 0$)

The droplet is held on a stainless steel capillary in the water phase which is at rest.[96] Figure 30 shows the variation of the solute (acetic acid) concentration in the toluene droplet of 0.49 cm diameter with an initial solute concentration of 29.4 mg/cm^3. To compare this curve with theory, the corresponding theoretical curves according to Newman[16] and Kronig-Brink[18] are also plotted. The first model assumes no movement within the droplet and the second one a laminar circulation within the droplet according to Rybczynski[6] and Hadamard.[7] Since in the initial phase, up to 50 sec, the measured curve is in good agreement with the theoretical prediction of Kronig-Brink, one can assume that during this time circulation prevails within the droplet. One can show that this movement is not caused by the eruptions of the interface, since under the experimental conditions the interface is stable,[68] but by circulation due to the droplet formation. With increasing age of the droplet these disturbances decay and after about 200 sec the droplet behavior can be described by the model of Newman.[16]

For different droplet diameters (Figure 31) and solute concentrations (Figure 32) the same behavior applies. However, at high droplet ages and with low solute concentrations the curves level off, because the solute is replenished after diffusion from the capillary.

To improve the time resolution for short transfer times and to compare the measured data with the theory, especially with the results of Brauer[9] and Schmidt-Traub,[10] the dimensionless

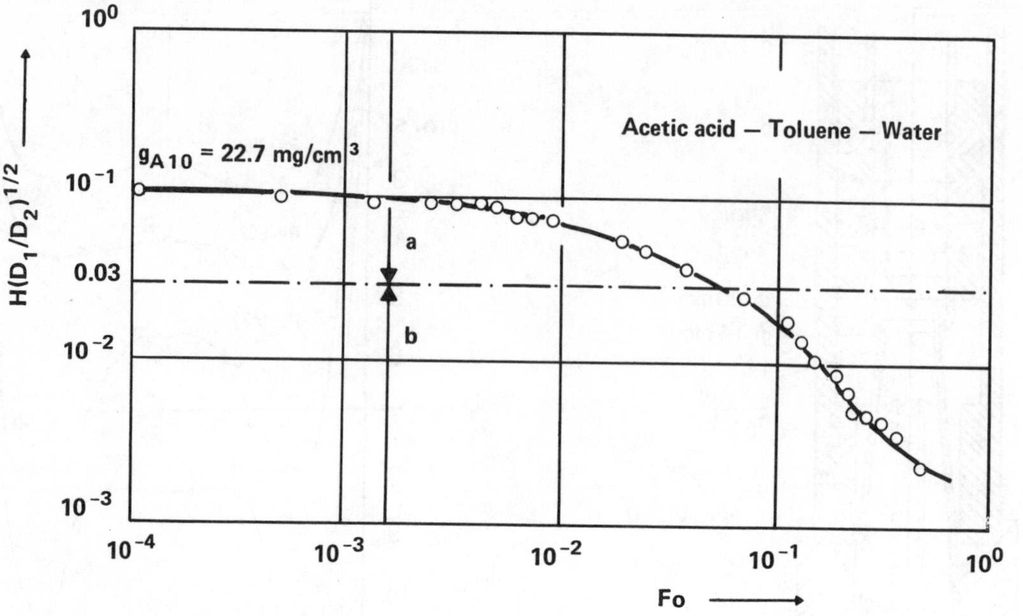

FIGURE 27. Criterion of the ratio of mass-transfer resistance $H(D_1/D_2)^{1/2}$ in droplets according to Brauer[9] as function of the Fo number for the water-toluene-acetic acid system (a, resistance in both of the phases; b, resistance only in the droplet phase). (From Streicher, R. and Schügerl, K., *Chem. Eng. Sci.*, 32, 23, 1977. With permission.)

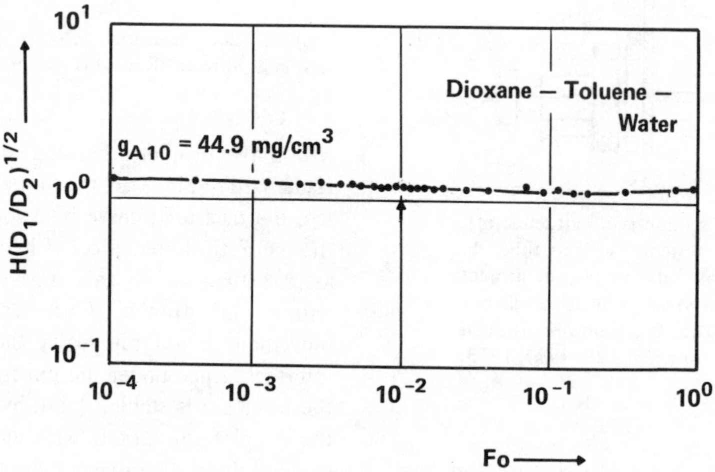

FIGURE 28. Criterion of the ratio of mass-transfer resistances $H(D_1/D_2)^{1/2}$ in droplets according to Brauer[9] as function of the Fo number for the water-toluene-dioxane system.

mean concentration $\bar{\xi}$ of the solute in the droplet was plotted as function of the dimensionless exchange time, the Fourier number Fo, on logarithmic scale (Figure 33). One can recognize that under initial conditions ($Fo < 6.10^{-3}$ no circulation prevails within the droplet (Newman model). After this initial period, at droplet ages of 6 to 10 sec, the mass-transfer mechanism changes from pure diffusion to laminar circulation (Kronig-Brink model). This initial phase corresponds closely to the time which is needed by a volume element in the droplet to move from the back-stagnation point along the axis of the droplet to the front stagnation point according to Schmidt-Traub.[10]

These results show that at small Fo numbers

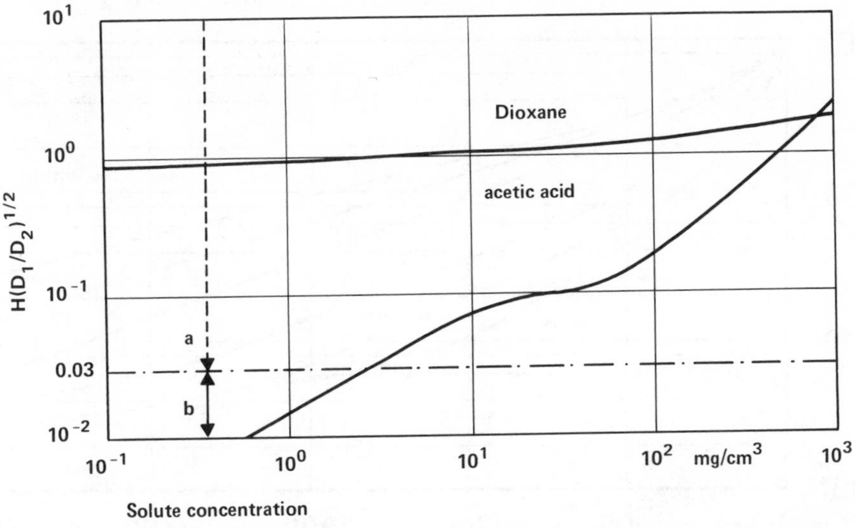

FIGURE 29. Criterion of the ratio of mass-transfer resistances $H(D_1/D_2)^{1/2}$ in droplets according to Brauer[9] as function of the solute concentration in droplet for water-toluene-acetic acid system (a, resistance in both of the phases; b, resistance only in the droplet phase).

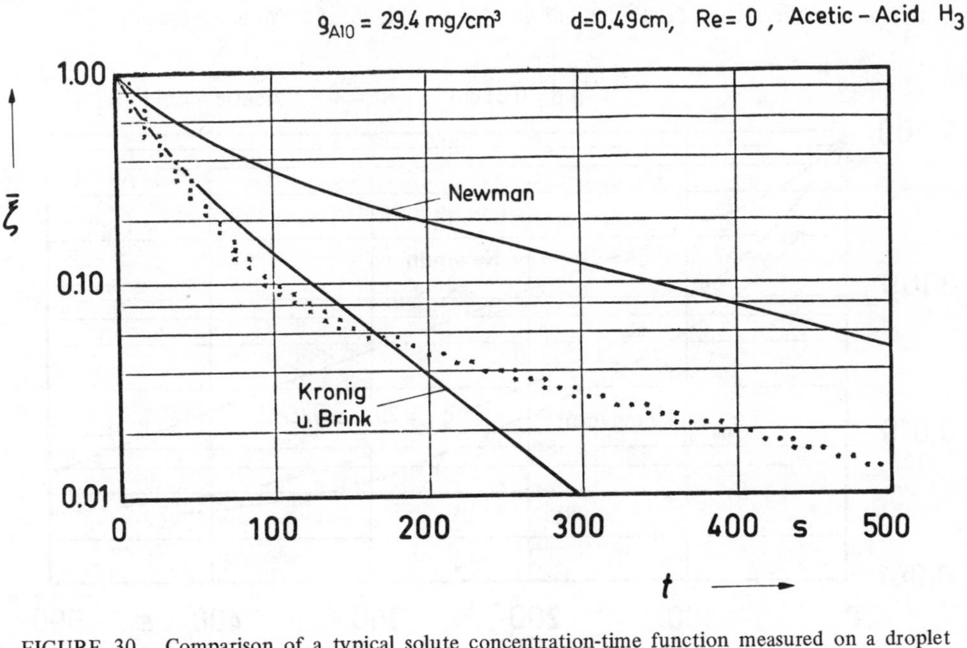

FIGURE 30. Comparison of a typical solute concentration-time function measured on a droplet with water phase in rest. C_0 = 29.4 mg/cm³, d = 0.49 cm, Re ≅ 0, Acetic acid-H^3 solute, with calculated ones according to Newman and Kronig-Brink. (From Streicher, R. and Schügerl, K., *Chem. Eng. Sci.*, 32, 23, 1977. With permission.)

the mass transfer occurs by diffusion alone up to the time t = 6 to 10 sec, at which time the circulation within the droplet begins to occur and therefore an acceleration of the mass transfer due to this circulation occurs. These circulations seem to prevail up to Fo ≅ 6.10^{-2} (t ≅ 60 sec). After this time the mechanism of mass transfer changes again to pure diffusion.

If one plots the course of the concentration change with the Fo number and shifts the meas-

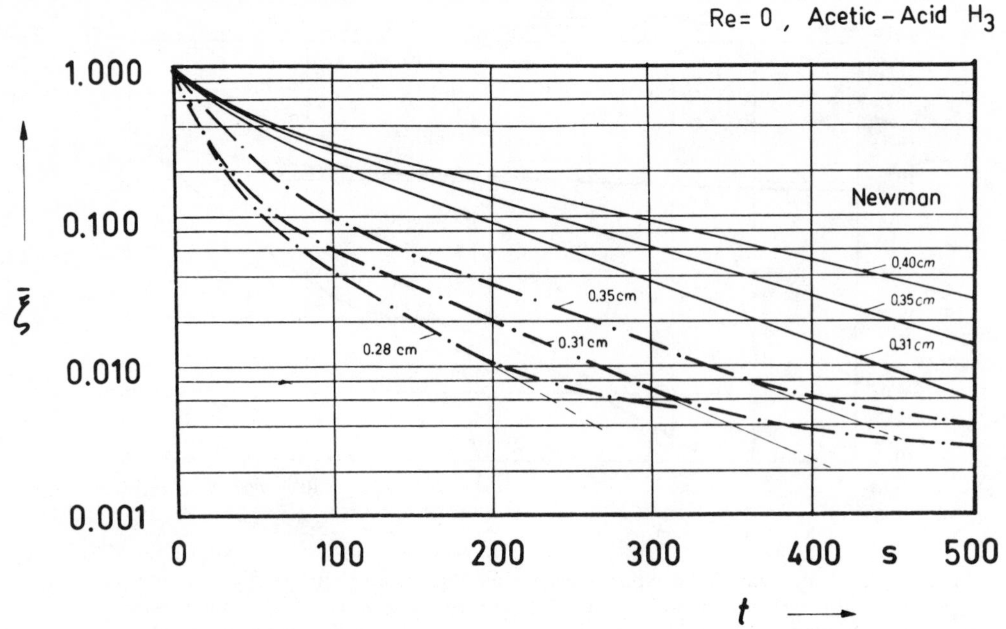

FIGURE 31. Influence of the droplet diameter on the concentration-time function. Parameter d (for C_0, Re, and solute see Figure 30). Comparison of the measured curves with the calculated one according to Newman. (From Streicher, R. and Schügerl, K., *Chem. Eng. Sci.*, 32, 23, 1977. With permission.)

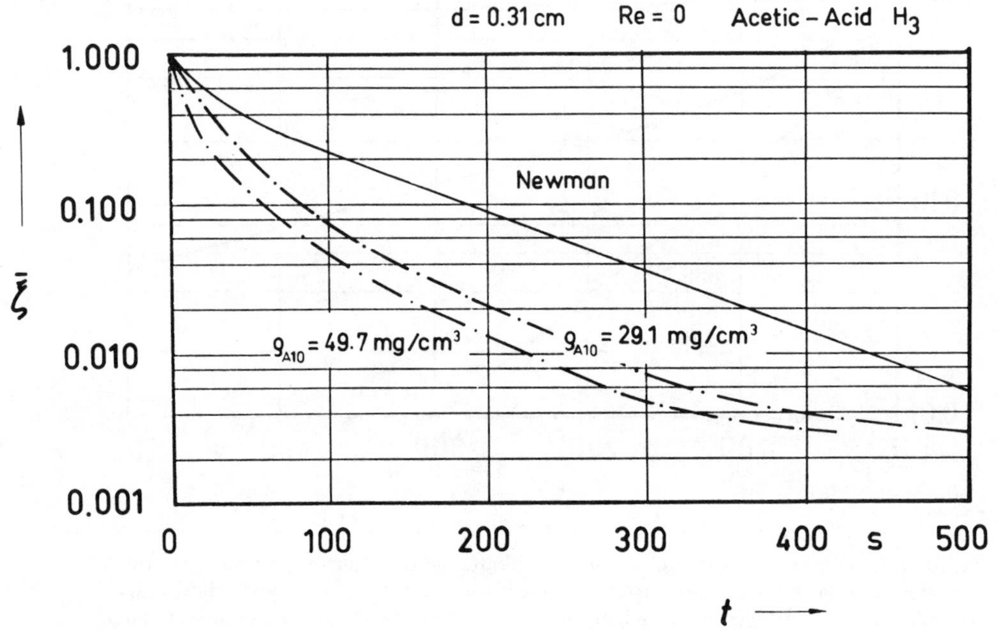

FIGURE 32. Influence of the initial concentration on the concentration-time function. Parameter C_0 (d = 0.31 cm, Re ≃ 0, acetic acid-H^3 solute). Comparison of the measured curves with the calculated one according to Newman. (From Streicher, R. and Schügerl, K., *Chem. Eng. Sci.*, 32, 23, 1977. With permission.)

ured curve by considering the state at t = 60 sec as the initial state, one obtains Curve 2, which corresponds exactly to the pure-diffusion mechanism of Newman.[16] This good agreement also proves that the resistance in the water phase can be neglected, as the theory of Brauer[9] demands.

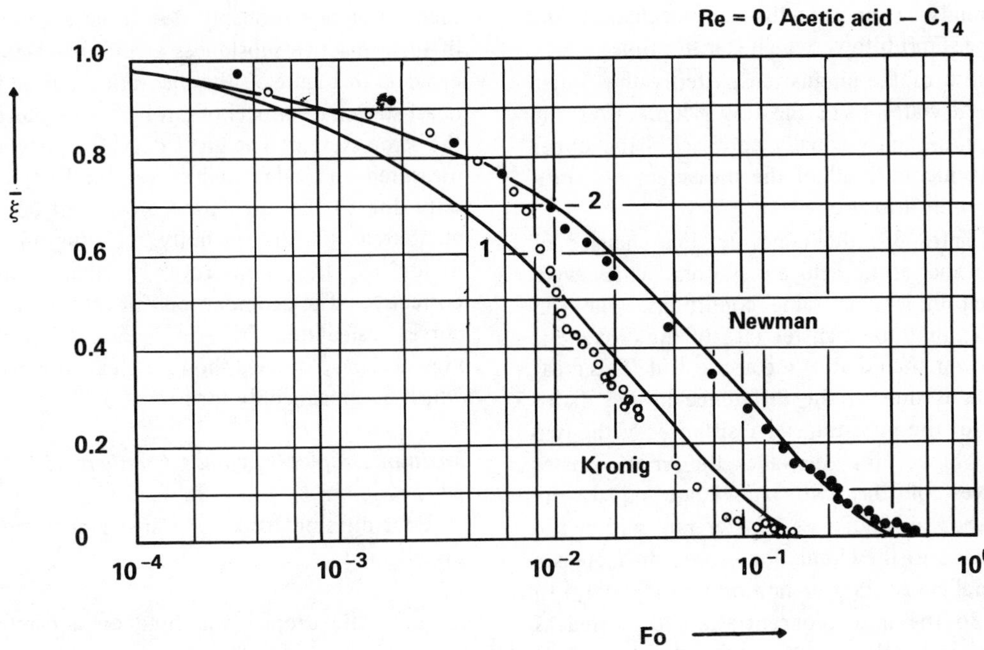

FIGURE 33. Mean concentration in the droplet as function of the Fo number (for d, Re, and solute see Figure 30). (1) Original measurement, (2) measurement recalculated by considering the concentration at t = 60 sec as initial concentration. Comparison of (1) and (2) with the calculated function according to Kronig and Brink and Newman. (From Streicher, R. and Schügerl, K., *Chem. Eng. Sci.*, 32, 23, 1977. With permission.)

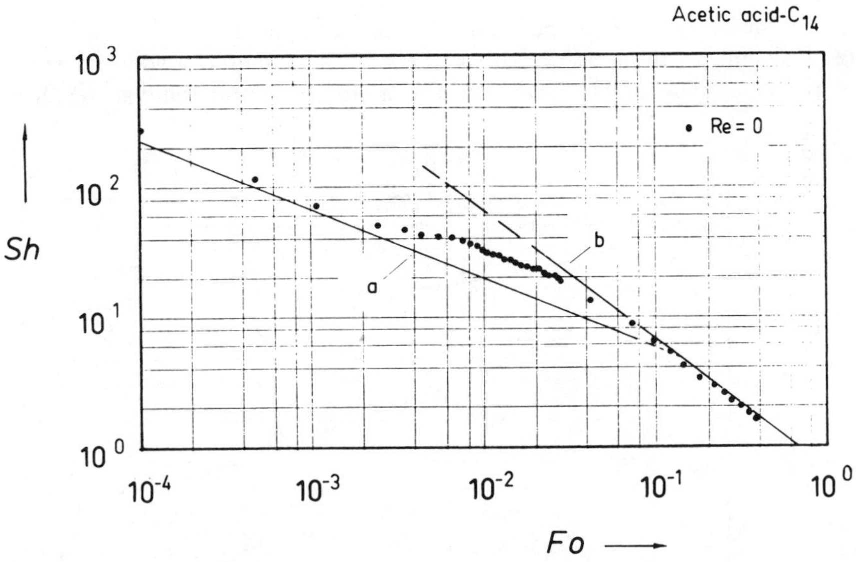

FIGURE 34. Mean Sherwood number as function of the Fourier number (for C_0, d, and solute see Figure 30). Comparison of the measured function with the upper and lower limit curves according to Brauer.[9] (From Streicher, R. and Schügerl, K., *Chem. Eng. Sci.*, 32, 23, 1977. With permission.)

In Figure 34, the upper and lower theoretical limits of the mean Sherwood number $Sh_1 = \frac{k_1 d}{D_1}$ and the corresponding experimental curve are plotted as function of Fo. The lower limit a corresponds to the pure-diffusion mechanism and the upper limit b to very high transfer times.

Because of the circulation patterns, the course of Sh_1 deviates from the lower limit after the initial phase and gradually approaches the upper limit. Incidentally all of the measurements fulfil the upper limit for $Fo > 10^{-1}$.

In Figure 35, the concentration changes of dioxane and acetic acid are plotted, which were measured under the same conditions. One can recognize that the transfer rate of the dioxane is much lower than that of the acetic acid. This great deviation is due to the difference in the distributions of the mass-transfer resistances of the two phases. Since for dioxane the mass-transfer resistances of the two phases are equal, the acceleration of the mass-transfer rate within the droplet due to the circulation movement increases the overall mass-transfer rate only moderately. In Figure 36 the mean concentration is plotted as function of the Fo number. Also, the theoretical curve of Brauer[9] for $H(D_1/D_2)^{1/2} = 1$ is plotted on the same figure. At low Fo numbers, the agreement between the measured and calculated curves is fairly good. At medium Fo numbers the mass-transfer rate increases because of the droplet circulation, and therefore the measured curve deviates from the theoretical one for pure diffusion. At high Fo numbers, the measured curve approaches a constant value higher than the theoretical one probably due to an accumulation of surface-active substances at the interface of the droplet. In Figure 37 the theoretical curves for the quasi-stationary model of Gröber[24] are plotted for the same system. The great deviation between the measured and calculated curves for Bi = 0 is not only due to the circulation movement but partly attributed to the inability of this model to describe the nonstationary mass exchange correctly. The comparison of the theoretical curves calculated by the quasi-stationary and nonstationary models shows a great disagreement, which disappears only for $H > 100$.[10]

Medium Droplet Reynolds Numbers (32 < Re < 215)

Four different types of transfer processes were investigated:[96]

1. The droplet was held on a capillary in water flow.
2. The droplet was formed on a capillary in pure water flow and then released to measure the mass transfer on the freely suspended droplet.
3. The droplet was formed on a capillary in stagnant pure water and then released and the mass transfer was measured on the freely suspended droplet.
4. The droplet was formed on a capillary in a stagnant water solution, which was in equilib-

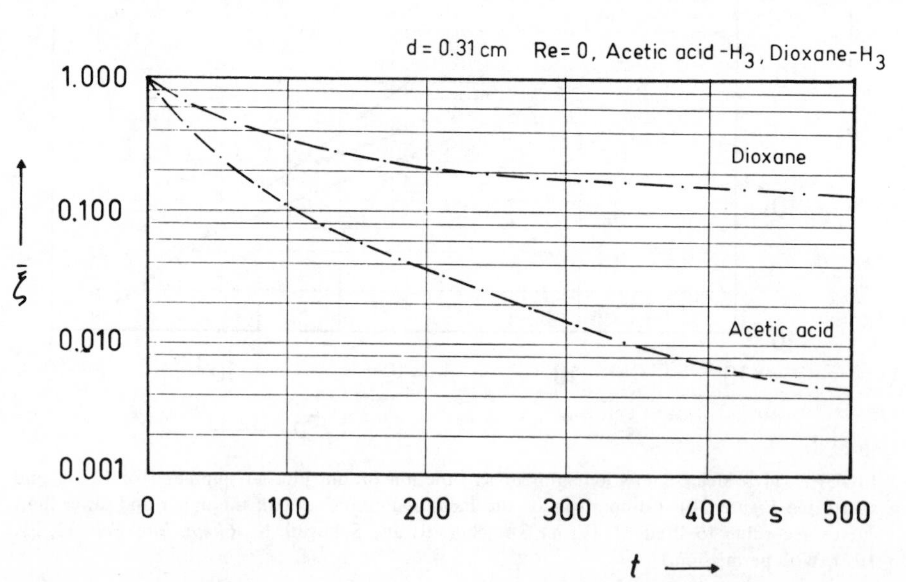

FIGURE 35. Mean solute concentrations in the droplet as function of the exchange time. Solute: dioxane-H^3 and acetic acid-H^3 (for C_0, d, and Re see Figure 32). (From Streicher, R. and Schügerl, K., *Chem Eng. Sci.*, 32, 23, 1977. With permission.)

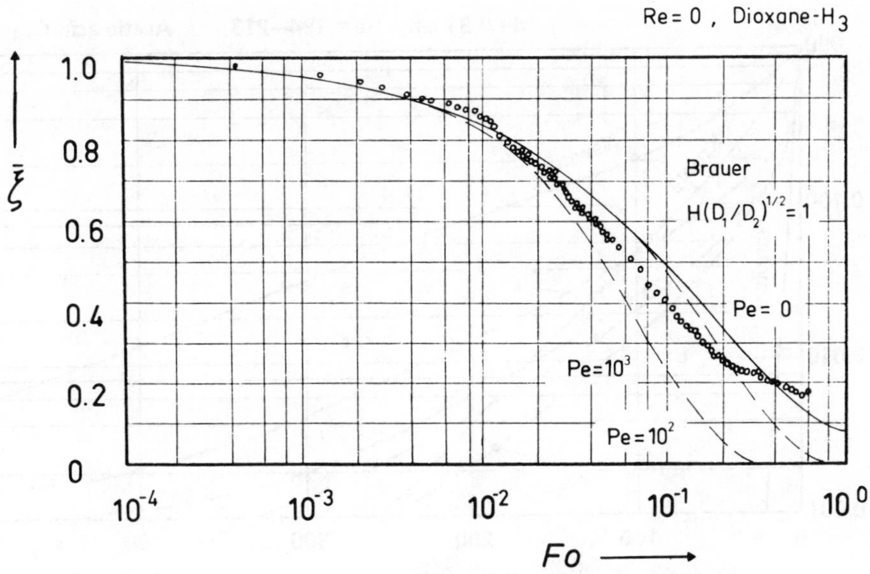

FIGURE 36. Mean solute concentration-Fourier number function. Comparison of the measured function with the calculated ones according to Brauer[9] for Pe = 0 and Pe = 10^2 and 10^3. Solute: dioxane-H^3 (for C_0, d, and Re see Figure 35). (From Streicher, R. and Schügerl, K., *Chem. Eng. Sci.*, 32, 23, 1977. With permission.)

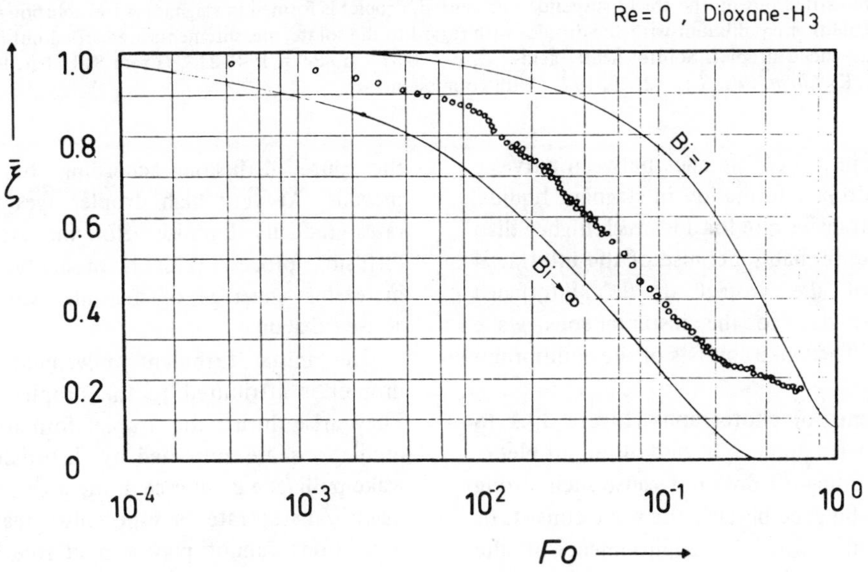

FIGURE 37. Comparison of the measured mean solute concentration-Fourier number function with one calculated by the Gröber model[23] for Bi = 1 and (for C_O, d, Re, and solute see Figure 36). (From Streicher, R. and Schügerl, K., *Chem. Eng. Sci.*, 32, 23, 1977. With permission.)

rium with the droplet. The droplet was then released from the capillary and the mass transfer was measured on the freely suspended droplet.

In Figure 38 typical curves are plotted for the acetic acid solute, which were measured by these four methods. The theoretical curves for pure diffusion (Newman[16]), for laminar circulation (Kronig-Brink[38]) and for turbulent movement (Handlos-Baron[20]) are also plotted. The difference between the curves a and b is slight, if one does not consider the after-diffusion effect for a. This is because the main mass transfer occurs at the front

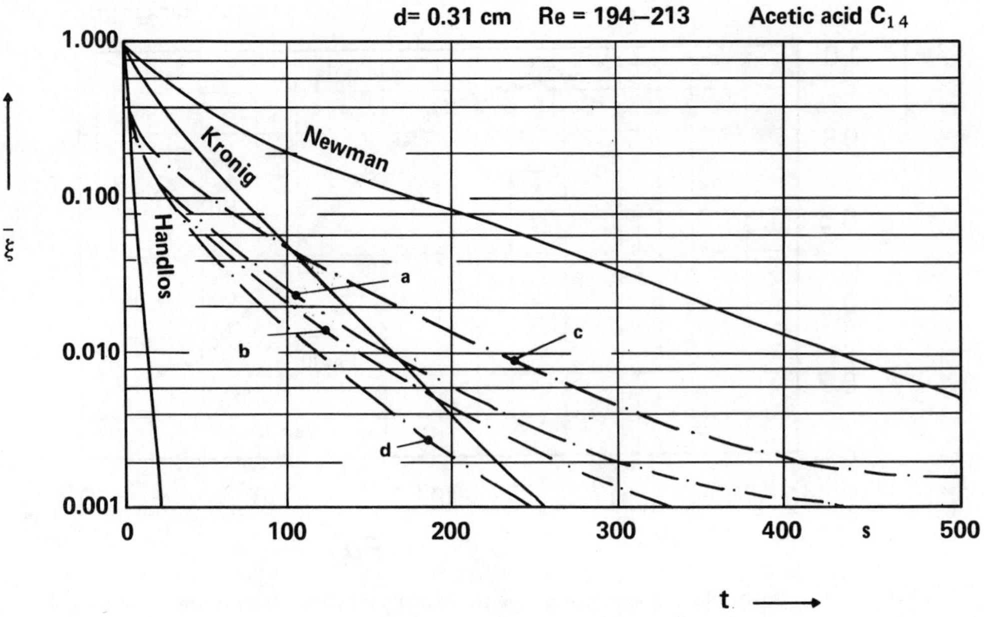

FIGURE 38. Comparison of the mean solute concentration-exchange time functions for four different systems: a, droplet is held on the capillary in water flow; b, droplet is formed in water flow on capillary, measurements are carried out on the freely suspended droplet; c, droplet is formed in stagnant water, measurements are carried out on the freely suspended droplet; d, droplet is formed in stagnant water solution which is in distribution equilibrium with the droplet with regard to the solute, measurements are carried out on the freely suspended droplet. Solute: acetic acid-C^{14}, d = 0.31 cm, Re = 194–213. (From Streicher, R. and Schügerl, K., *Chem. Eng. Sci.*, 32, 23, 1977. With permission.)

stagnation point. The difference between curves c and d, with droplet formation in stagnant liquids, is large. The transfer rate for d is much higher than the one for c, probably because of the interfacial turbulence of the droplet d; this interfacial turbulence is due to the instantaneous wake shedding-off. The wake consists of the equilibrium solution.

The sequence of photographs (Figure 39.1 to 39.8) show such a process. In case of the droplet c, the wake shedding-off does not cause such strong interfacial turbulence because the wake consists of water, and therefore the environment of the droplet does not change as dramatically as for droplet d.

For all of the four methods a to d with medium Re numbers the mass transfer takes place in the initial phase according to the model of Handlos and Baron.[20] This indicates that interfacial turbulence is combined by volume-turbulence.

This turbulent movement within the droplet gradually transfers to the laminar circulation according to Kronig and Brink[18] and finally dies out; and, for quite a long range of the droplet ages, the pure diffusion according to Newman[16] prevails. At very high droplet ages the transfer rates gradually diminish below the rate of the pure diffusion process. This is probably due to the increasing coverage of the interface by surface-active substances.

The initial turbulent movement within the droplet is attributed to the droplet oscillations. They arise during the droplet formation. If these oscillations are amplified by disturbances due to wake-pulling, e.g., in case d, the acceleration of the mass transfer rate is especially great. The free oscillations cannot play a great role because the Reynolds numbers are not high enough. This conclusion is also supported by Figure 40, from which the slight influence of the Re number on the transfer rate can be recognized. The theoretical curves are also plotted on this diagram for the nonstationary model at Re = 1[10] and the quasi-stationary model for Re >> 1[26] and considering only the resistance in the droplet phase. However, they can only be used as a qualitative comparison, since quantitative proof is only possible based on the numerical solution of the nonstationary

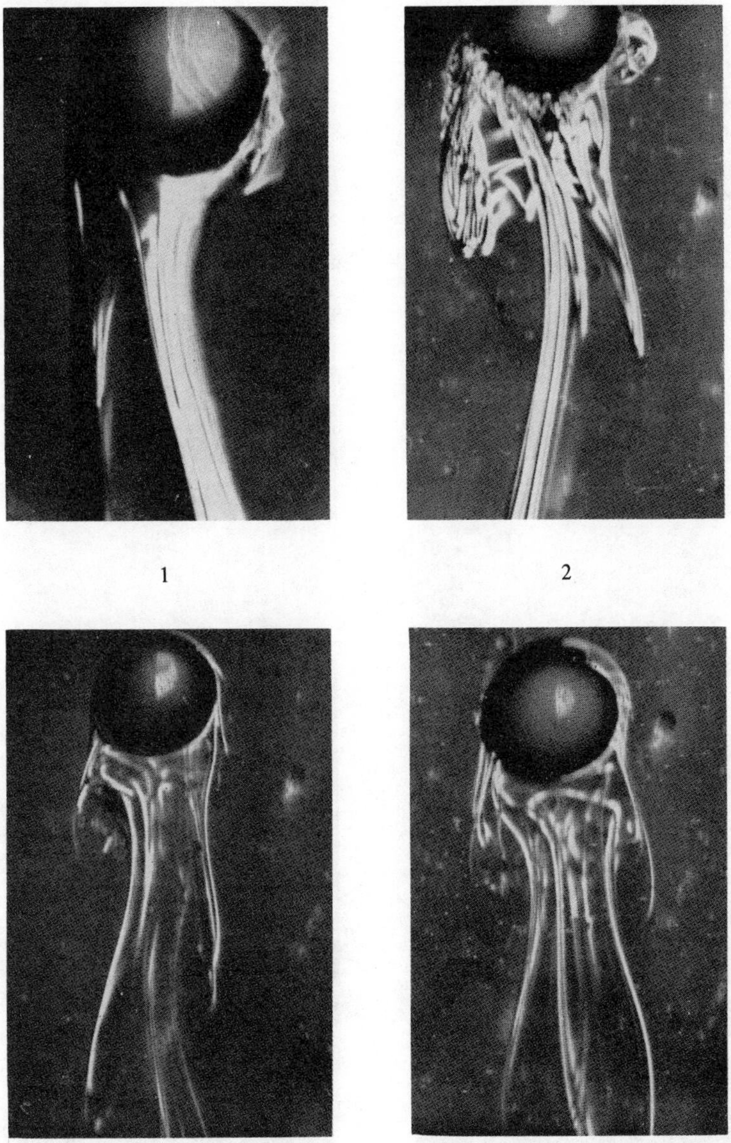

1 2 3 4

FIGURE 39. Behavior of a droplet which was formed in equilibrium solution, shortly after it has left the solution. Starting solute concentration in the droplet 6.3 weight % acetic acid; droplet volume 15 μl. Droplet formation time: 10 sec. Schlieren pictures were made with high pressure mercury lamp; shutter time 1/500 sec; diaphragm, 5.6; speed of the film 17 DIN. The droplet age is measured from the moment the droplet crosses the interface between the equilibrium solution and the pure water.[95] Droplet 1, 0.14 sec; 2, 0.5 sec; 3, 1.28 sec; 4, 1.72 sec; 5, 2.0 sec; 6, 2.3 sec; 7, 2.7 sec; 8, 3.0 sec. (From Grov, Ø., Otto, M., and Schügerl, K., *Chem. Eng. Sci.*, 24, 1397, 1969. With permission.)

differential equation for intermediate Reynolds number. No such a solution is known at the present. Since at the initial acetic acid solute concentration, 17.4 to 18.2 mg/cm^3, used in the present investigations, the criterion of the mass-transfer resistance ratio, $H (D_1/D_2)^{1/2}$, exceeds

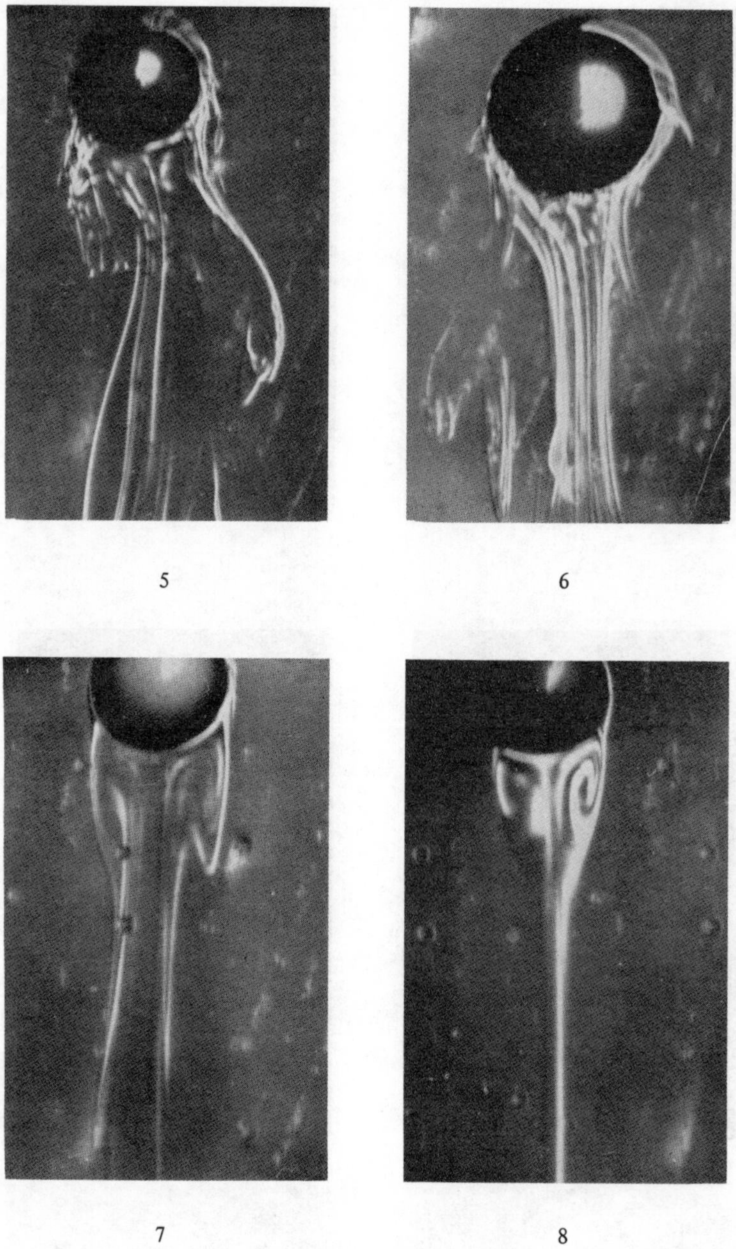

FIGURE 39. (continued)

the upper limit for the sole resistance in the toluene phase. On the other hand, with increasing transfer rate (decreasing concentration) this criterion falls below the upper limit (Figure 29); thus, it is necessary to consider this change with increasing droplet ages. For this purpose the resistance number h of Wellek and Skelland[21]

$$h = 512\left(1 + \frac{\mu_1}{\mu_2}\,\frac{k_2^*}{UH}\right) \tag{66}$$

is evaluated for the present system and is h = 6.2, if k^*_2 is calculated according to Gardner and Tayeban.[76,77] In Figure 41 the measured curves are compared with the calculated ones, which were evaluated for different h values.

At very low droplet ages, a low h value gives a better fit to the measured curve than the theoretical one. In the medium range of the Fo number the theoretical h = 6.2 gives a good description for

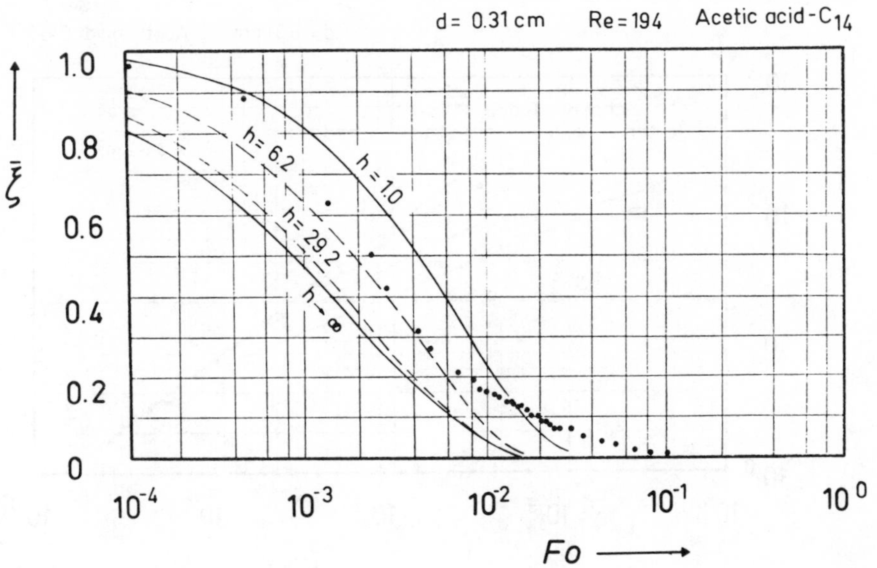

FIGURE 40. Comparison of measured mean solute concentration-Fourier number functions for different Reynolds numbers with the calculated functions of Schmidt-Traub[10] for Re = 1 and Patel and Wellek[26] for Re > 1. Solute: acetic acid-C^{14}, d = 0.31, parameter Re. (From Streicher, R. and Schügerl, K., *Chem. Eng. Sci.*, 32, 23, 1977. With permission.)

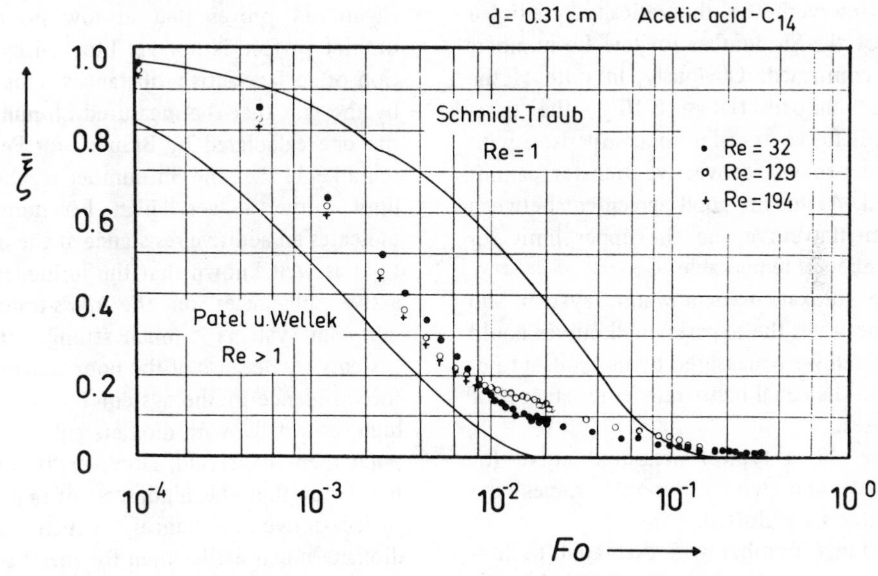

FIGURE 41. Comparison of measured mean solute concentration-Fourier number function with the calculated one according to the quasi-stationary model of Patel and Wellek[26] for different h values. Solute: acetic acid-C^{14}, d = 0.31 cm, Re = 194. (From Streicher, R. and Schügerl, K., *Chem. Eng. Sci.*, 32, 23, 1977. With permission.)

the present system. At high Fo numbers the measured curve levels off earlier than the calculated one, probably due to the adsorptive enrichment of the surface-active substances at the interface of the droplet. The same data are plotted in Figure 42 on a Sh-Fo diagram together with the limiting curves of Brauer[9] and Schmidt-Traub[10] for Re = 1.

Because of the high Re number, the initial Sh numbers are greater than the calculated ones for

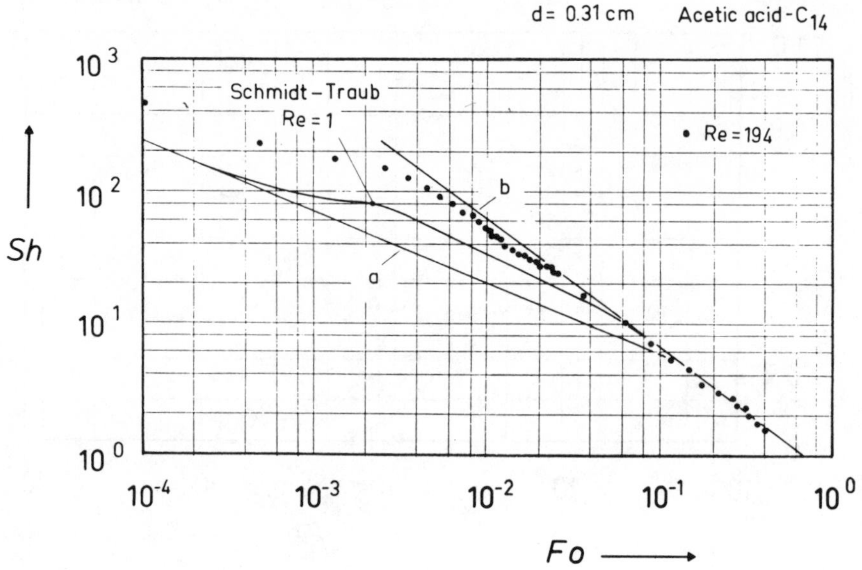

FIGURE 42. Comparison of measured mean Sherwood number-Fourier number function (Re = 194) with calculated one (Re = 1) and with the upper (b) and lower (a) limit curves according to Brauer.[9] Solute: acetic acid-C^{14}, d = 0.31 cm. (From Streicher, R. and Schügerl, K., *Chem. Eng. Sci.*, 32, 23, 1977. With permission.)

Re = 1. However, the theoretically predicted constancy of the Sh number for low Fo numbers cannot be confirmed. Obviously, in spite of the high Peclet numbers (Pe = 6.10^4), the time-dependent diffusive transfer in comparison with the time-independent convective transfer cannot be neglected. Again, the good agreement between the experimental curve and the upper limit for high Fo numbers is remarkable.

For the dioxane-toluene-water system no difference between the experimental curves could be found which were measured by methods a to d. This is due to the equal mass-transfer resistances of the two phases.

In Figure 43 a typical measured curve for dioxane solute and (with different h values) the calculated curves are plotted.

The resistance number was evaluated to h = 1.21. One can recognize from Figure 43 that the measured transfer rate is smaller than the calculated one for h = 1.21. The deviation between the calculated and the measured curves becomes greater with increasing Fo number. Remarkable is the relatively early leveling off of the experimental curve. This behavior should be attributed to the enrichment of the surface-active substances at the interface. This effect begins to act relatively early and gradually becomes dominant.

Also, the behavior of the mean Sh number in Figure 44 proves that at low Fo numbers the droplet surface is not yet blocked by the adsorption of surface-active substances. This is supported by the fact that the measured Sh number is above the one calculated by Brauer[9] for Pe = 10^4. It is remarkable that the Sh number reaches the upper limit curve at very high Fo numbers, which indicates an additive resistance at the interface.

It is well known that the influence of surface-active substances on the mass-transfer rate in nonpolar systems is much stronger than in polar systems.[82] Because of the nonpolar toluene phase, this influence in the system investigated is fairly high, especially with dioxane solute, which is less polar then acetic acid. However, it is necessary to point out that the hindrance of mass transfer by surface-active substances, which occured for dioxane much earlier than for acetic acid solute, is also due to the experimental conditions of the present measurements. The radioactive dioxane used in the present investigations had a greater age than that of the radioactive acetic acid. With increasing age of the radioactive solute or solvent, the chemical compounds in the solution (solute, solvent, and scintillator) gradually decompose due to radiochemical processes occurring in solution. By that, obviously different surface-active compounds are formed which are enriched at the droplet interface with increasing droplet age.

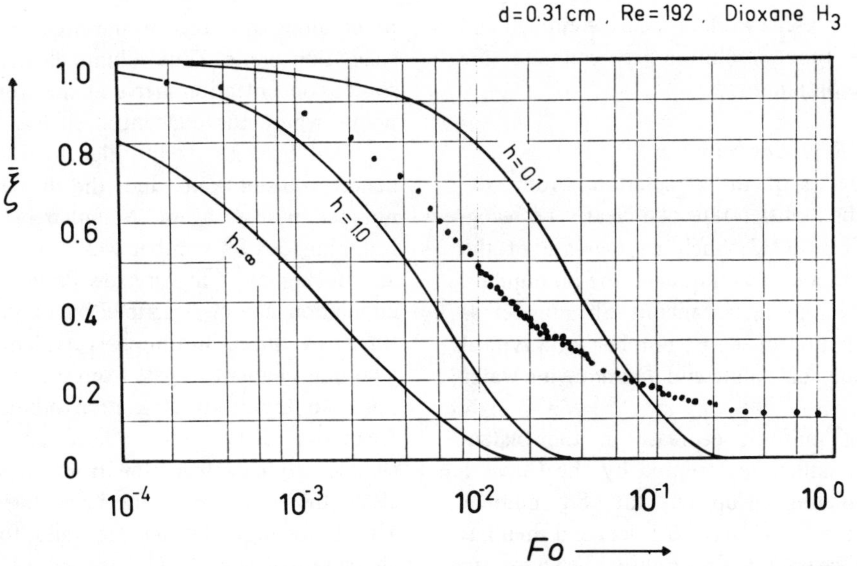

FIGURE 43. Comparison of measured mean solute concentration-Fourier number function with the calculated ones according to Patel and Wellek[26] for different h values. Solute: dioxane-H^3, d = 0.31 cm, Re = 192. (From Streicher, R. and Schügerl, K., *Chem. Eng. Sci.*, 32, 23, 1977. With permission.)

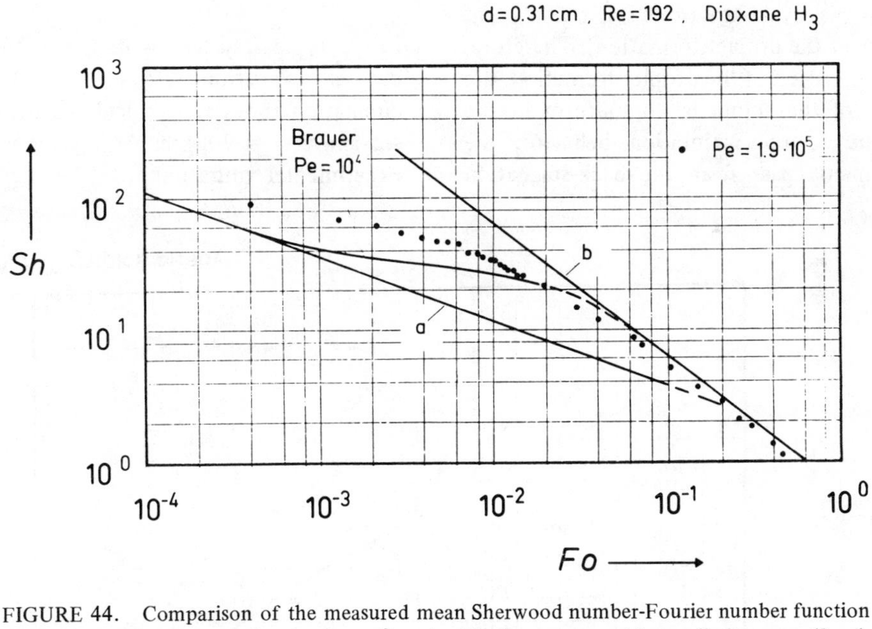

FIGURE 44. Comparison of the measured mean Sherwood number-Fourier number function with calculated one according to Brauer[9] and with the upper and lower limit curves (for d, Re, and solute see Figure 43). (From Streicher, R. and Schügerl, K., *Chem. Eng. Sci.*, 32, 23, 1977. With permission.)

Instantaneous Sherwood Numbers, $Sh = \frac{k_1 d}{D_1}$

If a circulation pattern arises within the droplet, a stepwise change of the instantaneous Sherwood number must appear.[10,78,79] Until now this stepwise change could only be shown by theoretical calculations. An experimental proof was not possible, because the applied methods of the concentration measurements were not accurate enough and they did not have the necessary time resolution to evaluate the differential change of the variation of the solute concentration within the droplet. The modified scintillation technique applied in the present work is accurate enough and has a high time resolution to estimate the instantaneous Sh numbers.

Low Droplet Reynolds Numbers

The influence of the circulation within the droplet on the transfer rate can clearly be recognized from Figure 33. Such an increase of the transfer rate should also influence the Sh number. In Figure 45 the instantaneous Sh number is plotted as function of the Fo number for a typical run with acetic acid solute and a nonmoving water phase.

Instead of uniform decrease in the instantaneous Sh number, represented by the Curve 1 for noncirculating droplets, the Sh number changes at Fo = 5.10^{-3} (t = 6.5 sec) and then has an oscillating character. This unusual behavior can be explained by means of Figure 46.

During the initial droplet formation, the mass transfer occurs only by diffusion, since during the initial lag time no circulation occurs within the droplet. In this lag time the concentration of the solute drops mainly at the front stagnation point (in direction of the droplet formation). Therefore, after the termination of the droplet formation, the distribution of the solute is nonuniform in the droplet. Due to the circulation behavior, the volume elements pass from the back-stagnation point along the axis of the droplet to the front stagnation point. Thus volume elements with high solute concentration arrive at the front stagnation point, where the concentration has already been depleted because of the high local transfer rate; hence transfer rate and the instantaneous Sh number increase again. A similar behavior of the instantaneous Sh number was also found by Johns and Beckmann[78] at very low Peclet numbers. The circulation can be described by two characteristic times: by the mean time Δt_1, which is needed for a volume element to pass from the back-stagnation point to the front stagnation point, and by the mean time Δt_2, which is necessary for a volume element to pass from the front stagnation point along the interface to the back-stagnation point. The following relations are valid for these two characteristic times[10] (Figure 46):

$$\Delta t_1 = \frac{6R}{U}\left(1 + \frac{\mu_1}{\mu_2}\right)$$
$$\Delta t_2 = \frac{8R}{U}\left(1 + \frac{\mu_1}{\mu_2}\right) \qquad (67)$$

For a typical system with a = 0.155 cm and a droplet formation rate U = 0.20 cm/sec the circulation times were calculated to be Δt_1 = 7.4 sec and Δt_2 = 9.8 sec. Δt_1 agrees well with the experimental duration of the lag time. The

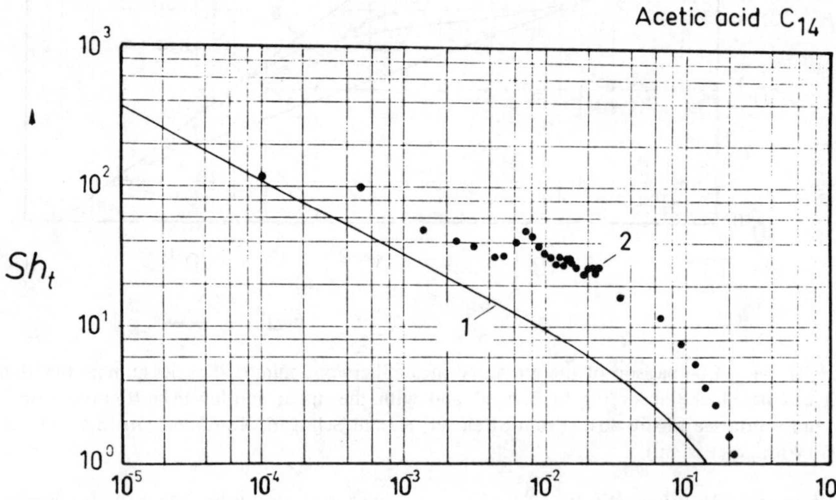

FIGURE 45. Comparison of the measured instantaneous Sherwood number-Fourier number function with the calculated function with (2) and without circulation movement (1) according to Schmidt-Traub.[10,79] Solute: acetic acid-C^{14}, Re ≃ 0. (From Streicher, R. and Schügerl, K., *Chem. Eng. Sci.*, 32, 23, 1977. With permission.)

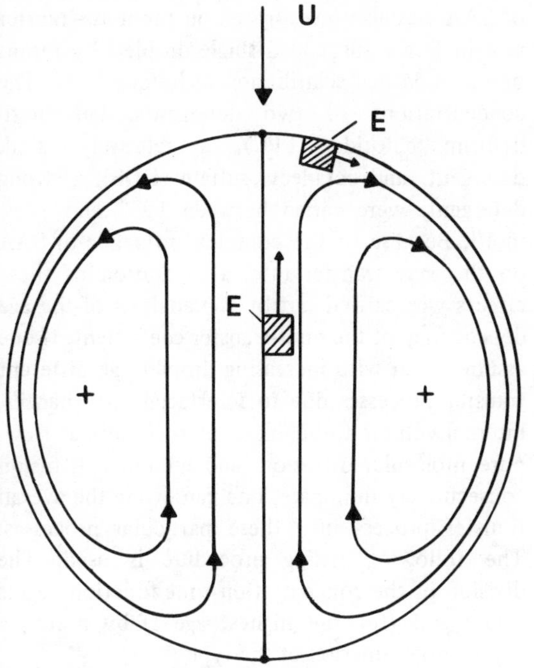

FIGURE 46. Schematic description of the circulation movement in the droplet. VS = front stagnation point; HS = back stagnation point; E = volume element. (From Streicher, R. and Schügerl, K., *Chem. Eng. Sci.*, 32, 23, 1977. With permission.)

instantaneous Sh number changes at the end of this lag time. This agreement between the calculated Δt_1 and measured duration of the lag time proves that the change in the mass transfer rate and the instantaneous Sh number after the lag time is due to circulation within the droplet.

Intermediate Droplet Reynolds Numbers

The change in the instantaneous Sh number in the droplet as function of the transfer time at intermediate droplet Reynolds numbers should indicate whether a laminar movement within the droplet prevails or if there already is a transition to the turbulent range.

The stepwise change in the instantaneous Sh number as function of the Fo number (which is found by Schmidt-Traub[79] for Re = 1 by means of the numerical solution of the nonstationary mass-transfer equation) is due to the circulation within the droplet. The instantaneous Sh numbers measured at intermediate Reynolds numbers show similar stepwise change as function of the Fo number. In Figure 47 a typical plot of the Sh number for Re = 192 is shown.

The circulation times measured from the duration of the lag time for Re = 192 and the

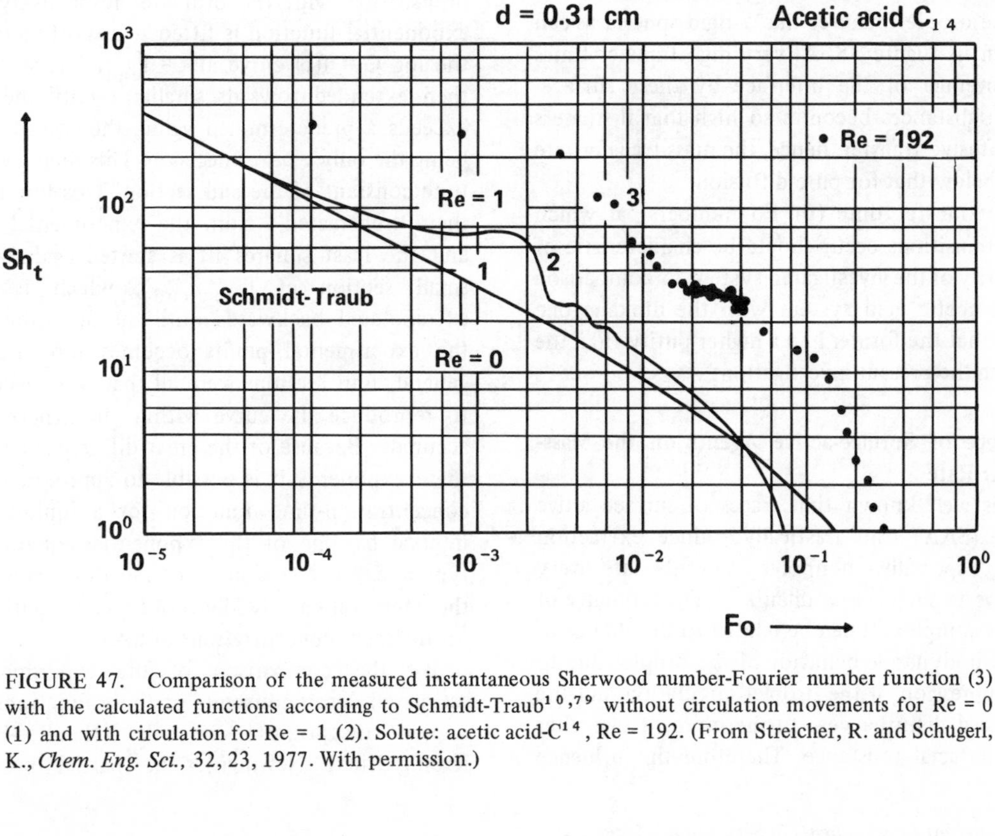

FIGURE 47. Comparison of the measured instantaneous Sherwood number-Fourier number function (3) with the calculated functions according to Schmidt-Traub[10,79] without circulation movements for Re = 0 (1) and with circulation for Re = 1 (2). Solute: acetic acid-C^{14}, Re = 192. (From Streicher, R. and Schügerl, K., *Chem. Eng. Sci.*, 32, 23, 1977. With permission.)

calculated one for Re = 1 do not agree as well as those for the case of the measurements with low Re numbers. Such a difference can be explained by the difference in the Re numbers and/or by the not exactly controlled behavior of the droplet in the initial phase of the mass transfer at higher Re numbers.

The presence of the circulation within the droplet at intermediate Re numbers (e.g., at Re = 192) is remarkable, since in general it is assumed that for Re > 50 no circulation occurs, but there is turbulent mixing within the droplet. Obviously there is a range of the Re number, in which a gradual transition of the laminar circulation movement to the turbulent mixing occurs. In this transition range the circulation must be increasingly overlapped by the stochastical turbulent motion. This transition is probably shifted to higher Re numbers in the presence of surface-active substances. Also in pure water flow with increasing transfer time the surface of the droplet is gradually covered by surface-active substances.

Thus the transition range of the Re number is shifted to such high values that at constant droplet Re numbers the droplet can again come into the laminar range. The turbulent movement (Handlos-Baron) transfers then into the laminar circulation state (Kronig-Brink), and later on this also dies out and the droplet behaves like a rigid sphere, as can be seen in Figure 38. At very high transfer times the coverage of the interface by these surface-active substances becomes so high that it hinders the diffusive transfer, hence, the mass-transfer rate drops below that for pure diffusion.

The transfer time (or Fo numbers) at which these transitions occur should be characteristic of the purity of the investigated system. A comparison of the acetic acid system with the dioxane one shows that the former had a higher purity than the latter in the present investigations.

Influence of Surface-active Agents on the Mass-transfer Rate

It is well known that traces of surface-active agents (SAA) can drastically reduce extraction rates. Especially nonpolar solvents are very sensitive to such contaminants.[82] The influence of SAA is complex. It can be related to the change of the hydrodynamic behavior of the droplet due to the suppression of the droplet circulation and the interfacial disturbances: furthermore, it can alter the interfacial resistance. Therefore the influence of SAA was also investigated on the mass-transfer rate in freely suspended single droplets by means of the modified scintillation technique.[40–42] The concentrations of two detergents, laurylpyridinium chloride (LPC), a relatively weak detergent, and octadecyl sulfate (DDS), a strong detergent, were varied between 10^{-8} and 10^{-3} mol/l. Because of the complex influence of SAA on the mass-transfer rate, a separation of these effects was carried out by the analysis of the age dependency of the mass-transfer coefficient. If one assumes that with increasing droplet age different transfer processes due to interfacial disturbances, internal volume turbulence, internal laminar flow, pure molecular diffusion, and hindered diffusion consecutively dominate, one can divide the overall transfer process into these particular processes. The following fitting procedure is used: The division of the concentration time function begins at its end (for the highest age t) by a simple exponential function of the type

$$a_i \exp(-b_i \cdot t) \tag{68}$$

By transformation of the last part of the function, it can be represented as a linear equation $\ln a_i - b_i t$. The values of b_i and a_i can be calculated from the slope and the point of intersection with the ordinate, respectively. The exponential function is fitted to a short section of the log C = f(t) curve at $t = t_{end}$. The section is then extended towards smaller t until the error exceeds a predetermined value, the size of which being the only *a priori* decision. This then gives the time constant of the end section. This function is then "subtracted" from the experimental curve and the least squares fit is started again with a small section at $t_{(new\ end)}$, which is again extrapolated backwards until the deviation from the experimental points becomes too large. In general, four sections were all that were necessary to reproduce the curve within our experimental accuracy. Because of the great difference between these exponents it is possible to approximate the concentration-time function for a limited time interval by one of the exponential equations of type $a_i \exp(-b_i t)$ alone. The ranges of validity of these terms are nearly identical for each solute, also for different concentrations of SAA.

By the comparison of the experimentally estimated decay constants of these functions with known mass-transfer models (Handlos-Baron, Kronig-Brink, Newman), the partial processes which are controlling the mass transfer in a given age range of the droplet were identified by the corresponding model processes.[41]

The influence of the SAA was then investigated on the decay constant of these consecutive processes. One found a very strong influence of the SAA on the interfacial disturbances which dominated the mass transfer during the droplet age t = 0 to 4 sec and on the internal volume turbulence, which controls the transfer process during the droplet age t = 4 to 16 sec. The presence of SAA apparently has no influence on the interfacial resistance until the droplet age becomes very high.[41] These results are in qualitative agreement with the measurements of Streicher[43] which were discussed in the previous section: furthermore, they agree with several theoretical investigations[30-32,80] and with the measurements of Sawistowski,[68,81] who investigated the influence of SAA on the mass transfer rate during drop formation.

These effects can be explained according to Sawistowski by reduced interfacial tension and interfacial compressibility and increased surface viscosity.[68] The reduced interfacial tension causes a lower dependency of the interfacial phenomena on solute concentration. The reduced interfacial compressibility diminishes surface renewal. The increasing surface viscosity reduces any movement in the interface. Hence only small amount of SAA suffices to eliminate or reduce to interfacial convection.[68]

Since the influence of the SAA on the droplet velocity is higher than on the mass-transfer rate, the relative velocity of the freely suspended single droplet to the continuous phase was measured and calculated by means of the equations of Saville.[32] For pure systems one obtains

$$\frac{U}{U_S} = 1.26$$

as expected. With c = 10^{-8} mol/l LPC the above equation is only approximately applicable. One obtains by means of this equation:

$$\frac{U}{U_S} = 1.08$$

With c = $5 \cdot 10^{-4}$ mol/l Equation 43b can be applied. It gives as expected

$$\frac{U}{U_S} = 1$$

For the intermediate range no relation was given by Saville.

A comparison of the U values measured for the pure system as function of the droplet diameter d is shown in Figure 48. One can recognize that for small d the droplet velocity is higher than the theoretical one with freely circulating droplet

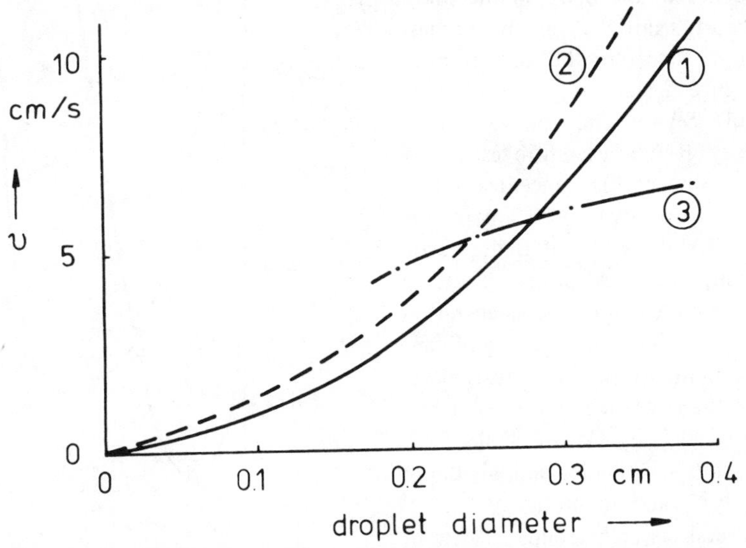

FIGURE 48. Relative droplet velocities U (cm/s) as function of the droplet diameter d(cm). System: toluene-water; (1) calculated according to Stokes[1]; (2) calculated according to Hadamard and Rybczynski[6,7]; (3) measured (Re = 63 to 230).

according to Hadamard and Rybczynski (H-R). With increasing droplet diameter, the measured U grows slower than the theoretical ones; therefore the experimental function U(d) crosses the H-R as well as the Stokes curves. This is probably due to droplet deformation.

Droplet velocities with nonspherical droplets in presence of SAA have not yet been treated theoretically. Therefore the experimental U values cannot be used to estimate the hydrodynamic state of the droplet in the intermediate range (between the Stokes and H-R limits). The experimentally estimated U values for small droplets, which are higher than the upper limit (H-R model) can possibly be explained by the following measuring technique.

To every droplet size belongs a volumetric flow rate of the continuous phase at which the droplet can be kept in a stationary freely suspended state in the test section. With these volumetric flow rates the velocity profiles in the test section were measured without droplet by a constant temperature anemometer as has already been discussed. The measured velocity in the center of the test section at the position of the freely suspended single droplet was considered as its relative velocity, U. It is possible that this velocity profile in the test section was influenced by the presence of the droplet, since the test section droplet diameter ratio amounted to only 6 to 10.

Since the influence of the SAA on the mass-transfer rate is most significant in the earliest period of the mass transfer, the initial mass-transfer rate was investigated as function of the concentration of SAA. The initial solute concentration decay B was therefore estimated and plotted as function of the concentration of LPC and ODC (Figure 49). With increasing concentration of SAA the constant B decreases, passes a minimum, increases again, passes a maximum and at the critical micelle concentration again sharply drops. Similar but less significant change (shallow minimum) in the mass-transfer rate as function of the concentration of SAA was also found in stirred cells by Davies et al.,[83,83a] for single bubbles by Voigtländer and Meiboom both experimentally[84] and theoretically,[85] and for droplets by several research groups (review in Reference 82). Voigtländer and Meiboom explained this behavior by the shape of the σ (c) function. Otto[40-42] related this effect to the change of the amplitude and frequency of the droplet oscillation due to SAA.

Since surface stretch caused by oscillations is nonuniformly distributed, all oscillations produce interfacial turbulence. Therefore, the enhancement of the amplitude of the oscillation, due to diminishing of the resonance frequency of the droplet with increasing concentration of SAA, can also increase the mass transfer. At very high concentrations of SAA micelles are formed at the interface which hinder the mass transfer.

OUTLOOK AND PROBLEMS TO BE SOLVED

In recent years developments on interaction of fluid dynamics, interfacial phenomena, and mass transfer have been fairly rapid. However, our knowledge is far from complete; several problems need to be solved. Some problems of current interest will be discussed below.

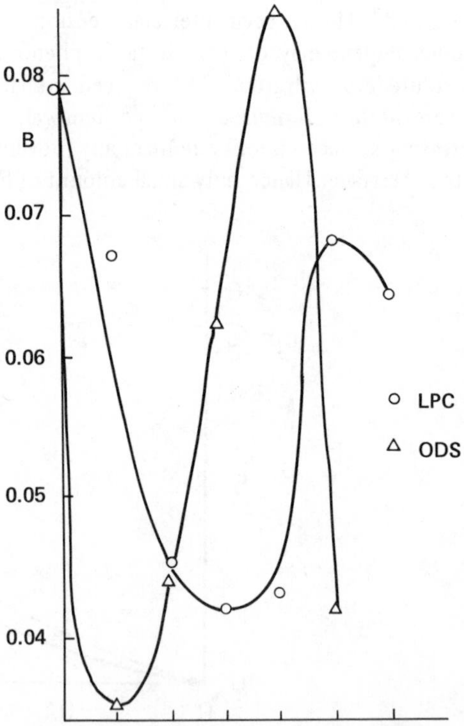

FIGURE 49. Decay constant B as function of the concentration of SAA. (From Otto, W., Streicher, R., and Schügerl, K., *Chem. Eng. Sci.*, 28, 1777, 1973. With permission.)

Theory

Two-phase Film Flow

It is important to find an appropriate mathematical formulation for the mass transfer in the phases near the interface which considers the chemical potential as driving force and the local variation of the activity coefficient near the interface. Furthermore, it is of current interest to find a proper model for the interfacial resistance. The lack of the necessary experimental data delays the development of such models.

Mass Transfer with Single Droplets

Two problems are of current interest:

1. The numerical solution of the non-steady-state mass balance equations (4) of the coupled phases (the resistances of both of the phases are important) for high Reynolds numbers is not available yet. At least two research groups are active in this field.[87,88]

2. The influence of SAA on the transfer rate has not yet been evaluated for the entire range between the Stokes and the Hadamard-Rybczynski limiting states.

Mass Transfer with a Swarm of Droplets

Dynamically interacting effects of surfactant impurities and neighboring particles on the transfer mechanism of momentum and mass transfer in particle swarms have already been considered for low Reynolds numbers.[90-92] It is necessary to extend this analysis to high Reynolds numbers.

Experimental Methods

The greatest problem with the investigation of the interaction of mass exchange with the fluid dynamics and interfacial phenomena is the lack of suitable experimental methods. In this report some new methods were presented. However, further improvement of these methods is necessary. In following the newest developments of these methods, which are already being tested, are discussed.

Two-phase Film Flow

The great disadvantage of Method C for the estimation of the interfacial solute concentration is that a large amount of tritium water with high activity is needed for the measurements. (In the present investigations, 50 l of tritium water with activity of about 1 Ci was used.) Therefore a great effort was put into Method C to improve it.[93]

Figure 50 shows the principle of the improved Methods J, K, and L. Method J corresponds to Method C. However, no tritium water is needed for this method. Instead of tritium, normal water is used in which B^{10} or Li^6 salts are dissolved. If these systems are radiated by neutrons, α-particles are formed by following nuclear reactions:

B^{10} (n, α) Li^7

or

Li^6 (n, α) H^3

One can use as neutron source an Am/Be or Cf^{252} source and the fast neutrons are moderated by D_2O or by graphite. When working with thermal neutrons of a nuclear reactor, no moderation is necessary.

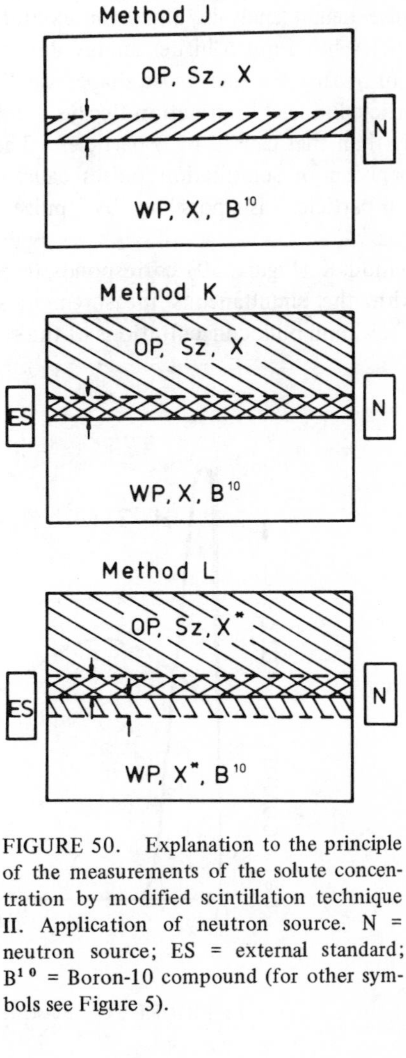

FIGURE 50. Explanation to the principle of the measurements of the solute concentration by modified scintillation technique II. Application of neutron source. N = neutron source; ES = external standard; B^{10} = Boron-10 compound (for other symbols see Figure 5).

The α-rays which are produced by neutrons in the water phase are monoenergetic. They penetrate into the organic solvent phase only to a depth of some microns depending on their energy and there excite the solvent and scintillator molecules. The latter emit light. The interfacial concentration of the solute can be estimated by its quench effect on this light emission, similar to Method C.

Since this measurement by (n, γ) nuclear reactions produces γ-particles, it is necessary to separate the light emission due to α-particles from that related to γ-particles. This is because the quench of the α-excited light emission is characteristic of the interfacial concentration of the solute in the organic solvent phase, and the quench of the γ-excited emission is characteristic of the bulk concentration of the solute in the organic solvent phase. This separation of the light pulses produced by α- and γ-rays is not possible by means of pulse height analysis. Since the excitation by α-particles has a much higher energy density than that for γ-particles, their pulse shapes are different (α-particle-induced scintillation decays much more slowly than that caused by γ-particles.) Therefore a separation of scintillation pulses caused by α- and γ-particles is possible by pulse shape analysis.[93]

Method K (Figure 50) corresponds to Method E, with the simultaneous measurement of the interfacial and bulk concentrations of the solute in the organic solvent phase, but now without applying tritium water. By varying the (n, α) nuclear reaction, the α-energy can also be varied. By that, the concentration of the solute in the thin films with different thicknesses can be measured at the interface. The concentration gradient can be estimated at the interface. Methods J and K have the advantages that they can also be applied in industry, because they do not need open radioactive sources.

Method L (Figure 50) presents a possible further development of Method K. The combination of Method K with tritium-labeled solute x could possibly allow us to measure the solute concentration in the solvent bulk phase as well as at the liquid interface, on both of its sides.

Mass Transfer with Droplets

β-Electrons produced by the disintegration of H^3 and/or C^{14} atoms do not have definite energy, but an energy distribution. Figure 51 shows the energy distribution of the applied β-emitters. In the liquid scintillation technique the height of the light pulses is characteristic for the energy of the β-particles and the number of the pulses for the concentration of the tracer.

By the quench process the pulse height distribution of the scintillation is shifted to lower energy range, as Figure 6 shows for a C^{14} spectrum. In the lower end of the energy spectrum a part of the low-energy pulses are lost by quenching because

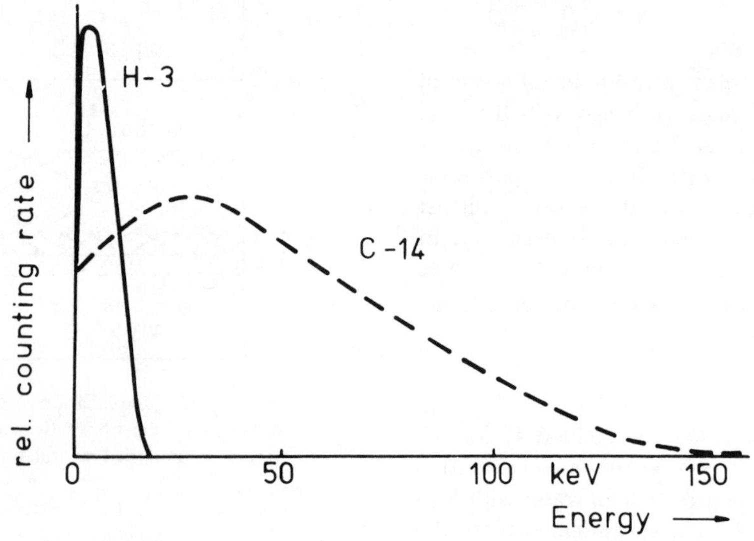

FIGURE 51. Pulse height distribution of β-emitter: H^3 and C^{14}.

they are shifted into the range of the background noise. This background is cut off by the lower discriminator during the measurements.

The optical quench causes a simple shift of the pulse height distribution to lower energies without distorting the distribution. The chemical quench shifts and distorts the distribution. Therefore not only the amount of the quencher but also its distribution in the droplet influences the pulse height distribution of the scintillation emission. According to the channel ratio method one divides the pulse height spectrum into two ranges (Figure 6) and forms the ratio of the counting rate of these two channels. If the solute is uniformly distributed within the droplet this channel ratio method and the simple counting rate method (the sum of the pulses in the two channels) must give the same results.

In fact, they yield the same amount of the solute during the initial phase of the mass-transfer process as long as the solute is uniformly distributed in the droplet. With increasing age of the droplet, a nonuniform concentration profile is gradually built up within the droplet which causes a deviation of the mean concentration evaluated by the channel ratio method from the one calculated by the counting rate method. This difference is due to the nonuniform distribution of the solute in the droplet.[43]

It certainly takes a great amount of very careful work to estimate the dependence of the shape of the pulse height distribution of the light emission from the solute distribution in the droplet. However, by fitting the calculated complete pulse height distribution to the measured one instead of using just the channel ratio method, it is in principle possible to evaluate not only the instantaneous amount of the solute in the droplet but also its spatial distribution by the modified liquid scintillation technique.

SUMMARY

One can conclude that it is possible to investigate the interaction of fluid-dynamical and interfacial processes with mass transfer in freely suspended single droplets and in two-phase film flow by the application of newly developed measuring techniques.

The results show that the mass transfer with droplets is strongly influenced by the fluid dynamics of the droplet and by interfacial phenomena. Because of their interaction with the mass transfer, the exchange rate is a complex function of time. Only non-steady-state models can correctly describe this process. The mechanism of the mass transfer significantly varies with the age of the droplet.

Furthermore, it is possible to measure the concentration of the solute at the liquid interface. The results indicate that the mass-transfer resistance at the interface is not always negligible. By further development of the measuring techniques, it should be possible to gain more information on the interaction of mass transfer with the fluid dynamics and interfacial phenomena.

ACKNOWLEDGMENT

The authors gratefully acknowledge the financial support of the Bundesministerium für Forschung und Technologie (German Federal Ministry of Research and Technology) and Deutsche Forschungsgemeinschaft (German National Science Foundation).

NOMENCLATURE

A	Cross-sectional area of the channel
a	Radius of spherical droplet
a_i	Constant of Equation 68
a_T	Activity coefficient of solute in the toluene phase
B	Decay constant
b	μ_2/μ_1 in channel flow
b_i	Constant of Equation 68
C	Concentration of solute
C_{DT}	Drag coefficient of droplet
D	Molecular diffusivity
d	Droplet diameter

E_m	$\frac{C_{A10} - \overline{C}_{A1}}{C_{A10} - (C_{A1})_{r=a}}$	degree of extraction
G_i	$\frac{wi}{C_{Ti}}$	
g	Acceleration of gravity	
H	$\left(\frac{C_{A1}}{C_{A2}}\right)_{equil.}$	Partition coefficient of the solute A between the phases 1 and 2
h	Interval of the equidistant grid points in 2.1 and 4	
h	Resistance number (Equation 66)	
j	Diffusion flux	
K_1	$\frac{Q_T}{Q_W}$	
K_2	$\frac{K_{w\ eff.}}{k_w}$	
k_T, k_w	Mass-transfer coefficients of toluene and water phases	
k_i^{-1}	Mass-transfer resistance of the interface	
k^*	$\left(\frac{dp_2}{dz}\right)/\left(\frac{dp_1}{dz}\right)$	(Equation 3)
p	Pressure	
Q_T, Q_W	Volumetric flow rate of toluene and water phases in the channel	
n	Integer	
R	Channel radius	
R	Gas constant	
r	Radial coordinate	
t	Time	
U	Relative drop velocity	
u_r, u_θ	Radial velocity along r, tangential velocity along θ in spherical coordinates	
u_0	Velocity at the droplet equator	
$V_{Z,1}, V_{Z2}$	Linear velocities of phases 1 and 2 in the channel along z	
V_m	Mean linear flow velocities in the channel along z	
$w_{(y)}$	Nonuniform linear flow velocity in the channel along z	
X	$\frac{\mu_1}{\mu_2}$	
x	Coordinate in the interface of the two-phase channel flow perpendicular to z	
y	Coordinate in the channel perpendicular to the interface	
Z	Coordinate along the channel axis	
Bi	$\frac{k_2 * 2a}{D_2}$	(droplet) Biot number with regard to the continuous phase
Fo	$\frac{t\,D_1}{a^2}$	(droplet) Fourier number
Pe	$\frac{2a\,U}{D}$	(droplet) Peclet number
Pe	$\frac{w\,R}{D}$	(channel) Peclet number
Re	$\frac{2a\,U}{\nu}$	(droplet) Reynolds number
Re	$\frac{w\,R}{\nu}$	(channel) Reynolds number
Sc	$\frac{\nu}{D}$	Schmidt number

Sh_1	$\frac{2a\,k_1}{D_1}$ (droplet) Sherwood number	
β	$\frac{\partial \sigma}{\partial \Gamma}$	
Γ	Concentration of SAA	
γ	$\frac{\partial \Gamma}{\partial c_S}$	
$\gamma_1, \gamma_2, \gamma_3$	Retardation coefficients in Equation 42	
δ	Thickness of diffusion layer	
ζ_1	$\frac{C_{A1} - HC_{A2}}{C_{A10} - HC_{A2}}$ Dimensionless solute concentration in the droplet	
η	Counting yield	
θ	Angular coordinate of spherical droplet measured counterclockwise from the point of incidence of the flow	
λ	Eigenvalues	
μ	Dynamic viscosity	
ν	Kinematic viscosity	
ρ	Density	
σ	Interfacial tension	
τ	$\frac{A}{2\,Q}$ Contact time	

Indices

1	Droplet phase Lighter phase (channel flow)
2	Continuous phase (droplet flow) Heavier phase (channel flow)
i	Interface
T	Toluene phase
w	Water phase

REFERENCES

1. **Levich, V. B.,** *Physicochemical Hydrodynamics,* Prentice Hall, Englewood Cliffs, N.J., 1962.
2. **Pietsch, G.,** Doctoral thesis, Technical University of Brunswick, 1970.
3. **Schadow, E.,** Doctoral thesis, Technical University of Darmstadt, 1972.
4. **Blaschke, H. G.,** Doctoral thesis, Technical University of Hanover, 1973.
5. **Brunke, U.,** Master's thesis, Technical University of Brunswick, 1975.
6. **Rybczynski, W.,** Uber die fortschreitende Bewegung einer flüssigen Kugel in einem zählen Medium, *Bull. Int. Acad. Sci. Cracovie,* A, 40, 1911.
7. **Hadamard, I.,** Movement permanente lent d'une shere liquide et visqueuse dans une liquide visqueux; *Compts Rendus,* 152, 1735, 1911.
8. **Abdel-Alim, A. A. and Hamielec, A. E.,** A theoretical and experimental investigation of the effect of internal circulation on the drag of spherical droplets falling at terminal velocity in liquid media, *Ind. Eng. Chem. Fundam.,* 14, 306, 1975.
9. **Brauer, H. and Mewes, D.,** *Stoffaustausch einschliesslich chemischer Reaktionen* (Mass exchange inclusive chemical reaction), Verlag Sauerländer, Aarau/Frankfurt, 1971.
10. **Schmidt-Traub, H.,** Instationärer Stofftransport an festen Partikeln, Tropfen und Blasen (Nonstationary mass exchange on solid particles, droplets and bubbles), DFG Research Rep. Br 260/30, 1973.
11. **Weber, M. E.,** Mass transfer from spherical drops at high Reynolds numbers, *Ind. Eng. Chem. Fundam.,* 14, 365, 1975.

12. **Harper, J. F. and Moore, D. W.,** The motion of a spherical liquid drop at high Reynolds numbers, *J. Fluid Mech.,* 32, 367, 1968.
13. **Brounshtein, B. I. and Fishbein, G. A.,** Study of the non-steady state transfer mechanism inside a moving drop and the end effect, *Theor. Found. Chem. Eng. U.S.S.R.,* 8(2), 186, 1974; *Teorteicheskie Osnovy Khimicheskoi Tekhnologiee,* 8, 196, 1974.
14. **Skelland, A. H. P.,** *Diffusional Mass Transfer,* John Wiley & Sons, New York, 1974.
15. **Ruckenstein, E.,** Mass transfer between a single drop and a continuous phase, *Int. J. Heat Mass Transfer,* 10, 1785, 1967.
16. **Newman, A. B.,** The drying of porous solids, *Trans. Am. Inst. Chem. Eng.,* 27, 310, 1931.
17. **Treybal, R. E.,** *Liquid-Extraction,* 2nd ed., McGraw Hill, New York, 1963.
18. **Kronig, R. and Brink, J. L.,** On the theory of extraction from falling droplets, *Appl. Sci. Res.,* 12, 142, 1950.
19. **Heertjes, P. M., Holve, W. A., and Talsma, H.,** Mass transfer between isobutanol and water in spray-column, *Chem. Eng. Sci.,* 3, 122, 1954.
20. **Handlos, A. E. and Baron, T.,** Mass and heat transfer from drops in liquid-liquid-extraction, *AIChE J.,* 3, 127, 1957.
21. **Wellek, R. and Skelland, A. H.,** Extraction with single turbulent droplets, *AIChE J.,* 11, 557, 1965.
22. **Orlander, D. R.,** The Handlos-Baron drop extraction model, *AIChE J.,* 12, 1018, 1966.
23. **Gröber, H.,** *Die Erwärmung und Abkühlung einfacher geometrischer Körper* (the warm-up and cool-down of simple geometrical bodies), *Z. Ver. Dtsch. Ing.,* 69, 705, 1925.
24. **Gröber, H., Erk, S., and Grigull, U.,** *Grundgesetze der Wärmeübertragung* (Fundamental Laws of Heat Transmission), Springer-Verlag, Berlin, 1963.
25. **Elzinga, E. R., Jr. and Banchero, J. T.,** Film coefficients for heat transfer to liquid drops, *Chem. Eng. Prog. Symp. Ser.,* 29, 149, 1959.
26. **Patel, J. M. and Wellek, R. M.,** Handlos and Baron model: Short contact times, *AIChE J.,* 13, 384, 1967.
27. **Heertjes, P. M. and De Nie, L. H.,** Mass transfer to drops, in *Recent Advances in Liquid-Liquid Extraction,* Hanson, C., Ed., Pergamon Press, Oxford, 1971, 367.
28. **Davis, R. E. and Acrivos, A.,** The influence of surfactants on the creeping motion of bubbles, *Chem. Eng. Sci.,* 21, 681, 1966.
29. **Boussinesqu, J.,** *J. Comp. Rend.,* 156, 983, and 1035, 1913; *Ann. Chim. Phys.,* 29, 349, 357, and 364, 1913.
30. **Savic, P.,** Circulation and distortion of liquid drops falling through a viscous medium, Mech. Eng. Rep. MT-22, National Research Council of Canada, 1953.
31. **Griffith, R. M.,** The effect of surfactants on the terminal velocity of drops and bubbles, *Chem. Eng. Sci.,* 17, 1057, 1962.
32. **Saville, D. A.,** The effects of interfacial tension gradients on the motion of drops and bubbles, *The Chem. Eng. Journal,* 5, 251, 1973.
33. **Brunke, U.,** Doctoral thesis, Technical University of Hanover, 1976.
34. **Ward, A. F. H. and Brooks, H.,** Diffusion across interfaces, *Trans. Faraday Soc.,* 48, 1124, 1952.
35. **Davies, J. T. and Wiggill, J. B.,** Diffusion across the oil/water interface, *Proc. R. Soc. London Ser. A,* 255, 277, 1969.
36. **Blaschke, H. G. and Shügerl, K.,** A novel method for the investigations of mass transfer across the interface of moving liquids, 77th National Mtg. Am. Inst. Chem. Engrs., Pittsburgh, 1974.
37. **Chandrasekhar, S. and Hoelscher, H. E.,** Mass transfer studies across liquid/liquid interfaces (use of analytical ultracentrifuge), *AIChE J.,* 21, 103, 1975.
38. **Mensing, W.,** Doctoral thesis, Technical University of Hanover, 1968.
39. **Mensing, W. and Schügerl, K.,** Mass exchange measurements on freely suspended single droplets, Part I. Measuring technique, *Chem. Ing. Tech.,* 12, 837, 1970; Part II. Results, *Chem. Ing. Tech.,* 12, 991, 1970.
40. **Otto, W.,** Doctoral thesis, Technical University of Brunswick, 1971.
41. **Otto, W. and Schügerl, K.,** Influence of surface active substances on mass exchange across the interface liquid-liquid, *Chem. Ing. Tech.,* 45, 563, 1973.
42. **Otto, W., Streicher, R. and Schügerl, K.,** Influence of surface active agents on the mass transfer across liquid-liquid interfaces. I. Dioxane-toluene water system, *Chem. Eng. Sci.,* 28, 1777, 1973.
43. **Streicher, R.,** Doctoral thesis, Technical University of Hanover, 1975.
44. **Colburn, A. P. and Welsh, D. G.,** Experimental study of individual transfer resistance in countercurrent liquid-liquid extraction, *Trans. Am. Inst. Chem. Eng.,* 38, 179, 1942.
45. **Licht, W. and Conway, J. B.,** Mechanism of solute transfer in spray towers, *Ind. Eng. Chem.,* 62, 1151, 1950.
45a. **Licht, W. and Pansing, F.,** Solute transfer from single drops in liquid-liquid extractions, *Ind. Eng. Chem.,* 45, 1885, 1953.
46. **Garner, F. H. and Skelland, A. H. P.,** Mechanism of solute transfer from droplets, *Ind. Eng. Chem.,* 46, 1255, 1954.
47. **Johnson, A. I. and Hamielec, A. E.,** Mass transfer inside drops, *Am. Inst. Chem. Eng. J.,* 6, 145, 1960.
48. **Nitsch, W.,** Mass transfer between liquid phases, *DECHEMA Monogr.,* 55, 143, 1965.
49. **von Berg, R.-I. and Henkel, W. M.,** Simultaneous heat and mass transfer in single drop liquid-liquid extractions, Int. Solv. Extraction Conf. London, 1971, p. 130.

50. **Bayadzhiev, L., Elenkov, D., and Kyuchukov, G.,** On liquid-liquid mass transfer inside drops in a turbulent flow field, *Can. J. Chem. Eng.*, 47, 42, 1969.
51. **Muntean, O., Dimian, A., and Hristescu, E.,** Mass transfer from drops, An experimental method, *Chem. Eng. Sci.*, 26, 1953, 1971.
51a. **Dimian, A. and Muntean, O.,** Transfer de masade la o picatura la faza continua in sisteme lichid-lichid, *Rev. Chim.* Bucharest), 23, 369, 1972.
52. **Lode, T. and Heideger, W.,** Single drop mass transfer augumented by interfacial instability, *Chem. Eng. Sci.*, 25, 1081, 1970.
53. **Yamir, A. and Taitel, Y.,** Adsorption mass transfer in the presence of axial diffusion in convective mass transfer, *Chem. Eng. Sci.*, 28, 1921, 1973.
54. **Beek, W. J. and Bakker, C. A. P.,** Mass transfer with a moving interface, *Appl. Sci. Res.*, A 10, 241, 1961.
55. **Byers, C. H. and King, J. C.,** Gas liquid mass transfer with a tangentially moving interface, *AIChE J.*, 13, 629, 1967.
56. **Tang, Y. P. and Himmelblau, D. M.,** Interphase mass transfer for laminar cocurrent flow of carbon dioxide and water between parallel plates, *AIChE J.*, 9, 630, 1963.
57. **Apelblatt, A. and Katchalsky, A.,** Mass transfer with moving interface, *Int. J. Heat Mass Transfer,* 11, 1053, 1968.
58. **Zogg, M.,** Der Stoffübergang an der freien Grenzfläche Laminarer Rieselfilme (Mass transfer on the free surface of laminar falling films), *Verfahrenstechnik,* 5, 328, 1971.
59. **Rotem, Z. and Neilson, J. E.,** Exact solution for diffusion to flow down an incline, *Can. J. Chem. Eng.*, 47, 341, 1969.
60. **Bojadjev, C. et al.,** Approximate equations of liquid phase mass transfer coefficients for falling films, *Chem. Eng. Sci.*, 29, 2127, 1974.
61. **Tamir, A. and Taitel, Y.,** Diffusion to flow down an incline with surface resistance, *Chem. Eng. Sci.*, 20, 799, 1971.
62. **Batschelet, E. and Grün, F.,** Numerische Behandlung der Diffusionsgleichung mit Konvektionsterm (Numerical treatment of the diffusion equation with convective term), *Z. Angew. Math. Phys.*, 7, 113, 1958.
63. **Crank, A.,** *The Mathematics of Diffusions,* Oxford University Press, 1975.
64. **Zurmühl, R.,** *Matrizen,* Springer-Verlag, Berlin, 1964.
65. **Birks, J. B.,** *The Theory and Practice of Scintillation Counting,* Pergamon Press, Oxford, 1967.
66. **Kristaller, G.,** Theoretische Aspekte der Flüssigkeitsszintillationsmesstechnik (Theoretical aspects of liquid scintillation measurement technique), 1. Symp. Nuclear Radiation Measurement Technique Munich, 1966.
67. **Koelzer, W.,** Grundlagen der Flüssigkeitsszintillationsmesstechnik (Foundations of liquid scintillation measurement technique), Course V 376, School of Nucleartechnique, Karlsruhe, 1970.
68. **Sawistowski, H.,** Interfacial phenomena, in *Recent Advances in Liquid-Liquid Extraction,* Hanson, C., Ed., Pergamon Press, Oxford, 1971, 293.
69. **Sternling, C. V. and Scriven, L. E.,** Interfacial turbulence. Hydrodynamic instability and the Marangoni effect, *AIChE J.*, 5, 514, 1959.
70. **Meyhack, U.,** Master's thesis, Technical University of Hanover, 1975.
71. **Vauck, W. and Müller, H.,** *Grundoperationen chemischer Verfahrenstechnik* (Unit operations), 4th ed., Steinkopf, Dresden, 1974.
72. **Shimbashi, T. and Shiba, T.,** The mass transfer rate through the liquid-liquid interface, Parts I, II, and III, *Bull. Chem. Soc. Jpn.*, 38, 572, 1965.
73. **Nitsch, W. and Matschke, K.,** Einfluss des Grenzflächenwiderstandes auf die Stoffübertragung zwischen flüssigen Phasen bei verschiedenen Strömungszuständen (Influence of the interfacial resistance on the mass exchange between two liquid phases at different flow conditions), *Chem. Ing. Tech.*, 40, 625, 1968.
74. **Nitsch, W.,** Schnelle Ionenreaktionen an der Grenzfläche flüssiger Phasen (Rapid ion reactions at the interface of liquid phases), *Chem. Ing. Tech.*, 42, 1229, 1970.
75. **Brun, B. and Gaufres, R.,** Mise en evidence d'une association eau-pyridine par mesure des coefficients propre de l'eau et de lay pyridine, *C.R. Acad. Sci.*, 260, 3636, 1965.
76. **Skelland, A. H. and Wellek, R. M.,** Resistance to mass transfer inside droplets, *AIChE J.*, 10, 491, 1964.
77. **Gardner, F. H. and Trayeban, M.,** The importance of the wake in mass transfer from both continuous and dispersed phase systems, Parts I and II, *An. R. Soc. Esp. Fis. Quim. Ser. B* (Madrid), 56, 479, 1960.
78. **Johns, L. E. and Beckmann, R. B.,** Mechanism of dispersed-phase mass transfer in viscous-single-drop extraction systems, *AIChE J.*, 12, 10, 1966.
79. **Schmidt-Traub, H.,** Unsteady mass transfer between fluid and a single sphere at Reynolds numbers $Re < 1$, GVC/AIChE Joint Meeting, Munich, 1964, G6-4.
80. **Berg, J. G. and Acrivos, A.,** The effect of surface active agents on convection cells induced by surface tension, *Chem. Eng. Sci.*, 20, 737, 1965.
81. **Sawistowski, H. and James, B. R.,** Einfluss von Oberflächenerscheinungen auf die Stoffdurchgangszahlen bei der Flüssing-Flüssig-Extraktion (Influence of interfacial phenomena on the mass transfer coefficient at liquid-liquid extraction), *Chem. Ing. Tech.*, 35, 175, 1963.
82. **Davies, J. T.,** Mass transfer and Interfacial Phenomena, in *Advances in Chemical Engineering,* Vol. 4, Drew, T. B., Hooper, J. W., Jr., and Vermeulen, T., Eds. Academic Press, New York, 1963, 3.

83. **Davies, J. T. and Mayers, G. R. A.,** The effect of interfacial films on mass transfer rates in liquid-liquid extraction, *Chem. Eng. Sci.,* 16, 55, 1961.

83a. **Mayers, G. R. A.,** The correlation of individual film coefficients on mass transfer in stirred cells, *Chem. Eng. Sci.,* 16, 69, 1961.

84. **Voigtländer, J. G. and Meyboom, F. W.,** A new method for measuring the transfer of oxygen in liquids. Measurements of oxygen transfer from bubbles in water and in water + 1-butanol, *Chem. Eng. Sci.,* 29, 799, 1974.

85. **Vogtländer, J. G. and Meyboom, F. W.,** Influence of surface active agents on the mass transfer from gas bubbles in a liquid, II, **Chem. Eng. Sci.,** 29, 949, 1974.

86. **Davies, J. T. and Rideal, E. K.,** *Interfacial Phenomena,* 2nd ed., Academic Press, New York, 1963.

87. **Brauer, H.,** Technical University Berlin West, personal communication.

88. **Krylov, V. S.,** Institute of Electrochemistry, Academy of Sciences of the U.S.S.R., Moskow, personal communication.

89. **Harada, M., Imamura, T., Fuyiyoshi, K., and Eguchi, W.,** Interfacial resistance in liquid-liquid mass transfer, *J. Chem. Eng. Jpn.,* 8, 233, 1975.

90. **Gal-or, B. and Hoelscher, H. E.,** A mathematical treatment of the effect of particle size distribution on mass transfer in dispersions, *AIChE J.,* 12, 499, 1966.

91. **Gal-or, B.,** On motion of bubbles and drops, *Can. J. Chem. Eng.,* 48, 526, 1970.

92. **Yaron, I. and Gal-or, B.,** Relative velocities and pressure drops in clouds of drops, bubbles or solid particles, *AIChE J.,* 17, 1064, 1974.

93. **Greger, U.,** Doctoral thesis, Technical University of Hanover, 1976.

94. **Sinfelt, J. H. and Drickamer, H. G.,** Resistance in a liquid-liquid interface. III. The effect of molecular properties, *J. Chem. Phys.,* 23, 1096, 1955.

95. **Grov, Ø., Otto, W., and Schügerl, K.,** Behaviour of freely suspended droplets shortly after their formation, *Chem. Eng. Sci.,* 24, 1397, 1969.

96. **Streicher, R. and Schügerl, K.,** Interchange of fluid mechanics and mass exchange in droplets, *Chem. Eng. Sci.,* 32, 23, 1977.

REMOVAL OF SALT FROM WATER BY THERMAL CYCLING OF ION-EXCHANGE RESINS

T. T. Shih and R. L. Pigford

TABLE OF CONTENTS

INTRODUCTION

Removal of salt from water can be achieved by several methods.[1,2] These can be classified into two groups. The first includes the processes that separate water from the solution, such as distillation, evaporation, crystallization, freezing, and reverse osmosis. The second group is composed of the processes that separate salt from the solution, such as electrodialysis, adsorption, liquid extraction, ion-exchange, and biological systems. The processes in the second group appear to have a theoretical advantage over those in the first category, since the quantities of salt that need to be processed are very much smaller than the quantities of water. On the other hand, conventional ion-exchange,[3-5] although basically an attractive process, has not been used widely for this purpose. For every equivalent of salt removed from the water, at least one equivalent of regenerant chemical must be used and most likely discarded into the environment. These facts make conventional ion-exchange processes economically and ecologically less attractive than evaporation, reverse osmosis,[6,26-28] and freezing.[7,29-31] In recent years, therefore, attention has been given to thermally regenerated ion-exchange resins[8] and regenerant recycle systems.[9]

In attempting to describe a new, thermally driven desalination process which requires less energy than conventional processes, this article concentrates on a separation process called Cycling Zone Adsorption (CZA), which was invented by Pigford et al.[10] The basis of the process is the cyclic adsorption and desorption of one or more solutes using an ion-exchange resin as a solid adsorbent. The result is an alternating solute-depleted and solute-enriched effluent phase.

Such a process has important long-term fundamental advantages, not all of which are possessed by other desalination processes. It avoids phase changes. Moreover, waste heat from other processes operating at higher temperature can be used. It requires no chemical regeneration or extreme temperature and pressure conditions. The availability of the large interfacial area between the resin particles and water, and the use of energy in its cheaper form – low-grade sensible heat – also favor reduced operating costs.

The knowledge obtained from this study is not only specific for desalination, but is widely applicable to separation processes involving thermally regenerable ion-exchange resins and solid adsorbents.

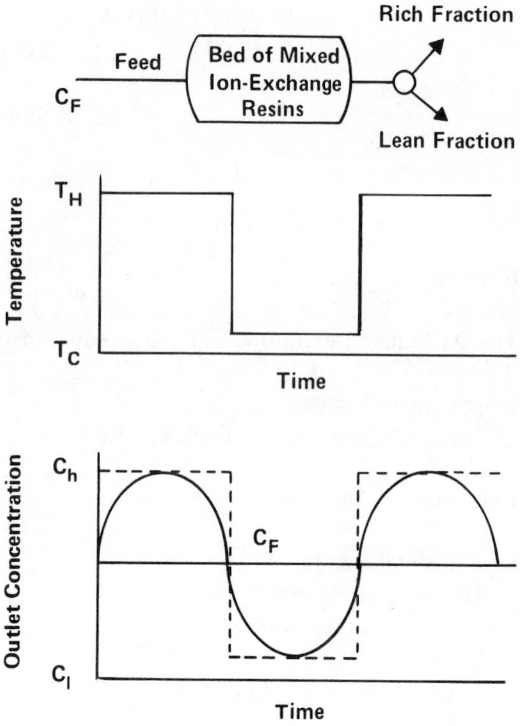

FIGURE 1. Sketch of single-stage Cycling Zone Adsorber.

THE QUALITATIVE DESCRIPTION OF CYCLING ZONE ADSORPTION

The ability of certain solids to adsorb substances preferentially from gas and liquid streams onto their surfaces has led to their use in widely varying separation and purification processes.[11,12,32] The mechanisms governing such separation techniques are well understood. However, use of continuous adsorption processes is sometimes limited by the required regeneration of the adsorbent, which is needed after it has become saturated with the feed. Ordinarily this can be accomplished either by chemical regeneration in place or by circulating the adsorbent particles continuously to a separate regenerator. The Cycling Zone Adsorption process, hereafter called "CZA," is a fundamental improvement upon the ordinary process of adsorption. It is possible in the CZA process to operate a packed column in a continuous fashion without the mechanical difficulties involved in the movement of the solid adsorbent particles.

Consider a fixed bed process as is shown in Figure 1. A fluid having a constant solute concentration is passed through a fixed bed of solid particles. The fluid and solid system can be shifted between two equilibrium distribution relationships by a shift in some thermodynamic potential, such as temperature, pressure, concentration of a third species, or electric or magnetic fields. Only changes in temperature are considered in this study. The system fluctuates between cold, T_C, and hot, T_H.

Suppose the system is initially in equilibrium at T_C. The solid particles are saturated with the solute in the feed and the effluent concentration is the same as that of the feed. If the temperature of the bed is raised to T_H, solute that was previously held on the solid will be expelled into the fluid as it passes by. The effluent will have a concentration above that of the feed until the particles and fluid come to equilibrium at the higher temperature. However, just before the feed concentration begins to emerge, if the temperature of the bed is decreased to the low temperature, T_C, the solid takes up solute from the fluid and temporarily holds it on the solid. During this period the effluent concentration is lower than that of the feed. Switching again to the high temperature just before feed concentration begins to emerge, the cycle is repeated. The result is a cyclically repeating wave of fluid concentration in the

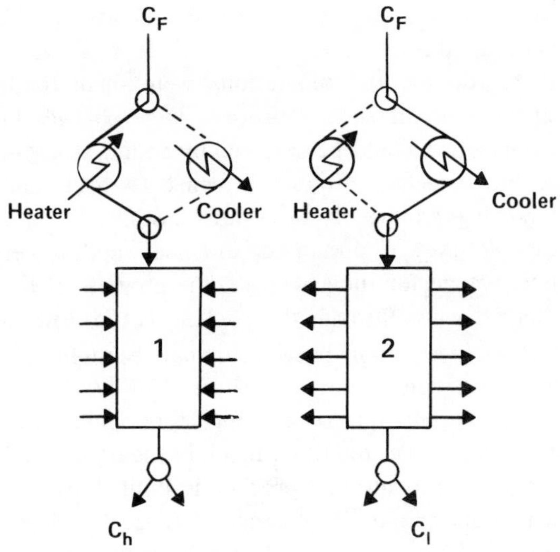

FIGURE 2. Single-stage operation of Cycling Zone Adsorber for continuous production.

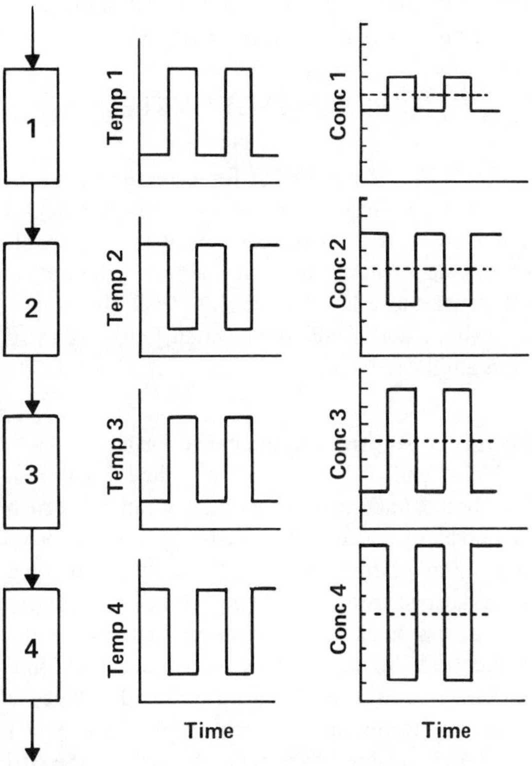

FIGURE 3. Multiple-zone operation of Cycling Zone Adsorber.

effluent from the bed, the stream consisting of alternating portions of enriched and depleted solution. These portions can be collected separately.

In an ideal CZA process, a square wave temperature change in the bed will produce a square concentration wave in the effluent as is shown by the dotted line of Figure 1. However, owing to the finite mass transfer resistance in the particles and to curvature in the phase equilibrium curve, the concentration wave is somewhat distorted. If twin parallel columns are used, one exactly one half of a temperature cycle out of phase with the other, as shown in Figure 2, separation can be achieved by periodically switching the outlet of each column. The result is a continuous production of two streams of different concentrations, one higher and one lower than that of the feed.

If the stream of varying composition from one column is sent to the second column, the separation can be further increased. An example showing four stages of CZA process is displayed in Figure 3. Each stage operates one half thermal cycle out of phase with the previous stage. The hot portion of fluid that leaves the first stage will experience high temperature in all succeeding beds, whereas that portion which is exposed to the cold wave in the first bed will be exposed to low temperatures in each successive bed. The solute will be removed from the cold fluid and will be added to the hot portion of the fluid in the following stages. Such a simplified series of zones should then be capable of producing very large separations of a binary liquid feed from single-zone separations. When applied to the removal of salt from water the process is theoretically capable of reducing the salt concentrations in the cold portion of the effluent stream nearly to zero while increasing the concentration in the hot portion nearly to double the feed concentration. The effluent concentration profiles for such an operation are also shown in Figure 3.

The key to the CZA process lies in the correct timing of the temperature changes of the solid adsorbent particles. There is an optimum switching time which depends on the time of passage of a concentration wave through the bed.

The optimum cycle time can be found theoretically if a simplified mathematic model is used. If the local equilibrium exists between the solid particles and the fluid, the optimum cycle time can be represented by the equation:[33]

$$t = \frac{1 + \frac{\rho_p}{\alpha}\left(\frac{\partial q^*}{\partial C}\right)}{v} L \tag{1}$$

It shows that in a fixed-bed column of constant physical properties the optimum switching time depends upon the length of the column, the flow rate, and the slope of the equilibrium curve.

Separations in CZA are dependent upon the concentration of fluid in the bed at the time of temperature change. The separations are therefore strongly affected by the way in which the temperature shifts are imposed. Detailed description of the CZA operation modes has been given elsewhere.[13,16] Only a brief summary is given in the following.

Standing Wave Mode

The temperature of the entire bed is shifted uniformly over its length. This requires heat transfer through the wall of the column, which is not very effective, and can only be achieved by tolerating a radial thermal gradient in the bed.

Traveling Wave Mode

The thermal wave travels longitudinally through the bed, which is insulated so that the only source of heat is the feed solution itself. The temperature of the feed is set by a heat exchanger just before the bed. The velocity of the thermal wave is determined by the fluid velocity, the ratio of the fluid and solid volumes, and the heat capacities of both phases.

There are difficulties encountered in the CZA operation. No real system permits very rapid heat exchange due to the finite values of heat transfer rates. As a result the thermal wave is attenuated and spreads as it travels through the bed. The entire column of adsorbent is not exposed to the maximum temperature shift. The separation capacity is therefore not fully utilized. Similar to other adsorption processes, the mass-transfer rates are usually low, especially in the case of an intraparticle diffusion-controlled system. The very slow fluid flow or space velocities that apparently are necessary to obtain a full response of the concentration changes restrict throughput rates. Also, nearly complete separation is more difficult to obtain. Longitudinal mixing and diffusion decrease the thermal and concentration wave amplitudes. This effect is even more evident at low fluid flow rates. However, the CZA process operates without flow reversal, as opposed to "parametric pumping."[34-37] Since no batch-type regeneration of the adsorbent is required, particle removal and possible sweep fluids are not needed.

The CZA process has been demonstrated successfully at a laboratory scale for gas-solid[14] and liquid-solid systems.[13,15,17] It was found that although the separations were small for a single zone in such a process, large changes in composition could be obtained by adding stages in series, recycling product streams to feed, and arranging groups of stages into cascades.[15] In a gas-solid system, due to the low heat capacity per unit volume of the gas phase, the progress of the thermal wave through the packing is too slow to give the best timing relationship between temperature and concentration changes. However, mass transfer occurs quickly and high throughput rates are possible. On the other hand, in the liquid-solid system, although the process is limited by the mass-transfer rate, heat transfer between fluid and solid is more rapid and a temperature wave moves through the bed more rapidly than a concentration wave, which is essential to the CZA process. Because of the wide variety of solid adsorbents and ion-exchange resins, many applications of such cyclic processing methods are possible.

ION-EXCHANGE SYSTEM

The basic requirements for economical use of ion-exchange resins for desalination of brackish water are that the exchanger must (a) be capable of being regenerated at almost theoretical efficiencies at a low temperature level, (b) operate at high capacity, and (c) have sufficient rates of mass and heat exchange.

Thermally Sensitive Ion-Exchange Resin

Weiss and others[18-21,40,45] have indicated that homofunctional electrolytic weak acids such as polyacrylic acid and weak bases such as epoxy amine can perform well in thermally regenerated ion-exchange processes. They have carried out extensive studies of the chemical structure of the acidic and basic components of a mixed ion-exchange resin bed. They have also developed a predictive technique[21] which enables us to select the best possible resin pairs based on the pH titration curve of the individual ion-exchange resins. The technique is based on the assumption that despite slow mass transfer in the process, fluid-solid equilibrium is closely achieved at all times during operation.

The following equation expresses the equilibrium between a mixed bed of resins and an aqueous solution of sodium chloride.

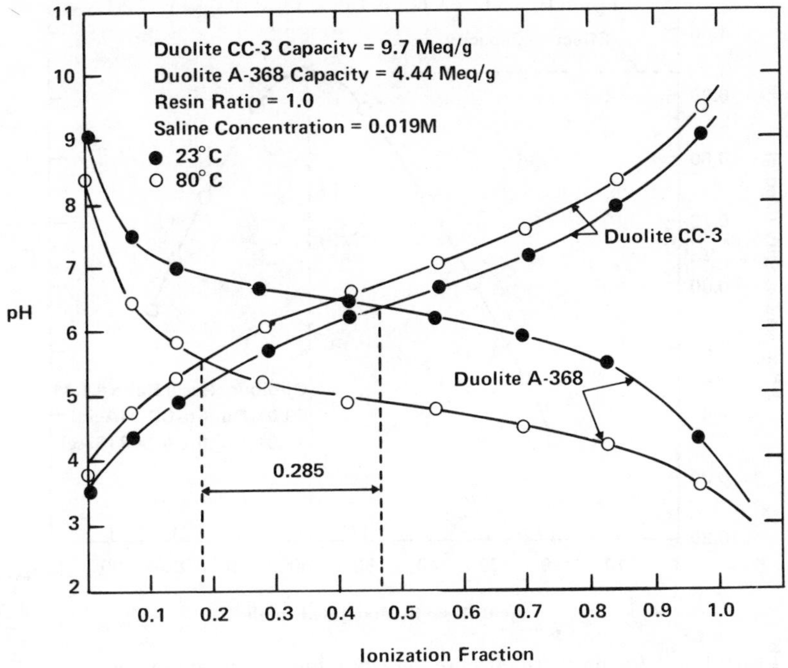

FIGURE 4. A matching of the titration curves for Duolite® CC-3 and Duolite A-368.

$$\overline{RCOOH} + \overline{R_3N} + Na^+ + Cl^- \rightleftharpoons \overline{RCOO^- Na^+} + \overline{R_3NH^+Cl^-} \quad (2)$$

The salt is adsorbed by the resins as a result of transfer of hydrogen ions from the acid to the base resin. This equilibrium is temperature dependent. There is a reduction in the number of exchange sites on both the acidic and basic resins upon heating and therefore salt is released into the solution. Conversely, salt is adsorbed onto the resin on cooling.

The equilibrium titration curves were obtained for several candidate acidic and basic resins at low and high temperature. Figure 4 is an example of such data from Light.[22] It shows the pH of the solution phase versus the fraction of resin neutralized when each type of resin is titrated separately. Since in the flow system two kinds of resins will be exposed to fluid having the same pH, the best resin combination would have the points on intersection of the curves at the two temperatures be as far apart as possible to obtain the maximum thermal effect. Thus the largest possible change in equilibrium salt adsorption on heating (the maximum effective capacity) was determined for each resin pair at the optimum resin ratio.

Figure 5 shows the variation of resin ratio to the capacity of a mixed-bed resin. It was concluded that Duolite® CC-3 (weak acid) and Duolite A-368 (weak base) resins were the best resin pair that Light studied. The optimum resin ratio for this particular resin pair was found to be 1.44 mol of CC-3 (acid) resin per mole of A-368 (base) resin, or 0.66 g CC-3 per gram of A-368. The maximum effective capacity is 0.937 meq/g at the optimum pH of 6.25 at 23°C. Both Duolite CC-3 and A-368 are manufactured by the Diamond Shamrock Chemical Company in Redwood City, California.

Latty[16] studied the rates of salt uptake and release by this particular mixed resin system. He concluded that the reaction of the weak acid resin particles is rate limiting for both salt uptake and release.

The adsorption rates exhibited by these resin beads are much too slow for satisfactory operation of the CZA process. The success of this process therefore depends primarily upon finding a way to improve mass-transfer rates of ions inside the particles. Since the rates of normal-size resin are low, resin beads of about 10 μm in diameter would have to be used for satisfactory resin utilization in an ion-exchange column. However, such microbeads cannot be used in a practical operation of

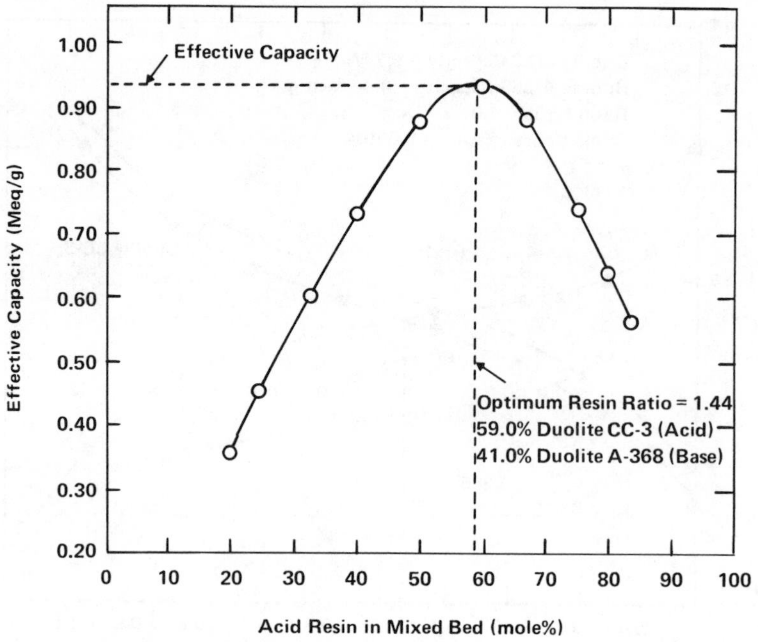

FIGURE 5. The predicted effective capacity versus the mixed-bed composition for Duolite® CC-3 and Duolite A-368.

the process because of the high pressure drop through a bed using small particles. Therefore, adequate rates of exchange must be achieved by using beads in the normal size range.

It has been shown that increasing the porosity of the resins improves the kinetics. Nevertheless, such improvements are still inadequate for practical purposes. An ion-exchange system having normal particle size but involving much shorter diffusion paths is therefore necessary. The significance of the particle size of ion-exchange resins has long been recognized. Attempts have been made to contend with this problem.[23] The approach was to prepare large, mechanically strong, and highly porous ion-exchange pellets by cementing a mixture of acid and base microresins together on an adequately strong and stable porous support. Recent attempts by Weiss[24] and Light[22] may be considered a modification of the early work. Detailed background and procedures of the development of the composite resin can be found elsewhere.[22,24] However, a brief review of such developments is informative.

Ion-retardation resins have the characteristic of reducing the diffusional path in large commercial resin beads. However, because the oppositely charged exchange sites are so close together, they tend to neutralize each other. This results in a low equilibrium capacity. The ion-retardation resins are therefore not adequate for use in the CZA process.

Attempts have been made to bind together microresin mixtures of individual weakly acidic and weakly basic resins. The criteria for binding together microresin mixtures are

1. The bonding agents should be able to swell as the resins swell, be hydrophilic, and be at least as ion-permeable as the individual resin particles. They should not block off exchange sites.

2. The two types of microresins must be evenly dispersed in a matrix of water-insoluble, ion-permeable, strong, and (most important of all) thermally stable polymeric material.

3. The matrix materials must also be strongly polar to be compatible with an aqueous salt solution.

The procedures adopted for making the composite resin based on the experimental equilibrium and rate data were the following. Two commercial ion-exchange resins, Duolite CC-3 and Duolite A-368, were ground separately using a ball mill to very small particle sizes in the range of about 10 μm. The optimum resin ratio was taken as its best equilibrium value, 1.44/1. Composite resin beads

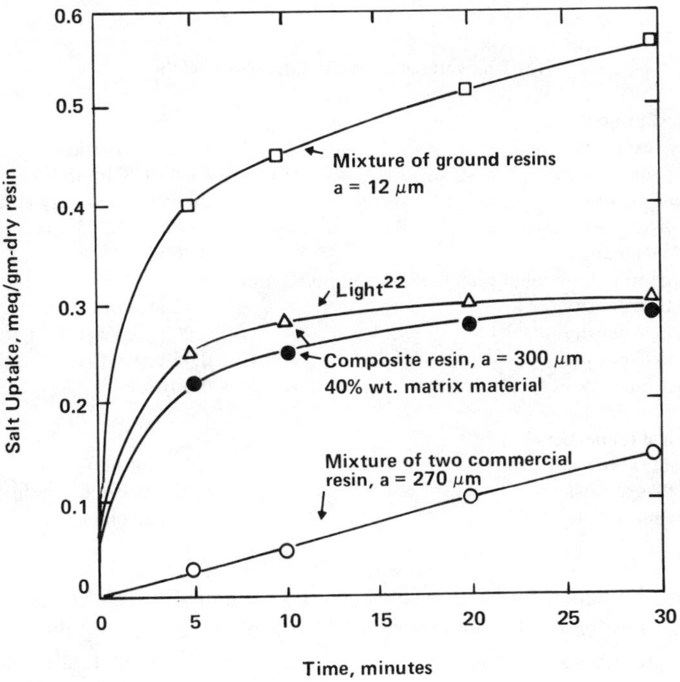

FIGURE 6. Salt uptake of various resins versus time in batch system.

were formed by dispersing the optimum ratio of a mixture of ground microbeads in a matrix of polyvinyl alcohol. Spherical beads of this mixture were formed by the suspension polymerization technique. Glutaraldehyde solution was used to react with the hydroxyl group in the polyvinyl alcohol, forming cross-links and providing mechanical strength. A ground resin mixture of the optimum composition was dispersed in an acidified aqueous suspension of polyvinyl alcohol, using a propeller mixer in a 250-ml beaker. Glutaraldehyde was added to the stirrer slurry and after about 1 min the reacting mixture was added quickly to about 0.75 l of a hydrocarbon oil. Stirring continued and resin beads were formed in the suspension as a cross-linking reaction occurred. After removing the oil and extensive washing with acetone and then water, the resin beads were cured at 90°C under vacuum overnight.

These resin beads were found to have about 90% of the ion-exchange capacity originally present in the resin and were fairly strong mechanically. The composite resin having the most rapid exchange rate contained 30 wt % of inert matrix material. "Holes" were made in the matrix to make it more ion-permeable. This was done by adding an amount of sodium chloride powder equal to 10 wt % of the resin. The holes were formed by leaching the salt out after the beads had been formed.

A quantity of composite resin large enough for pilot-scale experiments was custom-made by Diamond Shamrock Chemical Company according to the procedures described. It was found that the composite resin was lacking in equilibrium salt uptake capacity by only 10% on a per-weight-of-pure-resin basis.

The rate of salt uptake by the composite resin was much greater than that for the commercial mixed resin of similar particle size. The rates of salt uptake by various types of resin particles are shown in Figure 6. It can be seen that during the first 10 min the salt uptake by the composite resin, having only 50% of the capacity of the original resin, was about seven times greater than that of the commercial resin of approximately the same size.

The composite resin received from Diamond Shamrock Chemical Company did not exhibit as high an exchange rate as anticipated. There were many possible factors that could have affected the resin properties, such as the amount of water contained in the microbeads, the pH of the slurry prior to polymerization (which affects the rate of polymerization reaction), the extent of the initial grinding of the original resin particles, and the

TABLE 1

The Characteristics of the Composite Resin

Physical properties	
Physical form	Spherical particles
Moisture content (23 to 80°C)	51 to 62% by weight
Screen grading	28 to 60 mesh, dry (U.S.)
Particle size (radius)	0.072 to 0.563 mm
Mean radius	0.36 mm
Fraction by wt. between 0.25 mm and 0.52 mm	76%
Particle density, ρ_p	0.72 g/cc dry resin
Particle density, ρ	0.468 g/cc wet resin
Particle porosity, ϵ	0.45 cc void/cc wet resin
Heat capacity	0.8 Btu/lb/°F
Chemical properties	
Resin ratio, acid/base	1.44 mol/mol
Exchange capacity	0.937 meq/g dry resin
Swelling (23 to 80°C)	15% by volume

methods and conditions by which the resin beads were cured. The characteristics of the composite resin used in this study are shown in Table 1.

EXPERIMENTAL APPARATUS

A bench-scale thermally cycled ion-exchange apparatus was built to evaluate various process schemes and variables. The apparatus consisted of a jacketed ion-exchange column, a feed degassing system, two constant temperature baths, an automatic timer and controller, and a detection unit. The flow diagram of this apparatus is shown in Figure 7.

The feed solution of known concentration was prepared in the feed degasser. A small amount of formaldehyde (1 cc/30 l of salt solution) was added to prevent bacterial growth since microorganisms, some of which can cause deterioration of the ion-exchange resin, propagate in the salt solution. Feed solution was heated to its boiling point to remove soluble gases, especially oxygen. This degassing step was quite important since oxygen contained in the feed tended to oxidize the base resin and therefore to reduce its exchange capacity. The degassed feed was cooled and pumped first through the filter and then the rotameter.

In the cold portion of the cycles the odd-numbered solenoid valves and the cold water circulation pump were switched on for a predetermined time period. The salt solution was cooled to a desired production temperature before entering the column. During the hot portion of the cycles, only even-numbered valves and the other pump were turned on. Hot salt solution at the desired regeneration temperature was passed through the column. The cooling or heating water was also circulated inside the jacket of the column in correspondence with the temperature of the bed. The effluent solution was kept at a constant temperature of 25°C by the heat exchanger before it entered the electrical conductivity cell and the pH probe. These line connections were kept as short as possible to minimize the delay in the measurements and in the back-mixing in the solution. The temperatures at different points in the system were monitored by thermocouples in the 12-channel, 10-mV L & N Recorder. Particular attention was given to the temperature of the effluent solution prior to its entering the detecting instruments.

The cycle-averaged concentration and the separation factor were determined by planimeter integration of the recorder charts. For this purpose, the cycle was defined as the period of positive or negative deviation from the feed composition, rather than the period of heating or cooling, a difference of only a few minutes. The effluent samples were collected separately during different portions of the cycles. Their volumes were measured and the average concentrations were determined by $AgNO_3$ titration. These measured average concentrations were used as an independent check of the values obtained by planimeter integration. The characteristics of the ion-exchange column are shown in Table 2.

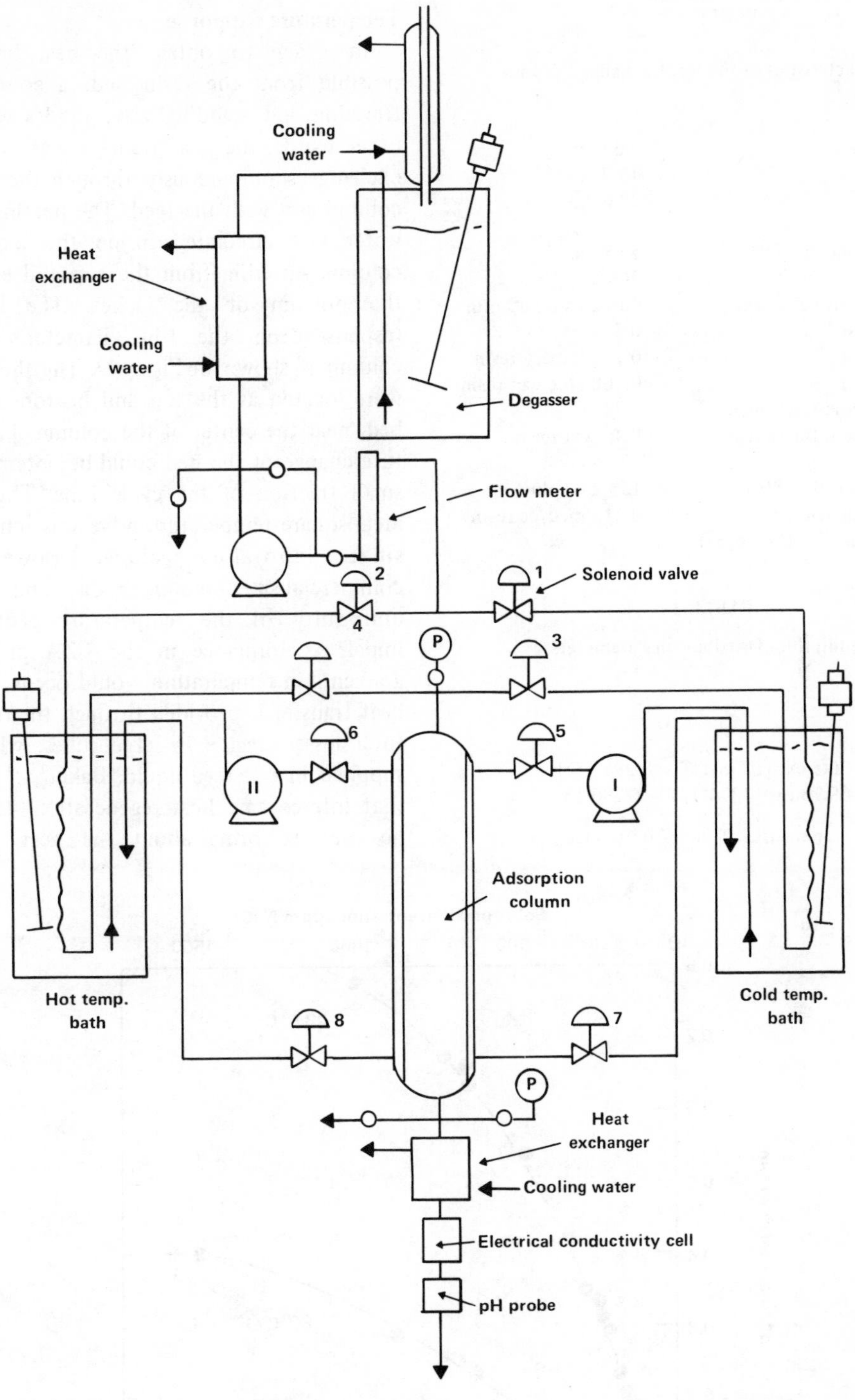

FIGURE 7. Process flow diagram for purification of salt water via Cycling Zone Adsorption.

EXPERIMENTAL RESULTS AND DISCUSSIONS

The experimental ion-exchange system described has a reasonably large temperature effect on the equilibrium distribution of the NaCl solution. The equilibrium isotherms for the composite resin-salt solution system are shown in Figure 8. These data can be expressed in the form of Langmuir isotherms. The coefficients for the Langmuir isotherms at two temperatures are shown in Table 3.

TABLE 2

The Characteristics of the Ion-Exchange Column

Column	
Inside diameter	2.54 cm
Length	45.7 cm
Bed depth	39.6 cm
Jacket	
Outside diameter	5.08 cm
Volume	360 cc
Radius of porous particles	0.072 to 0.563 mm
Mean radius	0.36 mm
Resin density, ρ_p	0.72 g/cc dry resin
Resin density, ρ	0.468 g/cc wet resin
Interparticle void fraction, α	0.38
Intraparticle void fraction, ϵ	0.45 wet resin
Resin volume	124.4 cc
Bed expansion (20 to 80°C)	15% by volume
Equilibrium capacity, Δq^* (20 to 80°C at C = 1000 ppm)	0.213 meq/cc resin

TABLE 3

Equilibrium Distribution Parameters

$$q^* = \frac{a_1 C}{1 + b_1 C}$$

$$a_1 = 100.5 \exp[2238(1/T - 1/296.15)]$$
$$b_1 = 69.78 \exp[1374(1/T - 1/296.15)]$$

Note: C in meq/cc, T in °K, q* in meq/g.

Temperature Response

In order to obtain the best heat transfer possible from the resin bed, a combination of traveling and standing wave modes was used. In other words, the heat transfer was done by heat exchange simultaneously through the wall of the column and with the feed. The heating or cooling water was circulated inside the jacket of the column, entering from the top and exiting from the bottom of the jacket. The temperature response from the 1-in. diameter, 15-in. long column is shown in Figure 9. The thermocouples were located at the top and bottom of the resin bed, near the center of the column. Full temperature change of the bed could be obtained within a small fraction of the cycle time. Thus, a nearly ideal square temperature wave was achieved in the small laboratory column. However, in a commercial-size column, radial and axial nonuniformity of the temperature profiles would impair performance in the CZA process. Such gradients in temperature would occur either when heat transfer is provided through the tube wall or, to a lesser degree in large tubes, when heat is supplied in hot feed liquid. Baker[13,46] suggested that intercolumn heat regeneration stages should be used to bring about the best relationship

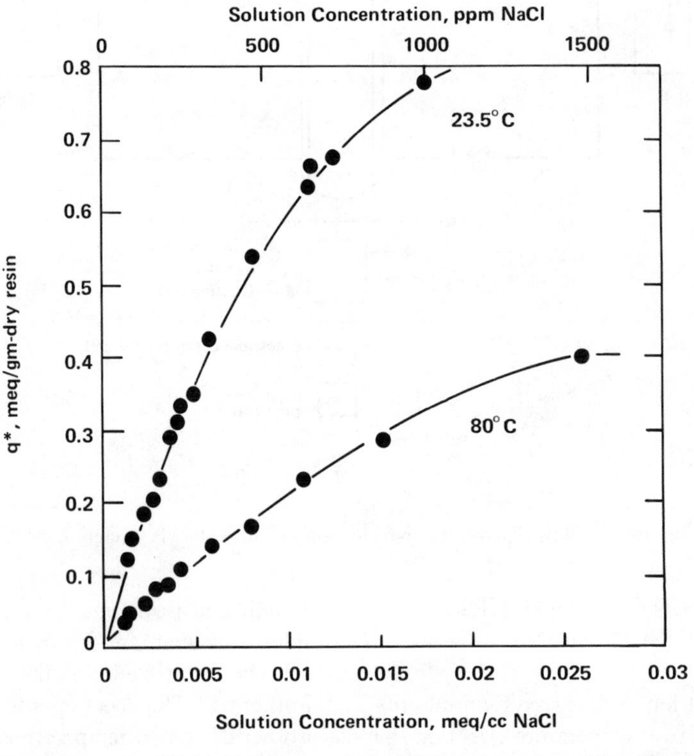

FIGURE 8. Equilibrium isotherms of salt and the composite resin system.

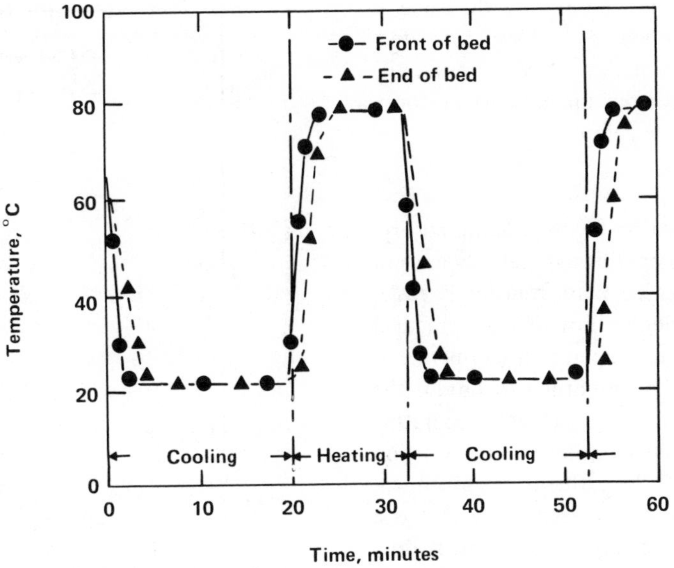

FIGURE 9. Temperature profiles for the experimental operation of a single zone adsorber (column diameter, 1 in.; superficial fluid velocity, 0.2 cm/sec; resin particle diameter, 0.072 cm).

between temperature and concentration waves in a staged system. A shell-and-tube heat exchanger could also be used as an ion-exchange column. Resin particles would be packed inside the tubes and heating or cooling water would be circulated alternately in the shell outside the tubes. This would allow a close approach to the ideal square wave temperature response in the resin bed, but would also increase the capital investment as well as operating cost of the process.

Equilibrium Breakthrough

Equilibrium breakthrough experiments were carried out using the laboratory column. The system was first brought to equilibrium with the feed at low or high temperature and then a step temperature change was introduced in the bed. The effluent concentration from the column was monitored continuously.

A typical graph of effluent concentration versus time is shown in Figure 10. In the adsorption step the rate of salt uptake by the resin was very fast initially. It was followed by a very sharp decline in the effluent concentration. During adsorption the minimum concentration was reached within about 5 min, after which the concentration began to return to the feed concentration at a relatively slow rate. The slow period lasted for a long time until the system came to equilibrium again. Then the feed concentration began to break through.

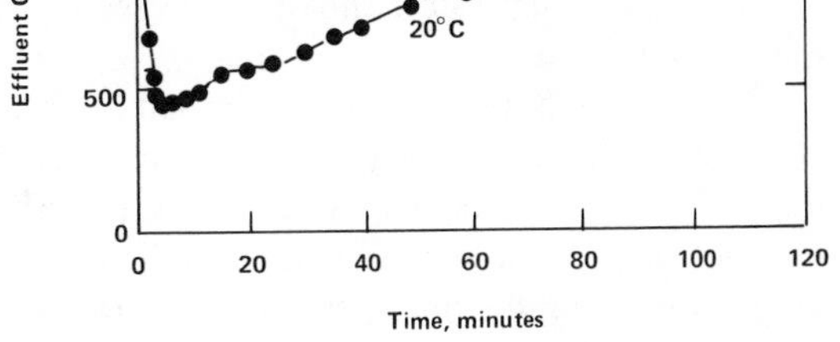

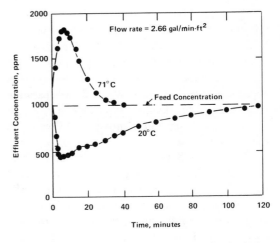

FIGURE 10. Effluent concentration profiles in elution experiments (superficial velocity, 0.181 cm/sec).

During a similar desorption step, shown by the upper curve at 71°C, the maximum change in concentration occurred at about the same time after the step change of temperature, and the rate of return to the feed concentration was more rapid.

Equilibrium conditions will not be reached in a practical CZA process. The ion-exchange resin particles and salt solution will not come to equilibrium before the temperature shift takes place for either the adsorption or the desorption cycles. Therefore, the behavior of the ion-exchange column will not be exactly the same as equilibrium breakthrough data have indicated. Nevertheless, the information obtained from the equilibrium study gives the upper limit performance of the ion-exchange column.

Cycle Time

Note that, as shown in Figure 10, the adsorption and desorption breakthrough periods are not equal, apparently because mass transfer is easier when the resin particles are hot. It is of practical importance in the column operation to operate at the optimum cycle time in order to obtain the maximum separation for those particular operating conditions. This involves minimizing the portion of the cycle for which the effluent has a concentration at or near that of the feed, since that is a region of little or no separation. However, if flow is to occur through a series of stages designed to increase the separation effect, it will be necessary to have equal periods for heating and cooling.

Equal Hot and Cold Periods

Figure 11 shows the effect of flow rate upon separation at different cycle times. The separation factor is defined as the ratio of the average salt concentration in the enriched portion of the effluent to the average concentration in the depleted portion. At low flow rates, the separation factor increases as the throughput rate increases. It reaches a maximum value, and starts decreasing as the flow rate increases.

The figure indicates that the separation is better at longer cycle times (low frequency) than that at high frequency. At high frequency, the particles did not experience the maximum temperature swing; therefore the mass-transfer driving force arising from the shift in the temperature was not fully realized. On the other hand, during low-frequency operation, the time required for the particles to reach their desired temperature amounted to only a small and insignificant portion of the cycle. The particles were exposed to the full temperature shift.

At lower flow rates, although the residence time was long enough for adequate mass transfer to take place, the effect of longitudinal diffusion was probably large. At high flow rates, however, the longitudinal diffusion effect was diminished and heat transfer was improved, causing maximum separation to be achieved. At even higher flow rates the fluid residence time was too short to

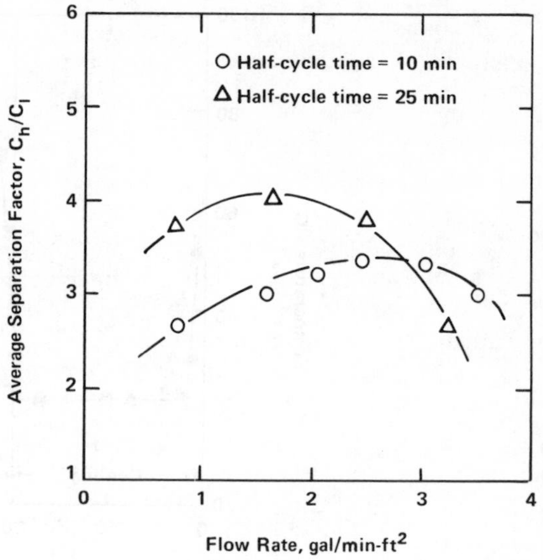

FIGURE 11. Effect of flow rate on the separation factor (equal cycle time operation).

permit adequate mass transfer, and separation therefore declined. Using long cycle times (low frequency) and high velocities in the vicinity of the optimum velocity is highly desirable.

Unequal Cycle Times

Due to the differing equilibrium isotherms and different mass-transfer rates at the higher and lower temperatures, the optimum half-cycle times for the hot and cold portions of the cycles are different. The optimum relationship can be determined semiquantitatively using the method of characteristics described earlier.[13]

If local equilibrium exists between the fluid and the particles, the optimum cycle time is approximately equal to the length of column divided by the concentration wave velocity, which depends upon the flow rate and the physical properties of the particles as well as the slope of the equilibrium isotherm. The predicted ratio of the two optimum cycle times for the two extreme operating temperatures of 22 and 80°C is about t_{80}/t_{22} = 0.6.

This predicted ratio agreed with the experimental observations, which gave a ratio of 0.63. The optimum cycle times predicted from the equilibrium theory of Equation 1 at temperatures of 22 and 80°C and a flow rate of 4.7 gal/min/ft^2 were 46 and 27.6 min, respectively, whereas experimental data showed the real values to be 30 and 18 min. The differences presumably arise from the theoretical assumption of local equilibrium between the particles and the solution.

Figure 12 shows that the average effluent concentration varied with the ratio of cycle times. At t_H/t_C = 0.63, the product concentration exhibited a minimum value for each of the two different flow rates, i.e., for two different cycle times. The same data were plotted in terms of average separation factor as is shown in Figure 13. The maximum separation occurred at t_H/t_C = 0.63 under the specified operating temperature conditions. These observations were consistent for all the flow rates investigated.

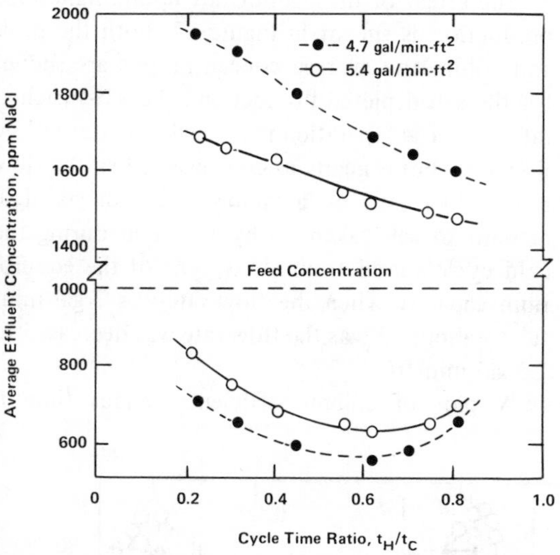

FIGURE 12. Effect of cycle time ratio on average effluent concentration.

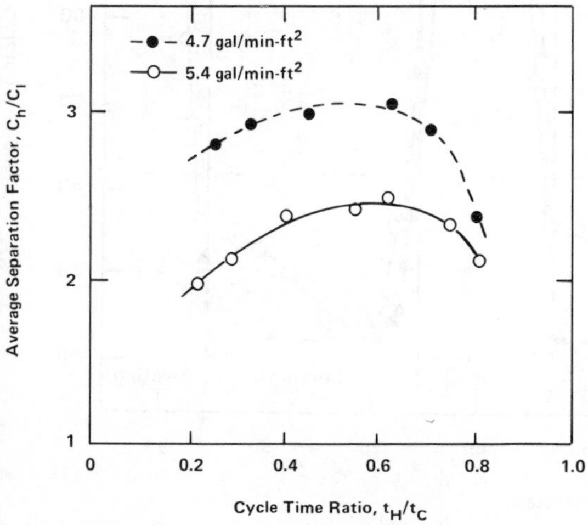

FIGURE 13. Effect of cycle time ratio on average separation factor.

Based on these experimental observations, the ratio of t_H/t_C = 0.63 was adopted throughout the later experiments in this study. The absolute cycle time for the cold cycle was first determined from the optimum value predicted by the equilibrium theory, and then a series of experiments was carried out in which the cold cycle time was decreased, but the ratio of t_H/t_C was kept constant at 0.63. The results are shown in Figure 14. The optimum switching time for the cold portion of the cycles was found to be about 30 min at a flow rate of 4.7 gal/min/ft^2 and t_H/t_C = 0.63.

Continuous Column Operation

During continuous operation, the optimum cycle time was first determined experimentally for the cold half-cycle. The ratio of t_H/t_C = 0.63 was then employed to calculate the optimum cycle time for the hot cycle. All the data shown here were taken at column steady state, such that the effluent concentration profile was repeated for each cycle, and under optimum cycle-time operation.

Measurements were taken, using pressure gauges at the inlet and outlet of the column, in order to determine pressure drop through the column as a function of the flow rate and the bed temperature. The results are shown in Figure 15. The differences in pressure drop at the two operating

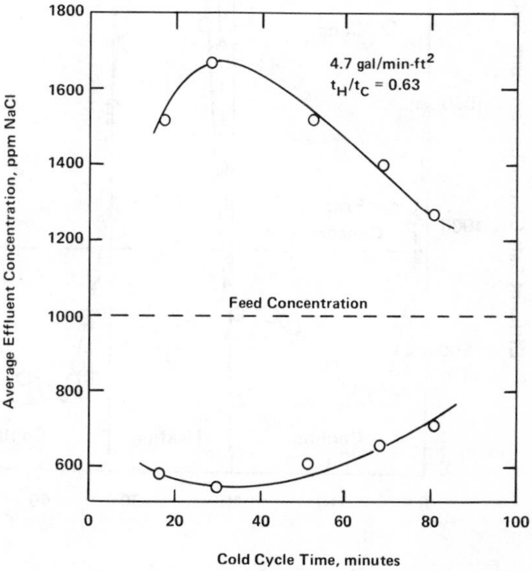

FIGURE 14. Average effluent concentration versus cold cycle time.

temperatures are due to the increased swelling of the resin at the highest temperature.

Typical plots of the effluent concentration and average temperature of the bed as they varied with time in the continuous operation are shown in Figure 16. Using a feed concentration of 900 ppm, a minimum effluent concentration of 300 ppm and an average concentration of 500 ppm were obtained in the 22°C fraction, while a maximum concentration of 2300 ppm and an average concentration of 1800 ppm were recorded in the 80°C fraction. In the adsorption cycle the effluent concentration declined very rapidly, reaching a minimum concentration in about 5 min and then rising slowly. The shape of the curve for the hot half-cycle reflects the higher desorption rate.

The thermal wave velocity closely matched the concentration wave velocity in this experiment. As the temperature reached its peak value, the concentration wave peak followed shortly. Under these circumstances, the advantages of CZA could be fully utilized.

The effect of throughput rate upon single-stage production is shown in Figure 17. Both the peak and volumetric average concentrations are shown for the salt-depleted product and the salt-enriched raffinate. The separation is somewhat better at low flow rate, but is nearly as good even when the flow rate is increased by a factor of five or six. The amount of salt taken up by the resin during the cold cycle varied from about 30% of the equilibrium capacity when the flow rate was 7 gal/min/ft^2 to about 55% as the flow rate was decreased to 1.3 gal/min/ft^2.

A plot of column efficiency versus time is

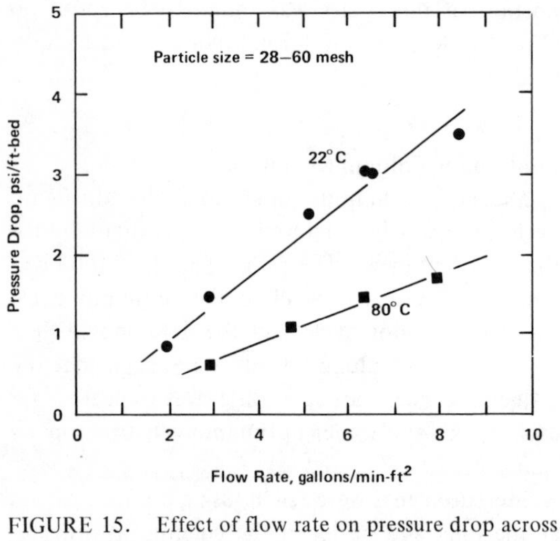

FIGURE 15. Effect of flow rate on pressure drop across the ion-exchange bed.

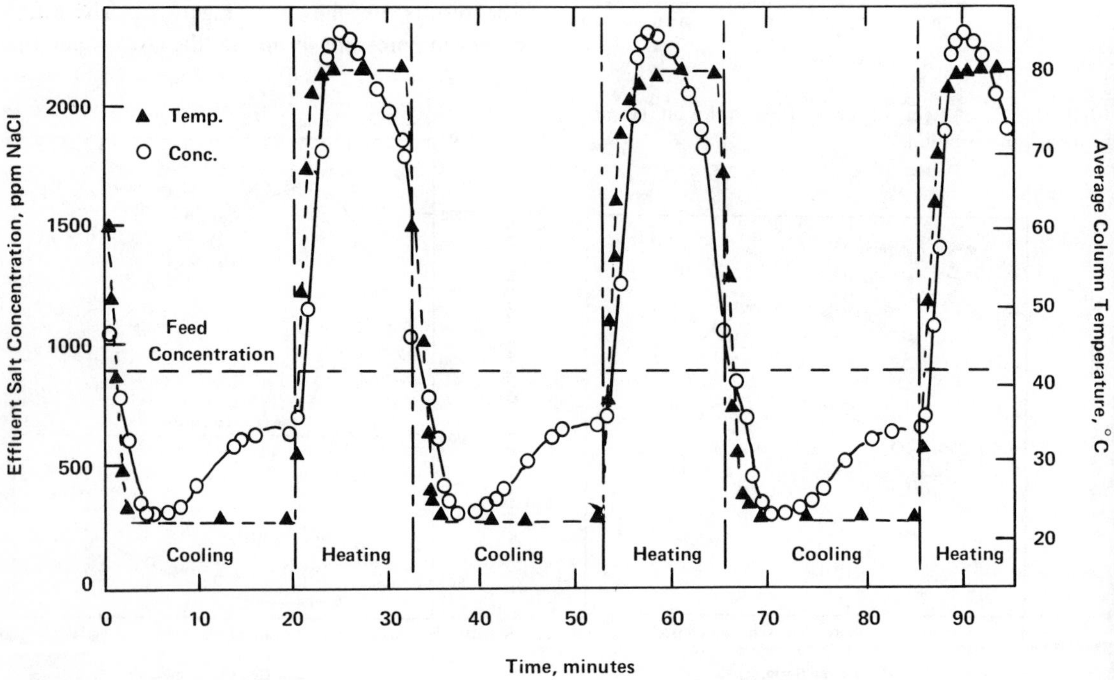

FIGURE 16. Average bed temperature and effluent concentration profiles in the continuous Cycling Zone Adsorption operation.

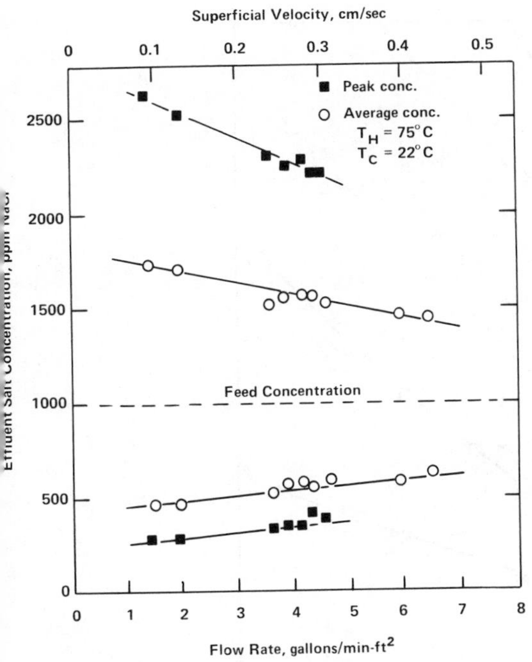

FIGURE 17. Effect of flow rate on product concentration.

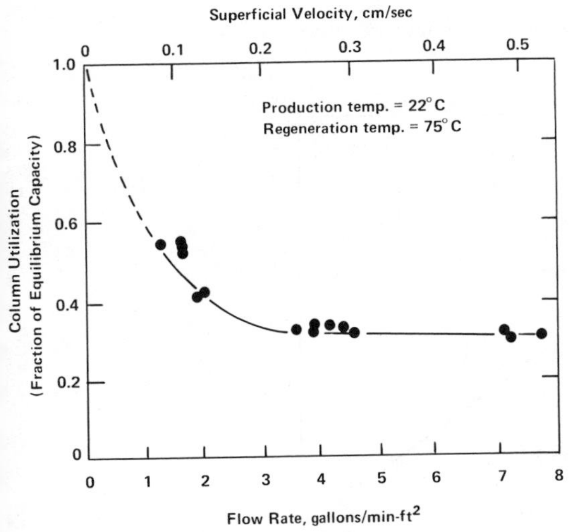

FIGURE 18. Effect of flow rate on column efficiency.

shown in Figure 18. The efficiency is defined as the ratio of the actual amount of salt taken up by the resin during the cold cycle to the amount of salt that would be adsorbed by the resin if the resin reached equilibrium with the feed. The efficiency increased as the flow rate decreased. At zero flow rate, that is for a stagnated system, the column is assumed to be fully utilized. This indicates that mass transfer was the limiting factor in the continuous operation.

At flow rates higher than 3 gal/min/ft^2, the column efficiency decreases very slowly. Since at higher flow rates the longitudinal diffusion effect became less important in the packed column, the sharp concentration wave front moving along the column was disturbed less. This led to increased separation when the residence time was long enough to permit adequate mass transfer.

The effect of changes in the feed concentration on the column performance is shown in Figure 19. The dotted line is the 45° line. Both peak and average concentrations of depleted and enriched raffinates are shown. With a feed NaCl concentration of 1000 ppm, for example, a minimum effluent concentration of 300 ppm and an average of 500 ppm were obtained. If the mixed effluent from one stage had been sent to a second stage, a product with an average concentration of 300 ppm would have been expected.

The fact that the peak and average effluent concentrations approach each other rather closely at low feed concentrations indicates that the effluent concentration profile is least distorted in that range. It can be seen from Figure 20 that the average separation factor decreased with increasing feed concentration. The large separation achieved at low feed concentrations must be weighed against the corresponding low column utilization, however, as shown in Figure 21. The CZA process appears to be particularly useful for treating low concentration feed streams in the region of about 1000 ppm. The less distorted concentration wave may be attributed to the linearity of the equilibrium isotherm of the system at low concentrations.

The effect of variations in feed pH values was also investigated. Figure 22 shows the effect of feed pH on the quality of water produced. The optimum pH for the original resin pair in the batch system had been found to be 6.2[22] when equilibrium was assumed. Under these ideal conditions the separation factor was expected to be rather sensitive to the feed pH. Under flow conditions, however, the volumetric average product concentration was not very sensitive to the pH of the feed so long as the pH was not far removed from the optimum value. The column utilization remained practically constant over the range of feed pH values. This indicates pH adjustment of the feed may not be necessary. Since pH adjustment of the feed represents a moderate portion of the operating cost in evaporation and in standard ion-

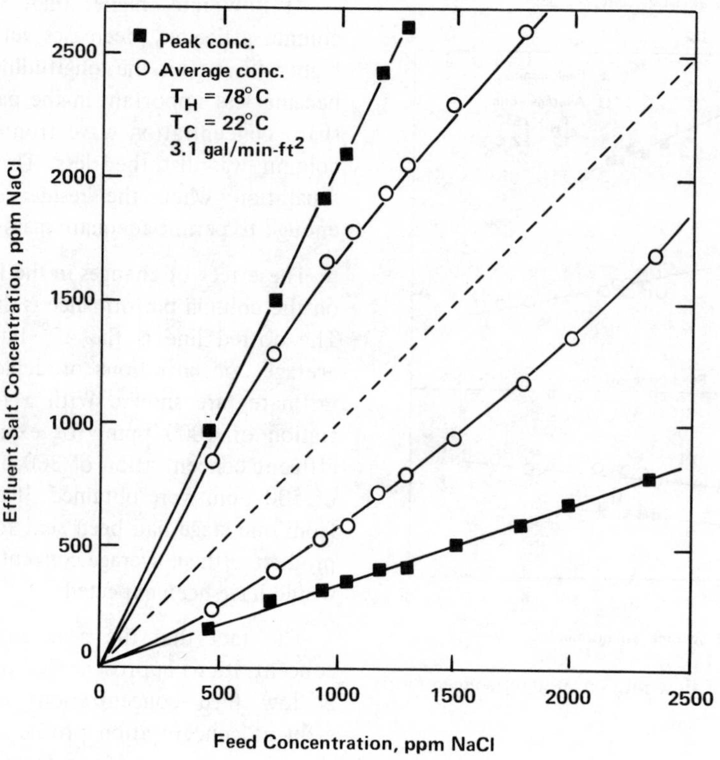

FIGURE 19. Effect of feed concentration on product concentration.

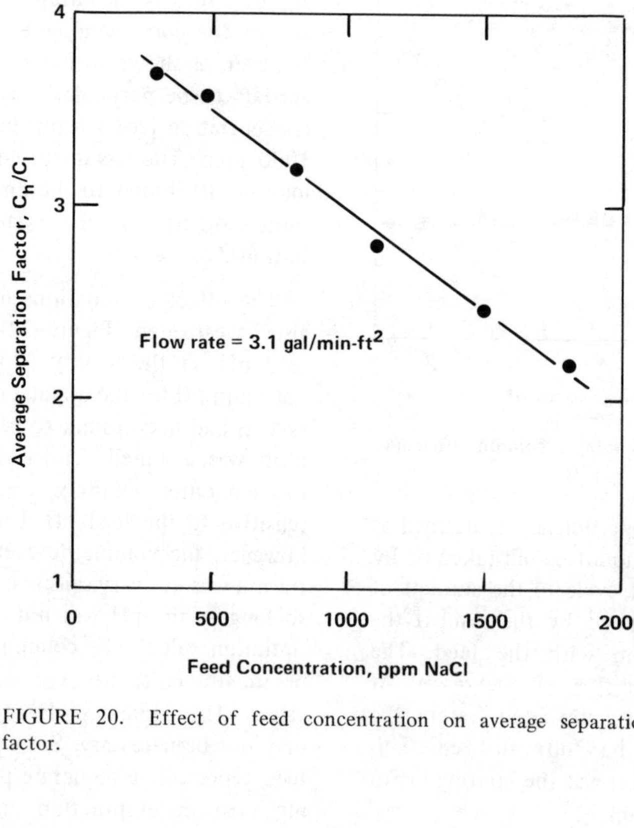

FIGURE 20. Effect of feed concentration on average separation factor.

exchange and reverse osmosis processes, this gives the CZA process an advantage.

The major objective of this study was to develop a new desalting process which would require less energy than existing or partially developed processes. The major concern, therefore, was with the amount and quality of heat required to regenerate the resin bed. If the ion-exchange resin can be regenerated effectively with a small amount of heat, and if low grade sensible heat or even waste energy can be used, an obvious economic advantage will be given to the process.

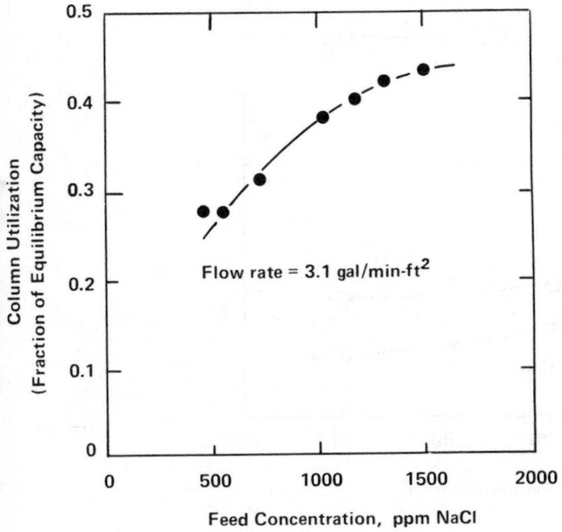

FIGURE 21. Effect of feed concentration on column efficiency.

The effect of regeneration temperature on one-stage performance is shown in Figure 23. Four different regeneration temperatures were tried, the lower production temperature remaining constant. Both the peak and the average effluent concentrations are shown. The separation improves somewhat as the temperature difference between the hot and cold portion of the cycle increases. The improvement is not proportional to the temperature difference, however.

The column efficiency increased only about 3% as the regeneration temperature was increased from 60 to 80°C. Operation of this process at a regeneration temperature of 80°C, or even 70°C, seems quite possible. This process could therefore use waste heat from nuclear or fossil fuel power generating facilities to produce purified water.

The experimental results from the composite resin system are compared to those of the original mixed-bed system[16] for CZA operation in Table 4. It is clear from Latty's results[16] that the

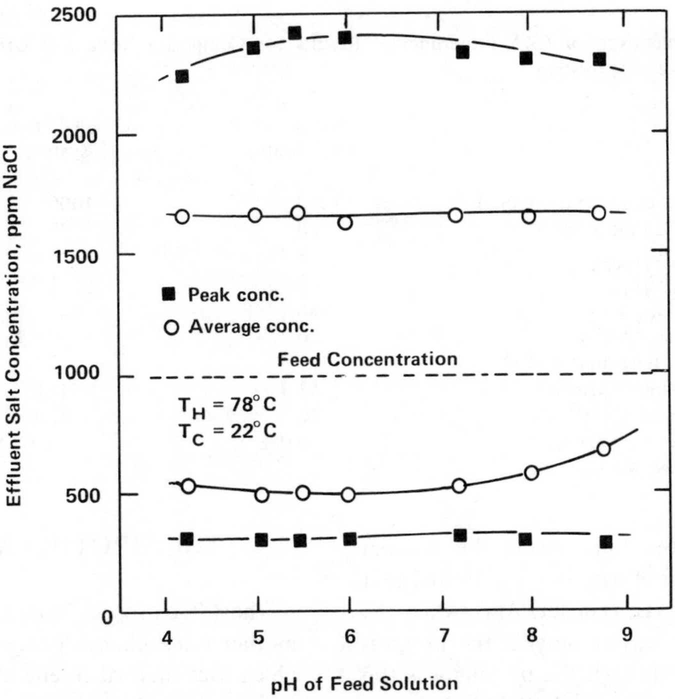

FIGURE 22. Effect of feed pH on product concentration.

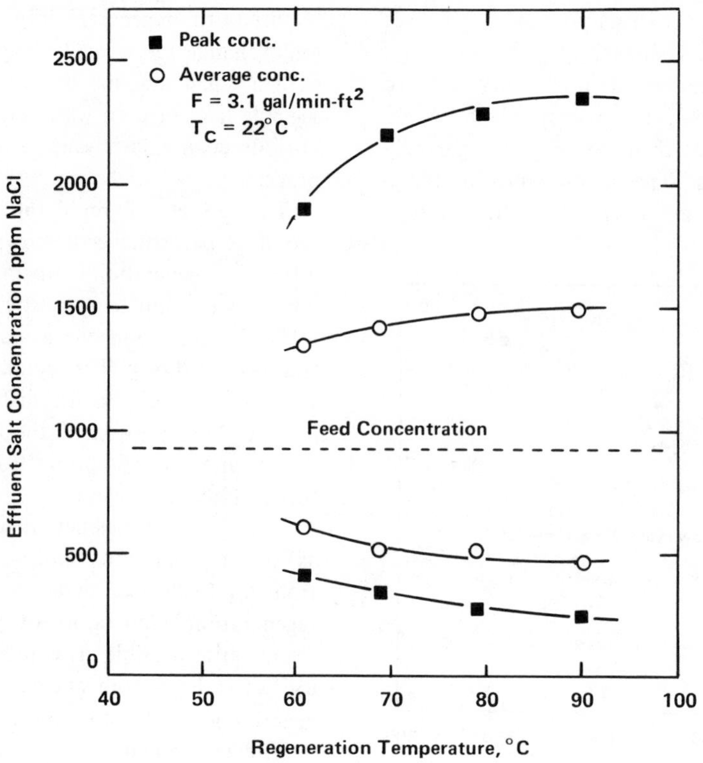

FIGURE 23. Effect of regeneration temperature on product concentration.

TABLE 4

Comparison of CZA Experimental Results for Composite Resin and Original Mixed-bed System

	Composite resin (this study)	Original mixed-bed system[16]
Feed concentration, ppm	1000	1000
Cycle time, min	60	72
$[C_h/C_l]_{peak}$	8.32	1.82
$[C_h/C_l]_{ave}$	2.62	1.74
$[C_l]_{ave}$, ppm	535	819
Space velocity $[\text{cc feed/min/cc bed}]_{ave}$	0.278	0.033
Volume % product	53.3	32.6
Volume % raffinate	46.7	42.1
Effective capacity (meq NaCl/cc bed)	0.066	0.0461

residence time of the fluid inside the column packed with commercial-size resin was insufficient to permit adequate mass transfer. Also, when the traveling wave mode was employed, the progress of the thermal wave through the packing was too slow to give the best timing relationship between temperature and concentration shifts.

THE SIROTHERM PROCESS

The CZA process bears a close resemblance to another ion-exchange process called "Sirotherm," which uses thermal regeneration. This process was developed jointly by the Commonwealth Scientific and Industrial Research Organization of Australia and Imperial Chemical Industries, Limited. The details of this process can be found elsewhere.[25,38,41-44]

The batch version of the Sirotherm process is operated in three flow cycles, adsorption, regeneration, and cooling, with five successive operations being required.

Sirotherm differs from the CZA process primarily in that multiple stages are not used and reversing flow is employed. The CZA process operates continuously without flow reversal, eliminating the need for large storage tanks. This has the added advantages of providing more efficient oxygen control and allowing for easier operation and maintenance.

CONCLUSIONS

The Cycling Zone Adsorption process using a composite resin to remove salt from water has been successfully demonstrated in this study.

The composite resin particles formed by cementing two types of ground fine particles together have been found to increase the exchange rate by a factor of seven over particles of commercial resins of the same chemical type.

Operation of this process at high throughput rates of up to 10 gal/min/ft^2 was found to be possible without losing too much of the potential capacity. It was also found that the separation of low concentration feeds was more effectively accomplished and that the effluent concentration wave was less distorted than for high concentration feeds. This is probably attributed to the nearly linear equilibrium distribution relationship at low concentrations. This phenomenon may make the Cycling Zone Adsorption process most useful for dilute feed streams and possibly for brackish water desalting. The pH values of the feed seemed to have an insignificant effect upon the product. Thus, a feed pretreatment to adjust the pH of the feed stream is not needed, reducing the capital as well as the operating costs of this process.

The energy requirement of this process was found to be much less than that for a competitive evaporative process. Regeneration at 80°C was sufficient to restore the resin capacity. Therefore, energy from nuclear and fossil-fuel power generating facilities can be used to produce purified water. Since low-grade sensible heat can be used, and since some of the heat can be recovered, this process should be particularly attractive. In comparison to conventional ion-exchange processes, the Cycling Zone Adsorption process requires no chemical regenerants. It extracts salt from water, rather than water from salt as do evaporative or reverse osmosis processes. It produces a waste stream that can easily be disposed of without serious environmental impact.

The major disadvantage of this process is still the rate of mass transfer of the ions inside the resin particles. The composite resin used in this study is not completely satisfactory; it is only the first effort toward improvement. The success of the process depends primarily upon developing a better resin. Work is needed to develop bifunctional resin particles containing both acidic and basic functional groups located at distances such that they will not neutralize each other. Prolonged experimentation should be carried out to determine the stability of the composite resin upon exposure to the temperature cycles and to repeated adsorption and release of salt. This should provide information for a reliable cost estimation.

The divalent ions which are the secondary contaminants in brackish water have not been investigated in this study. If experimentation should prove that it is not feasible to remove the divalent ions by the same resin system, certain pretreatment facilities of the feed might have to be used or other resin systems have to be developed. This would of course increase the cost of the water produced.

It has been shown by others[10,13] that staging Cycling Zone Adsorption units can amplify the concentration amplitude and enhance the separation. This should be investigated more carefully for the salt-resin systems. Such experimentation should provide enough information for a process flow sheet evaluation and detailed cost estimations of a version of the Cycling Zone Adsorption process in which energy and resin requirements would be more nearly optimum.

ACKNOWLEDGMENTS

The support of the Office of Saline Water (Grant 14-30-2922) and the Department of Chemical Engineering, University of California at Berkeley, is gratefully acknowledged.

NOMENCLATURE

a	Radius of wet resin particle, cm
a_1	Langmuir isotherm parameter, cc/g
b_1	Langmuir isotherm parameter, cc/meq
C	Solution concentration outside the particles, meq/cc
F	Flow rate, gal/min/ft^2
L	Total length of the ion-exchange column, cm
q^*	Equilibrium solid concentration, meq/g
t	Time, sec
T	Temperature, °C or °K
v	Interstitial fluid velocity, cm/sec
α	Interparticle void fraction
ϵ	Intraparticle void fraction, cc void/cc wet resin
ρ	Particle density, g resin/cc wet resin
ρ_P	Particle density including intraparticle void, g/cc

Subscripts

C	Cold
F	Feed condition
h	High concentration
H	Hot
l	Low concentration
P	Particle

REFERENCES

1. **Spiegler, K. S.,** *Salt Water Purification,* John Wiley & Sons, New York, 1962.
2. **Spiegler, K. S., Ed.,** *Principles of Desalination,* Academic Press, New York, 1966.
3. **Helfferich, F.,** *Ion Exchange,* McGraw-Hill, New York, 1962.
4. **Kunin, R.,** *Ion Exchange Resins,* John Wiley & Sons, New York, 1958.
5. **Applebaum, S. B.,** *Demineralization by Ion Exchange,* Academic Press, New York, 1968.
6. **Merten, U.,** *Desalination by Reverse Osmosis,* M.I.T. Press, Cambridge, Mass., 1966.
7. **Snyder, A. E.,** Freezing methods, in *Principles of Desalination,* Spiegler, K. S., Ed., Academic Press, New York, 1966, chap. 7.
8. **Weiss, D. E., Bolto, B. A., Macpherson, A. S., McNeill, R., Siudak, R., Swinton, E. A., and Willis, D.,** Thermally regenerated ion exchange process – An aid to water management, *J. Water Pollut. Control Fed.,* 38, 1782, 1966.
9. **Higgins, I. R.,** Ion exchange: Its present and future use, *Environ. Sci. Technol.,* 7, 111, 1973.
10. **Pigford, R. L., Baker, B., III, and Blum, D. E.,** Cycling Zone Adsorption Process, U.S. Patent 3,542,525, 1970.
11. **Sherwood, T. K. and Pigford, R. L.,** *Adsorption and Extraction,* 2nd ed., McGraw-Hill, New York, 1952.
12. **King, C. J.,** *Separation Processes,* McGraw-Hill, New York, 1971.
13. **Baker, B., III,** Cycling Zone Adsorption: Separation by Thermal Wave Propagation, Ph.D. dissertation, University of California, Berkeley, 1969.
14. **Blum, D. E.,** Cycling Zone Adsorption: Separation of Gas Mixtures, Ph.D. dissertation, University of California, Berkeley, 1971.
15. **Rieke, R. D.,** Large Separation via Cycling Zone Adsorption, Ph.D. dissertation, University of California, Berkeley, 1972.
16. **Latty, J. A.,** The Use of Thermally Sensitive Ion-Exchange Resins or Electrically Sensitive Liquid Crystals as Adsorbents, Ph.D. dissertation, University of California, Berkeley, 1974.
17. **Ginde, V. R. and Chu, C.,** Apparatus for desalination with ion exchange resins, *Desalination,* 10, 309, 1972.

18. **Weiss, D. E., Bolto, B. A., McNeill, R., Macpherson, A. S., Siudak, R., Swinton, B. A., and Willis, D.,** The Sirotherm demineralization process – An ion-exchange process with thermal regeneration. I. The place of a demineralization plant in an overall system of water management in arid areas, *J. Inst. Eng. Aust.,* 37, 193, 1965.
19. **Weiss, D. E., Bolto, B. A., McNeill, R., Macpherson, A. S., Siudak, R., Swinton, B. A., and Willis, D.,** An ion-exchange process with thermal regeneration. II. Properties of weakly basic resins, *Aust. J. Chem.,* 19, 561, 1966.
20. **Weiss, D. E., Bolto, B. A., McNeill, R., Macpherson, A. S., Siudak, R., Swinton, B. A., and Willis, D.,** An ion-exchange process with thermal regeneration. III. Properties of weakly acidic ion-exhange resins, *Aust. J. Chem.,* 19, 589, 1966.
21. **Weiss, D. E., Bolto, B. A., McNeill, R., Macpherson, A. S., Siudak, R., Swinton, B. A., and Willis, D.,** An ion-exchange process with thermal regeneration. IV. Equilibria in a mixed bed of weak electrolyte resins, *Aust. J. Chem.,* 19, 765, 1966.
22. **Light, W. G.,** Rate of Transfer into Weak Acid/Base Ion-exchange Resins, M.S. thesis, University of California, Berkeley, 1973.
23. **Holmes, E. L., Holmes, L. E., and Prescott, W. G.,** Deacidification of Water, British Patent 506,291, 1939.
24. **Weiss, D. E., Bolto, B. A., and Willis, D.,** Ion-exchange Resins, U.S. Patent 3,645,922, 1972.
25. **Battaerd, H. A. J., Blesing, H. V., Bolto, B. A., Cope, A. F. G., Stephens, G. K., Weiss, D. E., Willis, D., and Worboys, J. C.,** Sirotherm, paper presented to the 5th Federal Convention of the Australian Water and Waste-Water Association, Adelaide, May 1972.
26. **Lacey, R. E. and Loeb, S.,** *Industrial Processing with Membranes,* Interscience, New York, 1972.
27. **Channabasappa, K. C.,** Status of reverse osmosis desalination technology, *Desalination,* 17, 13, 1975.
28. **Podall, H. E.,** Reverse osmosis, in *Recent Developments in Separation Science,* Vol. II, Li, N. N., Ed., CRC Press, Cleveland, Ohio, 1972.
29. **Knox, W. G., Hess, M., Jones, G. E., and Smith, H. B., Jr.,** The hydrate process, *Chem. Eng. Prog.,* 57, 66, 1961.
30. **Barduhn, A. J.,** Desalination by crystallization processes, *Chem. Eng. Prog.,* 63, 98, 1967.
31. **Davis, H. E. and Fraser, H. J.,** Advances in concentrating chemicals and industrial waste by freeze crystallization, presented at the 1975 Separation/Exposition, Tarrytown, N.Y., October 23 to 24, 1975.
32. **Sherwood, T. K., Pigford, R. L., and Wilke, C. R.,** *Mass Transfer,* McGraw-Hill, New York, 1975.
33. **Shih, T-S. T.,** Removal of Salt from Water by Ion-exchange with Thermal Regeneration, Ph.D. dissertation, University of California, Berkeley, 1975.
34. **Sweed, N. H. and Wilhelm, R. H.,** Parametric pumping-separation via direct thermal mode, *Ind. Eng. Chem. Fundam.,* 8, 221, 1969.
35. **Wilhelm, R. H., Rice, A. W., Rolke, R. W., and Sweed, N. H.,** Parametric pumping – a dynamic principle for separating fluid mixture, *Ind. Eng. Chem. Fundam.,* 7, 337, 1968.
36. **Wilhelm, R. H. and Sweed, N. H.,** Parametric pumping – separation of mixture of toluene and *n*-heptane, *Science,* 159, 522, 1968.
37. **Sweed, N. H.,** Parametric pumping, in *Recent Developments in Separation Science,* Vol. I, Li, N. N., Ed., CRC Press, Cleveland, Ohio, 1972.
38. **Stephens, G. K.,** Sirotherm process assessment data, ICI Australia Ltd. and Diamond Shamrock Chemical Co., September 1974.
39. ICI Australia Ltd. and Diamond Shamrock Chemical Co., Sirotherm, hypothetical proposal, submitted to the Office of Saline Water, U.S. Department of Interior, 1974.
40. **Bolto, B. A., Eppinger, K., Macpherson, A. S., Siudak, R., Weiss, D. E., and Willis, D.,** Ion-exchange process with thermal regeneration. IX. New type of rapidly reacting ion-exchange resin, *Desalination,* 13, 269, 1973.
41. **Weiss, D. E.,** Pilot plant studies of partial demineralization of brackish waters by the Sirotherm process, *Ion Exch. Membr.,* 1, 109, 1972.
42. **Battaerd, H. A. J., Cope, A. F., Stephens, G. K., Worboys, J. C., Blesing, N. V., Bolto, B. A., Weiss, D. E., and Willis, D.,** Thermally regenerable ion-exchange resins – Sirotherm process, *Fresh Water from the Sea, Fourth International Symposium,* Vol. 3, Delyannis, A., Ed., European Federation of Chemical Engineering, 1973, 13.
43. **Battaerd, H. A. J., Cope, A. F. G., Stephens, G. K., Worboys, J. C., Blesing, N. V., Bolto, B. A., Weiss, D. E., and Willis, D.,** Desalination of brackish water by thermally regenerable ion exchange, *Effluent Water Treat. J.,* 14, 245, 1974.
44. **Battaerd, H. A. J., Cope, A. F. G., Stephens, G. K., Worboys, J. C., Blesing, N. V., Bolto, B. A., Weiss, D. E., and Willis, D.,** Desalination of brackish water by thermally regenerable ion exchange, *Effluent Water Treat. J.,* 14, 249, 1974.
45. **Weiss, D. E., Bolto, B. A., McNeill, R., Macpherson, A. S., Siudak, R., Swinton, B. A., and Willis, D.,** An ion-exchange process with thermal regeneration. V. Multistage operation, *Aust. J. Chem.,* 19, 791, 1966.
46. **Baker, B., III and Pigford, R. L.,** Cycling zone adsorption: Quantitative theory and experimental results, *Ind. Eng. Chem. Fundam.,* 10, 283, 1971.

ION EXCHANGE SEPARATION OF METAL IONS FROM WATER AND WASTE WATERS

W. S. Miller and A. B. Mindler

TABLE OF CONTENTS

INTRODUCTION

Ion exchange separation of metal ions from water is not a new technology, but applications of the technology have not found widespread acceptance by industry. Previously, the economics of ion exchange were frequently unfavorable unless the process was used primarily for producing a saleable product such as uranium. However, improvements to the ion exchange process such as countercurrent regeneration have reduced regenerant chemical requirements and consequently reduced operating costs. Experience in providing the proper pretreatment system and resin cleanup procedures for each application has also eliminated many of the fouling problems associated with prior ion exchange installations in the field of metal recovery.

With the increased pressure of federal effluent regulations, the ever-increasing price of metals, and the concern for resource conservation, ion exchange is now not only one of the most effective treatment methods for metals removal and recovery, but is also an economically justified treatment system.

METAL REMOVAL PROCESSES

Coagulation and Precipitation

The most common method for removing metals from water is to precipitate them from solution as insoluble metal hydroxides. Lime is generally used as the source of hydroxide ions and a coagulant is normally added to assist in the settling characteristics of the hydroxide floc. The residual metal values after treatment vary for each metal in direct proportion to the solubility of the metal hydroxides. Thus, the minimum effluent quality obtainable from a hydroxide precipitation is theoretically equal to the solubility of the metal hydroxide at the operating pH of the precipitator. Additional factors such as metals adsorbing on the surface of the floc may further reduce residual metals in the water. However, the remaining residuals often exceed many discharge limitations, thereby rendering the hydroxide precipitation process unsuitable in many instances. Even when the metal hydroxide is sufficiently insoluble to meet water quality standards, the problems of floc carry-over and the presence of complexing agents, which inhibit metal precipitation, can cause unreliable performance of hydroxide precipitation processes.

The problem of solubility of metal hydroxides and interference from complexing agents can be overcome by precipitation as the metal sulfide. The problems of hydrogen sulfide generation and formation of soluble complexes of sulfide ions are avoided by the use of a patented process known as "Sulfex".[1] This new process involves coagulation and precipitation of metals which have been reacted with slightly soluble ferrous sulfide. Table 1 shows the differences in solubilities between metal hydroxides and metal sulfides at pH 8.0. In general, sulfide precipitations give lower metal residuals in the treated effluent and can be done at lower pH than comparative hydroxide precipitation processes. An additional advantage to the Sulfex process is that it removes both hexavalent and trivalent chromium in one step, because the

TABLE 1

Calculated Solubilities of Metal Hydroxides and Sulfides at pH 8

	Solubility in mg/l at pH 8.0	
Metal	Hydroxide	Sulfide
Iron	2.2×10^{-15}	1.4×10^{-4}
Nickel	1.2×10^{2}	3.3×10^{-5}
Zinc	7.8×10^{-1}	1.0×10^{-6}
Cadmium	2.8×10^{3}	1.0×10^{-8}
Tin	1.7×10^{-11}	3.8×10^{-8}
Lead	2.5×10^{2}	5.8×10^{-9}
Copper	1.4×10^{-3}	1.6×10^{-13}
Silver	2.2×10^{3}	5.4×10^{-12}
Mercury	6.0×10^{-9}	1.3×10^{-21}

Data from Dean, J. A., Ed., *Lange's Handbook of Chemistry*, 11th ed., McGraw-Hill, New York, 1973.

Sulfex reagent, iron sulfide, has the ability to reduce hexavalent chromium by the following reaction:

$$CrO_4^{=} + FeS + 4H_2O \rightarrow Fe(OH)_3 + Cr(OH)_3 + S^0 + 2OH^- \qquad (1)$$

The hydroxide process only removes trivalent chromium, allowing the soluble hexavalent chromium to pass unchanged into the effluent. If hexavalent chromium is present, it must first be reduced to Cr^{+3} by a separate acidic reduction step before entering a hydroxide precipitator.

For either process, the metal values are not readily recovered from the sludge produced. Past practice has been to send the sludge to landfills, but with the concern over metals leaching into water supplies, permits for disposing of metal-containing sludges at landfill sites are becoming more difficult to obtain.

Reverse Osmosis

Reverse osmosis is the process in which the water to be treated is driven through a semi-permeable membrane by a pressure sufficient to overcome the osmotic pressure of the influent water when it is concentrated a number of times. Thus, only water and some gasses pass through the membrane while salts and particulate material are rejected and concentrated. Thus, for metals removal, reverse osmosis has found commercial applications in treating rinse waters from plating shops.[2] However, often the pretreatment required for reverse osmosis exceeds that required for ion exchangers, and the RO membranes commercially available have strict operating pH limits which must be maintained. Other disadvantages are that metals cannot be selectively removed from solution by reverse osmosis and the rejection of metal salts may only be 90 to 97%, which may be insufficient removal for meeting strict discharge limitations.

The technology of reverse osmosis is still young, and better membranes are being developed to withstand greater pH variations.[3] At the present time, the available membranes are designed to desalinate water and, therefore, application of reverse osmosis membranes for metals removal is restricted to a very limited market.

Carbon Adsorption

Metals can be removed from solutions by activated carbon due either to physical adsorption, precipitation, or exchange with weak acid groups on the carbon. Hexavalent chromium, mercury, and zinc are just a few of the metals which have successfully been removed from water by activated carbon.[4,5] As might be expected, capacities are low and regeneration of the carbon with acid or base is sluggish at best. In fact, capacities will vary from batch to batch of carbon because the amount of oxygenated groups found in carbon, which are largely responsible for the ability of carbon to remove various metals, is a function of the oxygen content of the environment during thermal processing of the carbon.

Investigations into the use of activated carbon for metals removal will continue due to the fact that carbon is a relatively cheap commodity when compared to ion exchange and chelating resins. Also, carbon can withstand rather severe operating conditions and may be less sensitive to competing salt backgrounds than conventional ion exchangers. Acceptance of activated carbon as a feasible treatment method for metals removal will be largely dependent on the ability of carbon manufacturers to provide carbons having reproducible capacities for metals removal.

Liquid Ion Exchange

Liquid ion exchange is the process of exchanging ions in water for ions contained in an oil-soluble and water-immiscible ionic organic compound. Generally, the organic ion exchange reagent is dissolved in an organic carrier solvent. Upon mixing of the organic and water phases, the ion exchange reactions occur. The two phases are then separated and the metal-bearing organic phase is then regenerated or "stripped" of its metal content by mixing with an aqueous phase which is capable of reversing the ion exchange equilibrium.[6]

This system has the major advantages of rapid kinetics and the ability to treat waters having moderate turbidity and suspended solids levels. A disadvantage is that some of the organic phase is transferred to the water phase, thereby creating a secondary waste treatment problem. Also, the separation of the oil and water phases is not always possible due to the formation of emulsions. The major field of application for liquid ion exchange has been in the uranium industry where the water phase is recirculated.

Resin Ion Exchange

Resin ion exchange is the reversible exchange of

ions between a solid and a liquid in which there is no substantial change in the structure of the solid. Modern ion exchangers are predominantly insoluble plastic matrices in the form of spheres, ranging in size from 0.3 to 1 mm diameter. The kinetics of ion exchange are largely dependent on ion diffusion through the liquid film surrounding the resin particles and on diffusion through the pore or gel structure. The size of the solid ion exchangers has been selected so that the kinetics are good while still maintaining a minimum pressure drop across the ion exchange bed during service. The plastic matrix is generally a cross-linked polystyrene structure, although some ion exchange resins have an acrylic structure. If the metals are in solution as a cationic species, such as Cr^{+3}, then removal from solution is done with cation exchange resins which have carboxylic or sulfonic acid functional groups. If the metals are in solution as an anionic complex, such as $CrO_4^=$, then anion exchange resins are used which have tertiary or quaternary amine functionality.

Since the ion exchange resins are insoluble solids, there are no problems with phase separations and additional pollution of the water with oils as found in liquid ion exchange systems.

A major disadvantage of ion exchange resins when used in packed columns is their inability to treat streams even only moderately high in turbidity or suspended solids. Ion exchangers also tend to be fouled by organics, particularly by large organic acids such as humic or fulvic, which accumulate on the resin beads, resulting in incomplete removal during regeneration. In such cases, capacity is lost not only to the ion exchange sites neutralized by the organic acids, but also by the physical blockage of other available exchange sites. In most cases, simple sand filtration is sufficient pretreatment for suspended solids and activated carbon does a good job of protecting ion exchangers from organic foulants.

The uranium industry has partly circumvented the problem of treating waters containing high levels of suspended solids with ion exchange resins by developing the resin-in-pulp process.[7] This process contains the resin in baskets which are dipped into the uranium-containing solution. Thus, suspended fine solids are not filtered out of solution to cause high pressure drops, bed packing, and possible crushing of the resin. Rather, the suspended solids are passed through the fluidized body of resin and are found in the ion exchange effluent.

The major advantage of ion exchange resins in metallurgical applications is their ability to not only remove the metals from solution sufficient to meet water discharge requirements, but to allow recovery and reuse of the metals.

The remainder of this chapter will review some of the more promising applications for ion exchange removal and recovery of metals.

ION EXCHANGE APPLICATION

Chromium

Plating Rinse Waters

The largest single source of chrome-bearing waste waters is the metal plating industry. These waste waters result from rinsing the plated material to free it of residual metals, brighteners, and chromic acid carried out of the plating bath with the finished product. This carryover of plating bath constituents is often referred to as "drag out" and results in both hexavalent and trivalent chromium contamination of the rinse baths. Countercurrent rinsing with recycled demineralized water has greatly reduced rinse water requirements while improving the quality of the plated product. The demineralized water is obtained from a standard two-step demineralizer. A strong acid cation resin operating in the hydrogen cycle will exchange H^+ ions for the trivalent chrome contaminant in the rinse water as well as any other cations. The strong base anion resin operating in the hydroxyl form will then exchange OH^- ions for chromates (Cr^{+6}) which will be present as $Cr_2O_7^=$ after hydrogen cycle exchange. The effluent water from the demineralizers is recycled back to the rinsing tanks. A simple flow sheet employing conventional ion exchange equipment is shown in Figure 1. Reciprocating flow ion exchange, a system which employs fine mesh resin and shallow beds, has also been used for this application.[8]

The concentration of chromate found in the rinse water can vary from 10 to 1000 ppm depending on the rinse flow rate, drag out time, etc., but normally concentrations of 100 to 200 ppm chromate are found. This chromate can be recovered either as sodium chromate or chromic acid. Elution of the anion exchanger with sodium hydroxide results in an eluant rich in sodium chromate. If chromic acid is desired, this eluate may be passed through another bed of a hydrogen cycle cation exchanger which will remove the sodium ions and replace them with hydrogen ions.

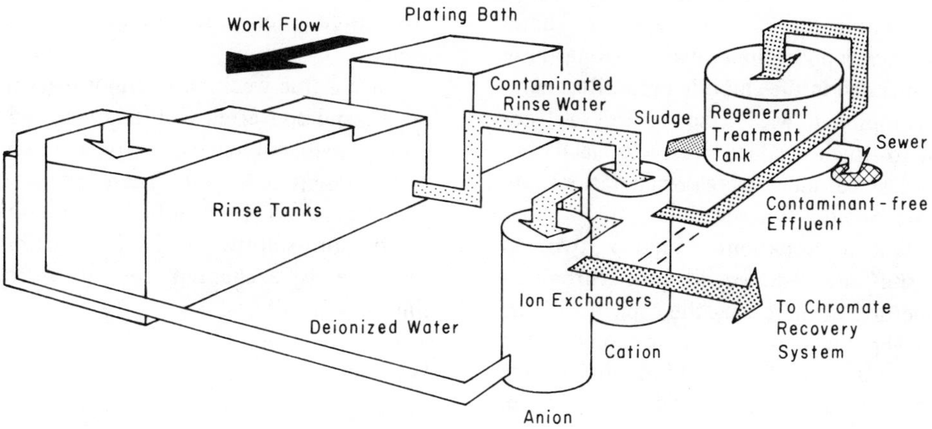

FIGURE 1. Closed-loop ion exchange treatment system for plating rinse waters. (Courtesy of Permutit Company, Paramus, N.J.)

The resulting 2 to 5% chromic acid solution can then be returned to the bath as make-up for evaporation losses.[9]

Regeneration of the cation exchanger used to remove trivalent chromium and other trace metal cations is done with sulfuric or hydrochloric acid. Recovery of the metal values from this regenerant eluant is neither economical nor desirable. Therefore, arrangements must be made for disposing of this concentrated waste stream. Neutralization and precipitation as the metal hydroxide is commonly employed with the sludge being dewatered and sent to landfill.

The process should be limited to those finishing processes that produce relatively dilute rinse solutions, that is, within a range of less than 500 ppm dissolved solids. It cannot be used on rinses containing metallic cyanides exclusively, but can be effective for treating certain percentages of cyanides in mixed rinses. The addition of a weak base exchanger before the strong base resin is one means of successfully treating rinse waters containing metal cyanides.

Cooling Tower Blowdown

Blowdown from high temperature duty cooling tower circuits which utilize zinc-synergized chromate-corrosion inhibitors constitutes a second major source of chromium pollutants entering the nation's waterways. A typical analysis for cooling tower blowdown from cooling circuits employing zinc chromate inhibitors is shown in Table 2. Normally, blowdown in the range of 500 to 3500 mg/l total dissolved solids are presently encountered. In the future, cooling systems will be

TABLE 2

Typical Analysis of Petrochemical Industry Cooling Tower Blowdown

Calcium (Ca)	200 mg/l
Magnesium (Mg)	30 mg/l
Sodium (Na)	400 mg/l
Zinc (Zn)	3 mg/l
Iron (Fe)	2 mg/l
Bicarbonate (HCO_3)	50 mg/l
Chloride (Cl)	520 mg/l
Sulfate (SO_4)	540 mg/l
Silica (SiO_2)	35 mg/l
Chromate (CrO_4)	20 mg/l
Suspended solids	40 mg/l
Total dissolved solids	1900 mg/l
pH	6.4

maintained at increasing cycles of concentration, with side stream treatment, resulting in blowdowns containing up to 10,000 mg/l dissolved solids. The high ratio of total anions to chromate requires a highly selective ion exchange process.

Strong Base Resins

The hexavalent chromium is present as $CrO_4^=$ in cooling tower blowdown and as such it can be removed by a strong base exchanger in the hydroxide or salt form:

$$2(R_4N^+)OH^- + CrO_4^= \rightleftharpoons (R_4N^+)_2CrO_4^= + 2OH^- \quad (2)$$

$$2(R_4N^+)Cl^- + CrO_4^= \rightleftharpoons (R_4N^+)_2CrO_4^= + 2Cl^- \quad (3)$$

Operation in the hydroxide cycle is not recommended due to the danger of forming metallic precipitates within the ion exchange bed. Therefore, industrial applications using strong base resins are operated in the chloride cycle. Regeneration is accomplished with 5 to 10 lb NaCl per cubic foot to which is added 2 to 5 lb NaOH per cubic foot, since incomplete regenerations are obtained with sodium chloride alone.

Notice that in Equations 2 and 3, two ion exchange sites are required for one chromium atom. A method of increasing the capacity of the ion exchanger for chromate is to convert the chromate ($CrO_4^{=}$) in the feed to dichromate ($Cr_2O_7^{=}$) by the addition of acid as shown in Equation 4.[10]

$$CrO_4^{=} \underset{OH^-}{\overset{H^+}{\rightleftharpoons}} Cr_2O_7^{=} \quad (4)$$

Acidification of the blowdown feed to a pH range of 4.5 to 5 takes full advantage of the increase in capacity obtained when loading with dichromate instead of chromate ion. For instance, at an influent pH of 6.5, the maximum chromate loading capacity for a strong base resin is 2 lb CrO_4 per cubic foot. At pH 4.9, the maximum capacity is 4 to 5 lb CrO_4 per cubic foot.

Several alternatives are available to direct in-line acidification. One method is to use a carboxylic weak acid exchanger in the hydrogen form ahead of the anion exchanger.[11] A second method is to load at a neutral pH and then acidify the chromate-laden resin. This will convert the chromate to dichromate and free an equivalent number of ion exchange sites for additional chromate loading.[12]

Weak Base Resins

The use of weak base resins for chromate removal was described in the literature as early as 1945.[13] Macroporous weak base resin is now becoming the resin of choice for chromate removal from cooling tower blowdown. This is due to the ability of macroporous weak base resins to resist fouling by organics because of their open and discrete porous structure, which permits easier diffusion of large organic molecules through the beads. Furthermore, they have a low ion exchange capacity for weak organic acids. Other advantages include their increased chemical and thermal stability properties. Also, elution of the dichromate with sodium hydroxide, which converts the resin to the equilibrium favored nonionized free base form, is very efficient, with little tendency to tail off as is common with salt regenerated strong base resins.

Once a true weak base resin is regenerated with caustic and converted to the nonionized free base form, it will not remove chromate from solution when present as the salt. Therefore, after elution, the resin must be acidified with either hydrochloric or sulfuric acid. During service, the chromate is exchanged for the corresponding chlorides or sulfates.

Loading cycle

$$2(R_3N^+H)Cl^- + Na_2Cr_2O_7 \rightarrow (R_3NH^+)_2Cr_2O_7^{=} + 2NaCl \quad (5)$$

Elution

$$(R_3N^+H)_2\ Cr_2O_7^{=} + 4NaOH \rightarrow 2R_3N\!: + 2Na_2CrO_4 + 3H_2O \quad (6)$$

The recovered sodium chromate is fed back to the cooling tower.

Acidification of resin

$$R_3N\!: + HCl \rightarrow (R_3N^+H)\ Cl^- \quad (7)$$

As noted for strong base resins, the pH of the influent will influence the capacity of the resin for chromate. Figure 2 illustrates the influence of pH and chromate concentration on the loading capacity of the sulfate-form resin at a constant salt background of 500 ppm chlorides and 500 ppm sulfates. Higher salt background will further reduce capacity.

Average leakages of 0.5 to 1 ppm Cr^{+6} can be obtained from a single column co-flow system. This leakage can be reduced to a level between 0.2 and 0.3 ppm with a polishing column. The lower values are obtainable when hydrochloric acid is used for the acidification step. Leakages below 0.1 ppm Cr^{+6} are readily obtainable from a counterflow regenerated system.[12] Counterflow operation not only yields the lowest possible leakage for any ion exchange system, but does so without the need for a polishing column, thus reducing resin and equipment inventory. The excellent elution of chromate from a counterflow regenerated weak base resin which was operated in the sulfate form is shown in Figure 3.

Copper

Recovery of copper from rayon wastes was one

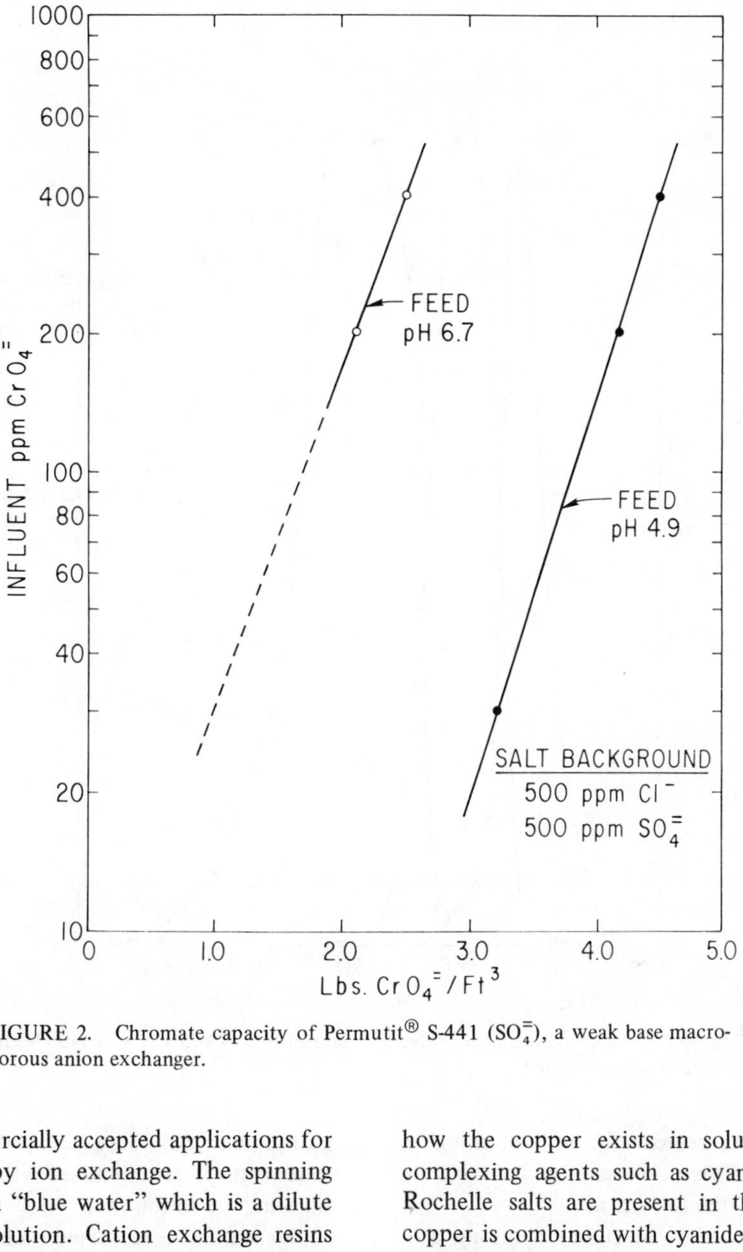

FIGURE 2. Chromate capacity of Permutit® S-441 ($SO_4^=$), a weak base macroporous anion exchanger.

of the first commercially accepted applications for metals recovery by ion exchange. The spinning process produces a "blue water" which is a dilute cuprammonium solution. Cation exchange resins are used to remove and recover the copper from this "blue water" in which the copper is present as $Cu(NH_3)_4^{++}$. The early resins used were phenol-formaldehyde and bisulfite condensation products.[14] Later, sulfonated coal and standard strong and weak acid resins were used.[15] Daily operating costs are minimized by regenerating the copper-laden cation resin with the sulfuric acid solution used for spinning rayon.

Removal of copper from plating rinse waters and wastes streams is also possible by ion exchange resins. However, a thorough analysis must first be made for each application to accurately determine how the copper exists in solution. Oftentimes, complexing agents such as cyanides, EDTA, and Rochelle salts are present in the wastes. If the copper is combined with cyanide, for example, the copper will not be removed by cation exchange resins. Rather, anion exchange resins are used to pick up the entire metal complex. When complexing agents are present in the waste stream, then a complete laboratory study is essential for selecting the proper ion exchange process.

Nickel

Nickel is readily recovered by strong acid ion exchangers. Rinse baths from nickel plating operations are purified by passing the nickel-bearing rinse water first through a cation exchanger to remove the nickel and then through a strong base

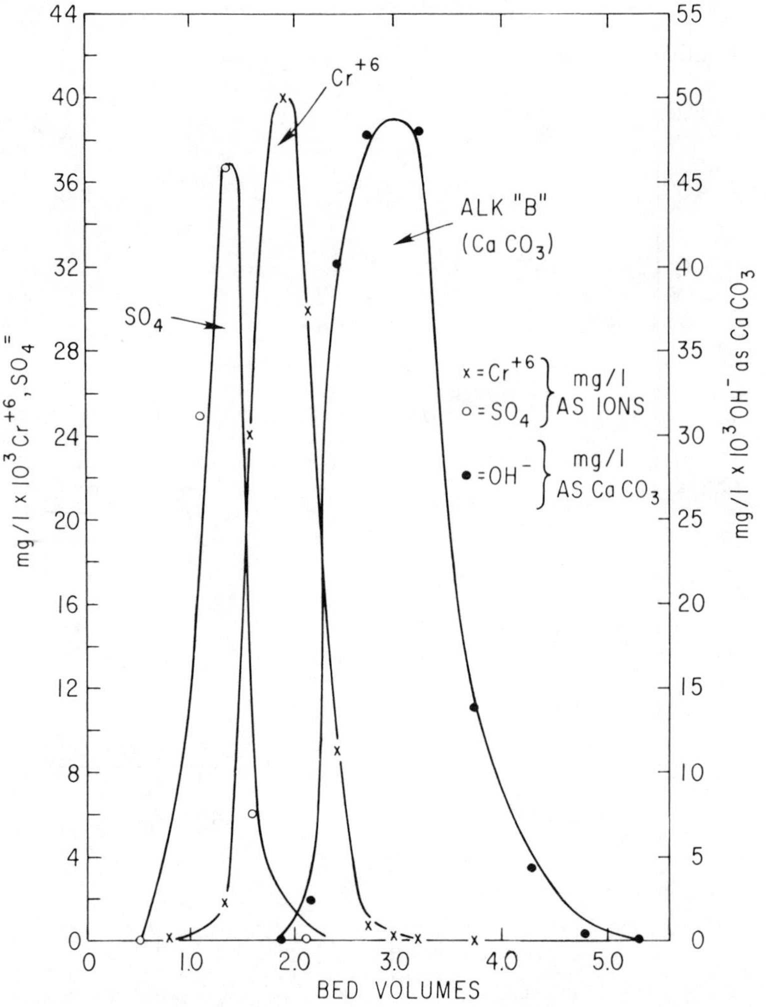

FIGURE 3. Chromate elution curve for Permutit® S-441 ($SO_4^{=}$) which has been counterflow regenerated.

anion exchanger to remove the sulfate, chloride, and borate ions. The nickel can be recovered by regenerating with 10% sulfuric acid.

Operating capacities for standard strong acid cation resins range from 1.2 to 1.8 lb of nickel recovered per cubic foot of resin. The loading capacities are affected by the acid dosage and the influent nickel concentrations, with the lower capacities being obtained with influent Ni concentrations below 50 ppm. Normally, 6 to 10 lb H_2SO_4 per cubic foot is required to regenerate the resin.

The organics present in the system must be removed by a carbon bed prior to the ion exchange columns. The strong base anion resin is generally the resin which is seriously fouled by organics, but the low pH condition present in the cation unit can cause precipitation of soaps and detergents present in mixed waste waters, thus also blinding the cation resin.

To maximize recovered nickel concentration, a split elution process is recommended. After sending the water in the resin voids to waste, the next portion of regenerant effluent will be the richest in nickel content. This portion is recovered as product for return to the plating bath. When the nickel content of the regenerant effluent decreases, the flow to the product tank is stopped and the remainder of the regenerant eluant is collected in one or more "save rinse" tanks. The recovered regenerant in the "save rinse" tanks is fortified with additional regenerant and used for the first part of the next regeneration sequence. Whenever a split elution technique is used for strong acid resins, it is imperative that the final portion of regenerant is essentially fresh regenerant uncontaminated with nickel ions.

By use of the split elution technique, nickel concentrations of 20 to 50 g/l (2.7 to 6.6 oz/gal) can be obtained. Both conventional fixed bed and reciprocating flow ion exchange have been successfully used for nickel recovery applications.[16]

Uranium

Introduction

By far, the largest single use of ion exchange resins in metal separation has been in the concentration and purification of uranium from its ores. The uranium production requirements of the 1950s and 1960s were largely satisfied by anion exchange separation of uranium from sulfuric acid leach solutions, based on the classic paper on metal removal by anion exchange by Sussman, Nachod, and Wood.[17] The first large plant to go into operation was in South Africa at West Rand Consolidated Mines in 1952. This technology was applied in more than 60 ion exchange plants throughout the world in South Africa, Canada, Australia, the Belgian Congo and the United States. Detailed histories and descriptions of these technologies may be found in the literature.[18-21]

With the current price of uranium at $40 per pound, there is a mounting incentive to obtain uranium from lower grade sources. Ion exchange as a means of separation is attractive because the concentration of uranium in the leach solution from low grade ores will be less than 300 ppm. In fact, uranium may be recovered from sources as low as a few parts per million in some well waters used for plant supply. The technique of direct precipitation from leach liquor is impractical in dilute solutions. Solvent extraction, which has been the major alternative to ion exchange as a concentration technique, loses much of its appeal because of solvent losses and a tendency to produce inseparable emulsions. Thus, ion exchange will, without a doubt, be depended on as the major separation means for uranium in the future.

Under contract by the United States Atomic Energy Commission (USAEC), Dr. Robert C. Merritt, Director of Colorado School of Mines Research Institute, has published an excellent history of this major development and a detailed summary and evaluation of the technology.[18] These works include an extensive bibliography, particularly the commendable work of the Watertown, Massachusetts Laboratory of USAEC.

Resin Characteristics

Chemistry of Process

Leaching of the ore with sulfuric acid or ammonium carbonate under oxidizing conditions results in the formation of the anionic complex uranyl sulfate or carbonate:

$$UO_2 + 1/2O_2 \rightarrow UO_3 \tag{8}$$

$$UO_3 + 2H_2SO_4 \rightarrow [UO_2(SO_4)_2]^{=} + H_2O \tag{9}$$

$$[UO_2(SO_4)_2]^{=} + SO_4^{=} \rightarrow [UO_2(SO_4)_3]^{-4} \tag{10}$$

The uranium must be oxidized from the plus 4 valence state to the plus 6 state for dissolution and formation of the soluble anionic complex. Control of oxidation is accomplished by emf potentiometric measurements.

In ammonium carbonate leaching, a similar set of equilibrium reactions results in the formation of tetravalent tricarbonate complex anion $[UO_2(CO_3)_3]^{-4}$. The divalent complex $[UO_2(CO_3)_2 \cdot H_2O]^{-2}$ is believed to dominate at low carbonate concentrations.

The reactions with the anion exchange resin may be shown as:

$$4RX + [UO_2(SO_4)_3]^{-4} \rightarrow R_4UO_2(SO_4)_3 + 4X^- \tag{11}$$

where R is the fixed ion structure, usually quaternary ammonium affixed to a cross-linked styrene copolymer, and X is the mobile ion.

In general, the affinity of ion exchange resins increases with the valence and for multivalent ions with decreasing solution concentration. Ions with higher atomic number are held more tightly because of smaller hydrated ionic volume. Thus, the tetravalent uranyl sulfate or carbonate ion may be expected to be adsorbed virtually completely from dilute solution even in the presence of substantial concentrations of other competing anions, and indeed it is. However, as will be cited in the section on resin poisoning, certain ions are held even more tightly than the uranyl sulfate.

While quaternary ammonium strong base anion resins have been used successfully for 25 years or more in uranium separation of both sulfate and carbonate complexes, during the last few years weak base tertiary amine resins have been applied to a limited extent to acid circuits.[22-24] The advantages claimed include greater selectivity for uranium with consequent higher purity and better recovery of nitrate after elution. True weak base resins will not function in carbonate solution, because their functional amine groups are insufficiently ionized in the presence of the hydroxyl ions in equilibrium with high carbonate concentrations.

Special resins developed for the nuclear energy industry having unique properties, such as stability to radiation attack, also showed excellent properties for uranium separation. These contain some pyridinium groups as the active amine; their properties are described by Merritt[18] and by Greer.[25]

Physical Characteristics

For use in conventional fixed beds with clarified uranium-bearing leach solutions, the ion exchange beads are of mesh size 95% through 16 on 50 (U.S. Standard series). For other types of contacting, such as resin-in-pulp (RIP), upflow contacting in columns, and most of the continuous countercurrent approaches of contacting, coarse mesh resin 90% through 10 on 20 mesh is employed.

Operating Characteristics

The capacity of strong base resin for the uranyl complex is approximately 1.0 to 1.2 meq/ml. Working capacities of 2 to 5 lb U_3O_8 per cubic foot are realized depending on the solution characteristics, on the type of resin, and on the efficiency of contacting. Virtually all of the early installations used a merry-go-round system of adsorption or loading in which two and sometimes three columns operate in series. When the lead column is fully loaded, it is taken off stream. A freshly eluted column is added at the tail end, and the pregnant feed solution is fed to the partially loaded column. The polisher column then picks up uranium which leaks through the lead column after it has reached breakthrough.

Elution can be achieved by the conventional practice of shifting the equilibrium by the mass action effect of applying relatively concentrated solutions of salts to reverse the ion exchange equilibrium in Reaction 11 to the left. Alternatively and preferably, elution is accomplished by changing the nature of the adsorbed anionic uranyl complex to one with lower valence, or uncharged form, or even to the cationic form. This is done in acid circuits by passing an acidified (0.1 *N*) salt solution of chloride or nitrate (0.8 to 0.9 *N*). The associated cation has some effect, particularly when the acidifying agent is H_2SO_4 in the order of $Mg^{++} > Na^+ > NH_4^+$.

Sulfuric Acid Leaching Systems

Leaching

Leaching is conducted of ore ground to pass 28 mesh using sulfuric acid at about 40 to 120 lb/ton of ore and 0.4 to 1% concentration in the presence of an oxidant so that the emf is -400 to -500 mV (hydrogen electrode potential = 0). Several oxidants have been employed with MnO_2 and $NaClO_3$ the most common. The presence of ferric iron expedites the oxidation by serving as a carrier of oxygen. The solution is then separated by clarifiers and/or countercurrent decantation techniques with ore washing. Flocculation aids have been a boon to clarification by settling. For fixed bed ion exchange, the leach solution is filtered to less than 5 ppm suspended solids.

Loading

The filtered leach solution is passed through the ion-exchange resin bed at 1.5 to 2 gal/min/ft^3, and the uranyl sulfate is exchanged onto the resin, releasing an equivalent amount of chloride or nitrate ions until these counter-ions have been removed from the active sites as "royal barren." Thereafter, uranyl sulfate complex exchange is for sulfate ions.

An outstanding feature of ion exchange concentration of uranyl sulfate is the separation accomplished by proper selection of the process. Among the unwanted metallic species frequently present in sulfuric acid leach solutions are iron, vanadium, molybdenum, and in South Africa, cobalt cyanide complexes. Other impurities are polythionates and, in some ores, organic compounds.

Ferric iron sulfate complexes and vanadium adsorption is depressed by adjusting both the pH to 1.3 to 1.5 and the emf to -400 to -500 mV to assure that ferrous iron is present to reduce vanadium to the tetravalent state. Then, when two columns are operating in series in a merry-go-round mode, most of these ions are displaced forward by the uranyl sulfate. Since ion exchange is an equilibrium process, not all competing ions will be displaced forward and, consequently, some will be found on the loaded resin. Most of these ions will be removed by the elution solutions. Special precipitation techniques must then be used to avoid U_3O_8 yellow cake contamination.

Elution

After adsorption or loading, the bed is backwashed to loosen and regrade it, removing any dirt which may have accumulated from the feed.

Frequently, a split elution technique is used in which the elution effluent, after discharge of the water in the voids of the resin bed, is separated into a product fraction and recycle fraction. Recycle is fortified by adding salt and acid before reuse in the next cycle. Uranium concentrations in solution going to precipitation are 5 to 10 grams U_3O_8 per liter for chloride and 10 to 20 g/l for nitrate, representing a concentration factor of 20 or 30 to 1 when feeding conventional leach concentrations of 0.5 to 1 g U_3O_8 per liter.

Precipitation

Precipitation of the uranium as a mixture of diuranates, hydrated oxides, and basic uranyl sulfates is accomplished in one, or more frequently two, steps by neutralizing the acidic elution effluent with lime and caustic soda, magnesia, or ammonia, under relatively closely controlled conditions, sometimes with seeding. The "yellow cake" is then dewatered, dried, packaged, and shipped to the sintering plant and market.

Eluex Process

The Eluex Process is a modification of the elution-precipitation step which is designed to keep nitrate and chloride out of the system and to produce a purer yellow cake. In this process, elution in the acid circuit is done with 90 to 120 g/l H_2SO_4 and the elution effluent is extracted with either amine or phosphate solvent. Stripping from the solvent is then accomplished with carbonate for phosphate solvent and with ammonium sulfate for amine solvent. Yellow cake precipitation then follows standard procedure.

Resin Poisons

Some ions are adsorbed more strongly than the uranyl sulfate, accumulating on the active sites of the resin or physically blocking the resin pores. Among these are molybdate, pentavalent vanadate, cobalt cyanide complexes, polythionates, and certain organic acids, notably humic and fulvic acids. Some of these form polymer-like compounds. Other poisons are oil and asphaltic materials which coat the resin. Silica may form polymers or gels within the resin structure due to the increase in internal pH as a result of the Donnan equilibrium effect.

Fouling results in sluggish kinetics of the resin, early breakthrough, high leakage, lower capacity, and decreased concentrations going to precipitation.

Caustic soda is the usual treatment used for regenerating poisoned or fouled resin. Alkaline treatment followed by a salt treatment removes trithionate and thiosulfate. Strong (12 *N*) sulfuric acid treatment has been used effectively to regenerate resins fouled with titanium, zirconium, molybdenum, thorium, iron, silica, and organics. Sometimes, a caustic treatment is also necessary after acid. Even more drastic types of treatment may be necessary, sometimes lasting for several days to allow diffusion to take place.

No data are available on the relative poisoning susceptibility of the macroporous resins, as these were developed long after the processes described above were adopted. However, porous resins are expected to be less likely to foul than tightly structural resins and, if fouled, they should be more readily regenerated or cleaned.

Alkaline Leaching Systems

Leaching

Uranium ores which are high in calcite or other acid-consuming constituents may be leached with sodium or amonium carbonate-bicarbonate solution in the presence of oxidizing agent to solubilize the uranium and form the uranyl tricarbonate anion complex.

The increasing scarcity of ores 0.2% or higher in grade has necessitated reliance on resources containing much less U_3O_8, mostly 0.1% or less. At $28 per ton for underground mining and $12 for open pit, the cost of mining and hauling such low grade ores is prohibitive. In addition, the skills necessary for such work are largely unavailable in the remote areas where uranium is found.

These circumstances and the ability to realize rapid cash flow have led to a revolutionary movement toward *in situ* mining – a technique of leaching the ore by circulating the leach solution through the ore body to solubilize the uranium. *In situ* mining eliminates much of the plant equipment required for conventional hydrometallurgical operations, such as transport and handling of the ore, milling, leach processes, and liquid-solid separation. Thus, a great deal of engineering, fabrication, and construction time and costs is eliminated. Consequently, a production facility can be brought on stream quickly. The ore body must be suitably located not over 500 ft below the surface but under the water table, and must be of adequate porosity. The solutions used for *in situ* mining are ammonium carbonate of approximately 3000 ppm to 5000 ppm concentration applied through injection wells to the ore body, usually located several hundred feet below the surface. Small amounts of oxidants such as chlorate or hydrogen peroxide are added. The solutions are withdrawn by production wells located 20 to 50 ft from the injection well in a pattern similar to those developed for secondary and tertiary recovery operations in oil production.

In solution mining, uranium concentrations of pregnant solution from the various production wells vary greatly depending on the nature of the ore body and leach solution, how long the well has been producing, ground water influx, rates of pumping, and other factors. Blending of solutions from numerous wells results in concentrations ranging from 50 to several hundred parts per million U_3O_8.

Pretreatment

In solution mining, it is not necessary to go through the elaborate liquid-solid separation and solids washing techniques of conventional hydrometallurgical processes. However, the solutions are pressurized and supersaturated with calcium carbonate. The $CaCO_3$ is derived from two sources. Some comes from dissolution of the calcite by the acidity produced during the oxidation of sulfur compounds from the pyrites usually present and some comes from ion exchange of calcium in the clays. As carbon dioxide is released from the solution, calcium carbonate comes out of solution and deposits. Also present are small amounts of fine particulates of clay and silica from some wells.

Clarification is accomplished by the application of conventional water softening by lime or ammonia reacting with bicarbonate to form substantially insoluble calcium carbonate:

$$Ca(HCO_3)_2 + Ca(OH)_2 \rightarrow 2CaCO_3\downarrow + 2H_2O \qquad (12)$$

$$Ca(HCO_3)_2 + 2NH_4OH \rightarrow CaCO_3\downarrow + (NH_4)_2CO_3 + 2H_2O \qquad (13)$$

Conventional lime softening also removes the major portion of calcium hardness, but produces a voluminous wet sludge which occludes considerable amounts of uranium.

A modification of this conventional process utilizes a fluidized bed contactor, called a Spiractor,[26] to promote crystallization of calcium carbonate on small sand particles, called "catalyst," causing the particles to grow in size until they are large enough to separate as beads at the bottom of the tapered conical vessel. The operation is shown in Figure 4. Periodically, the beads, now grown to 1/16 to 1/8 in. diameter, are removed from the bottom of the unit and dewatered by vibrating screen to 90% solids. The radium present in the production well leach water coprecipitates with the $CaCO_3$ hardness to form manageable granules instead of a voluminous sludge of only 5 to 10% solids.

The Spiractor effluent, softened to 10 to 20 ppm $CaCO_3$ depending on carbonate level, contains 10 to 15 ppm suspended solids and therefore must be filtered before contacting fixed bed ion exchange. After filtration, it is stabilized by recarbonation to assure that no $CaCO_3$ precipitates out of the saturated solution.

Loading

The stabilized, clear solution is then passed through strong base anion exchange beds at flow rates up to 3 gal/min/ft^3 where the uranyl tricarbonate anion of valence minus 4 exchanges for carbonate ions on the resin. A tabulation of the most commonly used resins is shown in Table 3. Capacity is about 4 to 6 lb U_3O_8 per cubic foot, and the uranium complex is adsorbed in preference to most other anions present except vanadate. Vanadium is not present in south Texas ores where *in situ* mining is practiced. Molybdenum is displaced almost quantitatively as shown in Figure 5.[27] At first, both uranyl carbonate and molybdate are adsorbed, virtually completely. Then, the moly breaks through and uranyl carbonate displaces most of the moly which had been adsorbed. Finally, an equilibrium is reached where the moly in the effluent is equal to that in the influent, but some residual molybdenum remains on the resin proportional to the concentration ratio to uranium in the influent.

Elution

Elution of adsorbed uranyl carbonate may be accomplished by using 1 *M* NaCl or $NaNO_3$ solutions. Small amounts of sodium carbonate or bicarbonate expedite the elution.

Alternatively, uranyl carbonate may be eluted with 1 *M* amonium carbonate solution, as shown in Figure 6.[27] By the split elution technique, in which the latter portion of eluate effluent is used as the first portion in the next run, uranium oxide concentrations of product fraction for precipita-

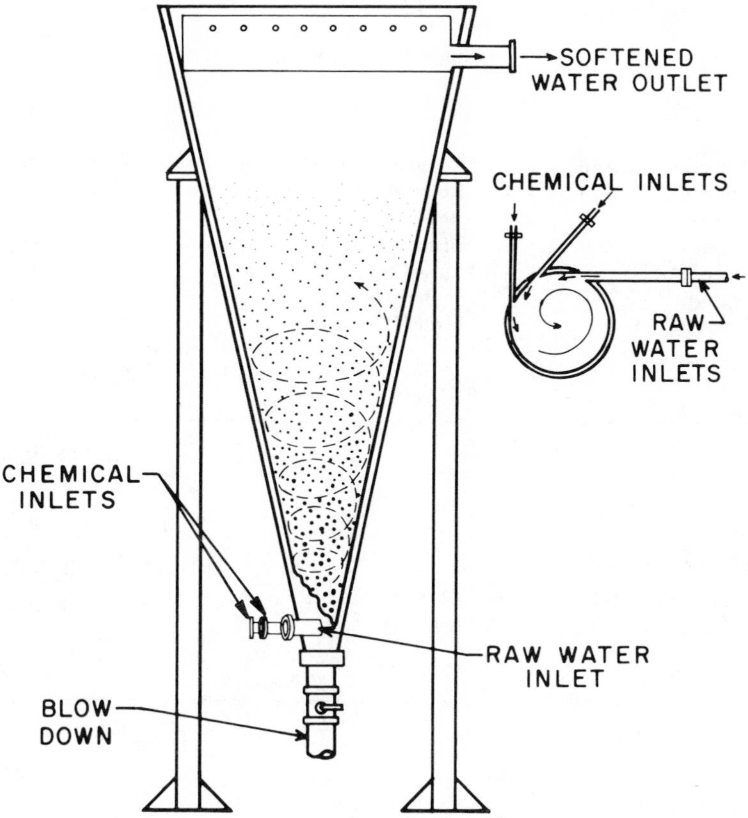

FIGURE 4. Cross-Sectional view of Permutit Spiractor. Insert gives detail of arrangement of raw water and chemical inlets. (Courtesy of Permutit Company, Paramus, N.J.)

tion average 20,000 ppm U_3O_8 with only about 200 ppm molybdate. The volume of solution going to precipitation is 2.5 to 3.5 bed volumes for resins with good kinetics.

Precipitation

Steam stripping is an effective precipitation means, driving off the amonia and carbon dioxide to precipitate uranium oxides. Other means may be used, such as addition of strong base, acidification, or hydrogen reduction.

Ion Exchange Equipment

Fixed Beds

In South Africa, Belgian Congo, and Canada, most of the ion exchange plants installed in the 1950s were conventional, automatically operated, fixed bed systems. The sets of columns were operated in merry-go-round mode. Usually, two columns were loading in series while the third column was eluting. For conditions where poisoning took place, four column sets were used. The fixed bed downflow contacting method provides an efficient, reliable method of separating U_3O_8 with a minimum of operating and maintenance problems.

Moving bed column systems were employed in six Canadian plants and a few U.S. plants.[28] In these systems, the loaded resin is hydraulically transferred from the lead column of sets of columns used for adsorption and elution to a common backwash tank. After backwash, the resin is transferred to another set of columns for elution; also three in series. After elution, it is returned to the adsorption system in the polishing position.

Other Contacting Methods

Two other techniques of applying ion exchange were developed to contact resin with unclarified leach liquor containing slimes. One method uses large mesh resin in baskets made of screening, 4- to 6-ft cubes, containing 15 to 40 ft^3 of resins 10 to 20 mesh size. Fourteen of these baskets were used

TABLE 3

Uranium Removal Resins

Resin	Manufacturer or distributor	Mesh size
Amberlite® IRA400	Rohm and Haas Company	Conventional
Amberlite® IRA430	Rohm and Haas Company	Large bead
Dowex® 21K	Dow Chemical Company	Large bead
Duolite® A101D	Diamond Shamrock Corp.	Conventional
Ionac® A-580	Ionac Chemical Company	Conventional
Permutit® S-700	Permutit Company	Conventional
Permutit® SK	Permutit Company	Conventional

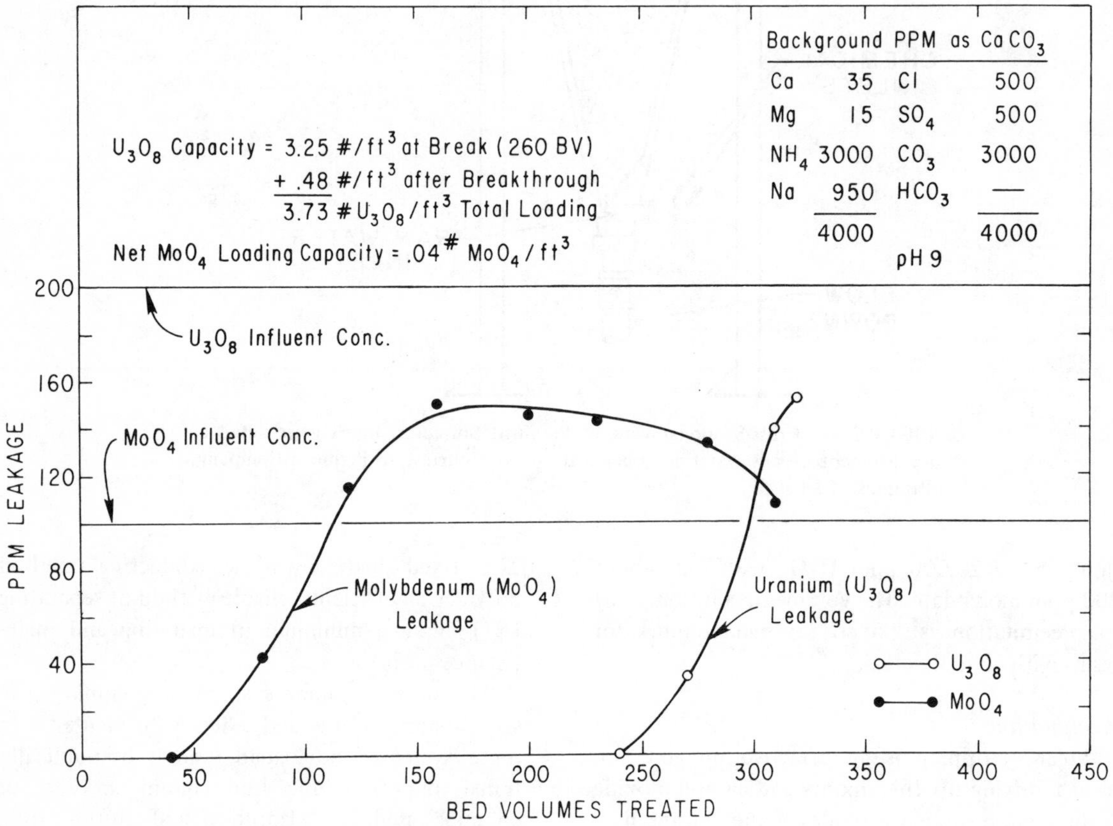

FIGURE 5. Uranium and molybdenum loading curves for Permutit® S-700.

in a system, ten for adsorption and four for elution. The baskets were mechanically moved up and down at a frequency of 6 to 12 strokes per minute.[29] This is the resin-in-pulp or RIP method.

Another method of contacting resin with leach solution containing slimes is the Bureau of Mines sieve plate column.[30] Both adsorption and elution are conducted in a tall, multistage column in which unclarified leach liquor is passed upflow through partitioned beds of resin moving downflow to provide six or more stages of contact. Partitioning of the stages is provided by sieve plates for solution to pass upflow against resin passing downflow through ports in the plates. Loaded resin is withdrawn from the bottom stage and transferred to the top of a smaller elution column of similar design and operation.

Still other types of contactors have been or are

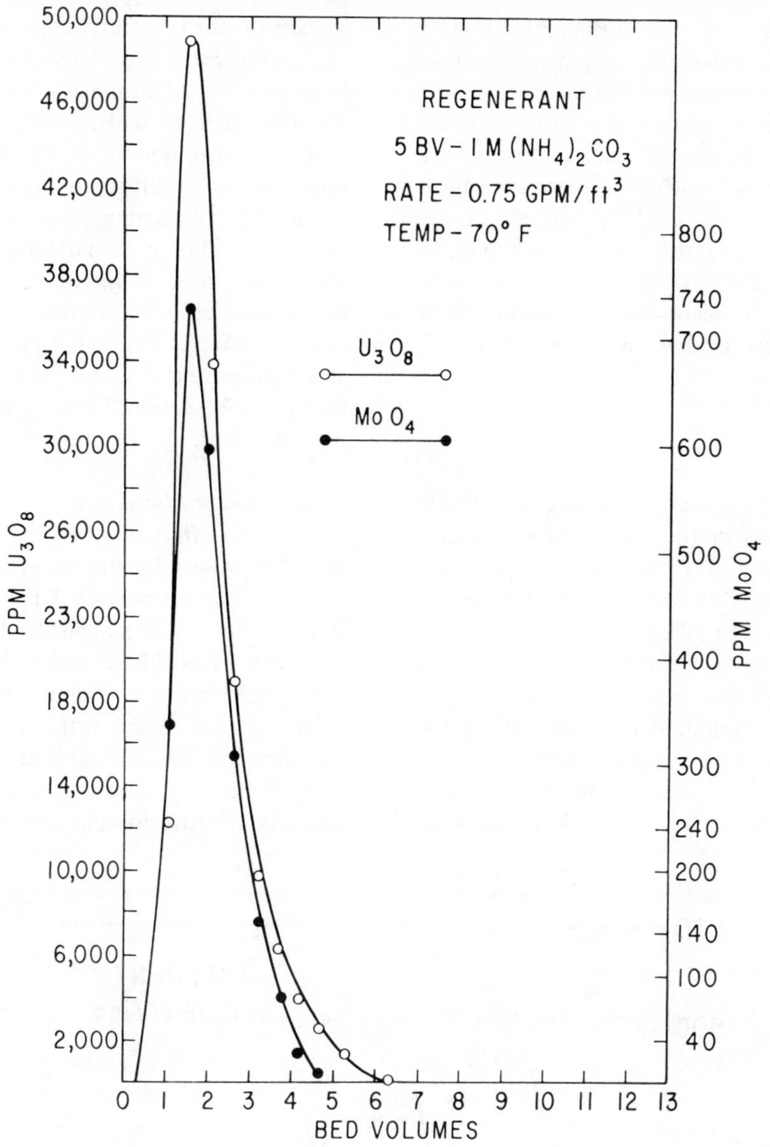

FIGURE 6. Uranium and molybdenum elution curves for Permutit® S-700.

being investigated, including the Porter contactor, the Stanton contactor, the Higgins contactor, the Himsley contactor, the Cloete-Streat contactor, and the NIM contactor of South Africa. All these depend upon movement of resin in a counter-current method through adsorption and elution. All have the disadvantage of requiring a careful balancing of adsorption flow rates and elution flow rates to balance the chemical and stoichiometric requirements of the system. Most of these processes require careful attention to operation and frequent maintenance. Resin attrition and osmotic shock are further factors which must be considered when comparing these systems with conventional fixed bed ion exchange systems which require clarification of feed.

Costs

Ion exchange equipment costs represent 15 to 17% of uranium mill costs when using columns for acid circuits, and 26 to 32% when using resin-in-pulp. Mill costs for the 1950s are summarized by Merritt in his book.[18] No updating to current mill costs has been published and estimates are hazardous because of the high cost of field installation, wide ranges in equipment selection and design, and unknown inflation rates. Some unpublished studies indicate that for a 10-year depreciation, the annualized capital cost of the ion exchange equipment including pretreatment is about 15 cents/lb of U_3O_8 produced. Consequently, there is little justification for skimping on this, the heart of such a unique process, capable of separating and concentrating uranium from resource solutions as low as a few parts per million.

Zinc

Rinse Waters

Zinc removal by ion exchange originally found major applications in the rayon industry where zinc sulfate is used as a hardener in sulfuric acid coagulation baths. Consequently, the rinse waters contain about 100 to 500 ppm of zinc and up to 0.3% acid. Strong acid cation exchangers effectively remove the zinc from this solution despite the low pH background. For instance, at sulfuric acid concentrations below 0.1%, zinc removal is virtually complete.[31] Higher than 0.5% acid background for 500 ppm Zn influent causes some leakage of zinc to occur, but generally not over 5% at reasonable acid backgrounds. Significant leakages occur when the acid background exceeds 1%. These data are plotted in Figure 7.

Zinc is also used in the kaolin industry, which uses zinc hydrosulfite to improve the color of kaolin by solubilizing iron contaminants. Conventional sodium cycle softening using strong acid resins has been suggested for this application where plant effluents contain from 10 to 60 ppm zinc.[32] Leakages below 0.4 ppm Zn are reported at a regeneration dosage of 18.7 lb NaCl per cubic foot as 20% solution. Capacity was 2 to 2.5 lb Zn per cubic foot.

Cooling Tower Blowdown

Zinc can effectively be removed from cooling tower blowdown by the use of sodium-form weak acid resin. Levels below 0.1 ppm Zn are possible. Regeneration is accomplished by removing the zinc with hydrochloric acid and then putting the resin back into the sodium form with caustic. Work has been done with hydrogen-form weak acid resin but only 50% zinc removal was reported.

Unfortunately, standard weak acid resins are not very selective for zinc over calcium.[34] There-

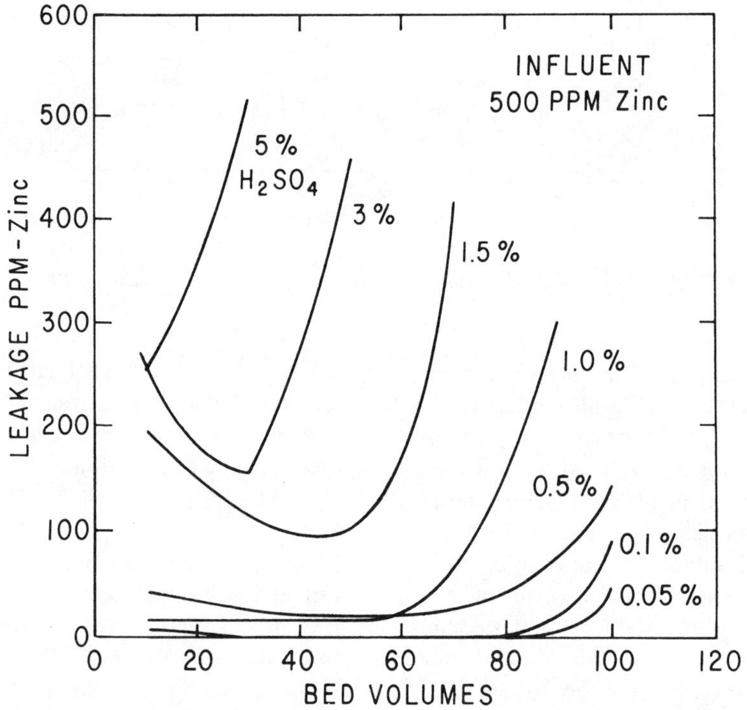

FIGURE 7. Permutit® Q-101 removal of zinc from sulfuric acid influent.

fore, in removing the zinc, the hardness will also be removed thus exhausting the resin much faster than desired. However, the high capacity of these resins for hardness removal allows treatment of three times the amount of blowdown between regenerations compared to standard strong acid resins.

Chelating resins are zinc selective, but they have not yet found wide acceptance mainly due to economic factors. Generally, a chelating resin will cost several times as much as conventional ion exchangers because they are a low volume specialty item for most resin manufacturers. Since the chelating resins are much more specific for zinc than calcium, the chelates are capable of treating many more bed volumes of waste than nonchelating resin counterparts. Operating costs are thus greatly reduced and even capital savings on equipment are possible due to reduced vessel sizes. Resins capable of specificity toward particular ions are destined to be used increasingly, resulting in greater production and thus lower costs in the near future.[35]

Figure 8 compares a standard weak acid resin breakthrough curve with a chelating resin when operating in the sodium cycle on a feed containing 30 ppm Zn, 250 ppm Ca, and 400 ppm Na as ions. This particular chelating resin allowed treatment of 2.5 times the volume of influent than is possible with the standard weak acid resin. Previous work by Chamberlain reported the use of a phosphonic resin for treating a 5.5-ppm zinc influent containing 16.2 ppm Ca, 10 ppm Mg, and 169 ppm Na as ions. Five times the amount of blowdown could be handled by the phosphonic resin than by a conventional carboxylic exchanger.[34] Unfortunately, phosphonic resins are no longer commercially available. The development of a moderately priced chelating resin with high selectivity for zinc could lead to an economical zinc recovery process from cooling tower blowdowns.

EQUIPMENT DESIGN CONSIDERATIONS

Ion exchange, as a unit operation, has unique capabilities for removing, separating, and concentrating metal ions in process solutions whether they be dilute rinse waters or relatively concentrated leach solutions. Counterflow operation in either the fixed bed version or any of the multitude of moving bed versions has great appeal in reducing resin inventory and in increasing operating efficiency. However, in contrast to the utter simplicity and reliability of conventional

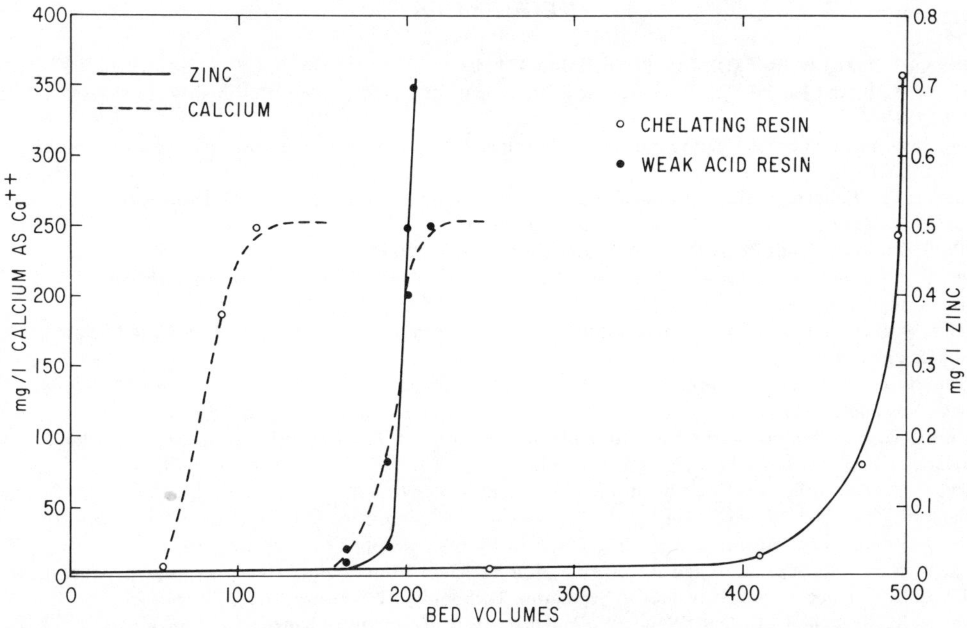

FIGURE 8. Zinc breakthrough curves comparing the performance of a standard weak acid resin vs. a chelating resin.

co-flow ion exchange processes, any counterflow ion exchange process has limitations and drawbacks which must be carefully evaluated before adoption.

Foremost among the major advantages of conventional fixed bed co-flow ion exchange is the 60-year-old technology which has led to extreme reliability under field operating conditions. This reliability is capable of providing efficient repetitive performance despite drastic changes in the concentration and nature of the feed solution. Lapses in attention by the operator are not as critical. Maintenance and costly resin losses are minimized in conventional fixed bed operation.

This is not to say that there is no place for continuous ion exchange systems in metal recovery. There are many benefits to be gained in improved ion exchange efficiency and degree of removal, in minimizing rigorous pretreatment, and in decreasing resin inventory. Thus, a careful evaluation of all of the factors entering into the application of ion exchange as a unit operation must be made before selecting the treatment system. The experience of many years of intimate association in applying ion exchange to a wide variety of actual field problems is perhaps the most vital factor.

CLOSING

As we continue to deplete our sources of high grade ores and begin to enforce our pollution laws governing toxic metal discharges, additional opportunities will be available for ion exchange technology and its unique capabilities.

With the development of resins having higher capacity, improved physical stability, improved resistance to oxidation and organic foulants, and possessing enhanced selectivities for specific metals, resin ion exchange is expected to become the leading treatment process for pollution abatement and conservation of metal resources.

This chapter is an attempt to summarize some of the technology of ion exchange in metal recovery and hydrometallurgy with particular attention to commercialized applications. Excellent theoretical and scientific treatments of this subject have been published by Dorfner,[36] Helffrich,[37] Calmon,[38] Kunin,[39] Nachod,[40] Arden,[41] and others.

REFERENCES

1. **Anderson, J. R. and Weiss, C. O.,** U.S. Patent 3,740,331, 1973.
2. **Luttinger, L. B. and Hoché, G.,** Reverse osmosis treatment with predictable water quality, *Environ. Sci. Technol.,* 8(7), 614, 1974.
3. **Anon.,** New membranes for treatment of metal finishing effluents by reverse osmosis, *Plating Surf. Finishing,* 63(1), 64, 1976.
4. **Maruyama, T., Hannah, S. H., and Cohen, J.,** Metal removal by physical and chemical treatment processes, *J. Water Pollut. Control Fed.,* 47(5), 962, 1975.
5. **Smith, S. B.,** Trace Metals Removed by Activated Carbon, EPA-902/9-74-001, 1973, 55.
6. **Lewis, C. J.,** Liquid ion exchange in hydrometallurgy, in *Recent Developments in Separation Science,* Vol. 2, Li, N. N., Ed., Chemical Rubber Co., 1972, 47.
7. **Mindler, A. B.,** Application in hydrometallurgy, in *Ion Exchange Technology,* Nachod, F. C. and Schubert, J., Eds., Academic Press, New York, 1956, 306.
8. **Hunter, R. F. et al.,** Proc. Conversion of Waste to Profit Symp., Canadian Soc. Chemical Engineering, Toronto, Canada, November 8, 1971.
9. **Morrison, W. S.,** Chromium recovery from plating solutions, in *Ion Exchange Technology,* Nachod, F. C. and Schubert, J., Eds., Academic Press, New York, 1956, 321.
10. **Arden, T. V. et al.,** Anion exchange in chromate solutions, *J. Appl. Chem.,* p. 229, July 11, 1961.
11. **Yamamoto, D., Yabe, K., and Kurita, A. O.,** Recovery of Chromate from Cooling Tower Blowdown by Ion Exchange Resins, paper presented at Cooling Tower Institute, Houston, Tex., February 1975.
12. **Miller, W. S.,** Metals Separation and Recovery by Ion Exchange from Cooling Tower Blowdown, paper presented at Technical Conference on New Advances in Separation Technology, Tarrytown, N.Y., October 24, 1975.
13. **Sussman, S., Nachod, F. C., and Wood, W.,** Metal recovery by anion exchange, *Ind. Eng. Chem.,* 37, 618, 1945.
14. **Gerstner, F.,** Recovery of copper from rayon wastes, in *Ion Exchange Technology,* Nachod, F. C. and Schubert, J. Eds., Academic Press, New York, 1956, 340.
15. **Dorfner, K.,** *Ion Exchangers, Properties and Applications,* Ann Arbor Science, Ann Arbor, Mich., 1972, 106.

16. **Brown, C. J., Davey, D., and Simmons, P. J.,** Nickel Salt Recovery by Reciprocating Flow Ion Exchange, paper presented at the 62nd Annual Technical Conf. American Electroplaters Society, June 1975.
17. **Sussman, S., Nachod, F. C., and Wood, W.,** Metal recovery by anion exchange, *Ind. Eng. Chem.,* 37, 618, 1945.
18. **Merritt, R. C.,** *The Extractive Metallurgy of Uranium,* Colorado School of Mines Research Institute, Golden, Colorado, 1971, 137.
19. **Ayres, D. E. R. and Westwood, R. J.,** *The Use of the Ion Exchange Process in the Extraction of Uranium from Rand Ores with Particular Reference to Practice of the Randfontein Uranium Plant in South Africa (1946–1956),* Vol. 2, A Joint Symposium, Hartaro Ltd., South Africa, 1957, 85.
20. **Mindler, A. B. and Termini, J.,** The vital role of ion exchange in uranium production, *Eng. Min. J.,* 157(9), 100, 1956.
21. **Galkin, N. P. and Sudarikov, D. N., Eds.,** *Technology of Uranium,* AEC-tr-6638, Israel Program for Scientific Translations, Wiener Bindery, Jerusalem, 1966.
22. **Kunin, R. et al.,** Ion exchange resins for uranium hydrometallurgy, *Eng. Min. J.,* 170(7), 73, 1969.
23. **Gardner, H. E. and Kunin, R.,** Application of a Weak Base Anion Exchange Resin for Recovery of Uranium at Uravan, Colorado, U.S.A., Proc. Int. Ion Exchange Conference, Cambridge, England, July 27, 1976, p. 41.1.
24. **Naden, D.,** Development of a Fluid Bed Weak Base Ion Exchange Process for the Recovery of Uranium, Proc. Int. Ion Exchange Conference, Cambridge, England, July 27, 1976, p. 42.1.
25. **Greer, A. H., Mindler, A. B., and Termini, J. P.,** New ion exchange resin for uranium recovery, *Ind. Eng. Chem.,* 50(2), 166, 1958.
26. Permutit Spiractor, Sales Bulletin 5852, Permutit Company, Paramus, New Jersey.
27. **Miller, W. S.,** unpublished data.
28. **Maltby, P.,** Use of moving bed ion exchange in the recovery of uranium at Cam-Met Explorations Ltd., Blind River, Ontario, Inst. Mining Metall., London, Trans., 69, 95–109, 291–295, 1959–1960.
29. **Pruess, A. F. and Kunin, R.,** Uranium recovery by ion exchange, in *Uranium Ore Processing,* Clegg, J. W. and Foley, D. D., Eds., Addison-Wesley, Reading, Mass., 1958, 191.
30. **George, D. R. et al.,** By-product uranium recovered with new ion exchange techniques, *Eng. Min. J.,* 20(1), 73, 1968.
31. **Mindler, A. B., Gilwood, M. E., and Saunders, G. H.,** Metal recovery by cation exchange, *Ind. Eng. Chem.,* 43(5), 1081, 1951.
32. **Anderson, R. E.,** Some Examples of the Concentration of Trace Heavy Metals with Ion Exchange Resins, EPA-902/9-74-001, 1973, 46.
33. **Yamamoto, D., Yabe, K., and Kurita, A. O.,** Recovery of Chromate from Cooling Tower Blowdown by Ion Exchange Resins, paper presented at Cooling Tower Institute, Houston, Tex., February 1975.
34. **Chamberlain, D. G.,** Selective Removal of Zinc from Cooling Tower Blowdown by Ion Exchange, Proc. Int. Water Conference, Pittsburgh, Pa., 1970.
35. **Calmon, C. and Gold, H.,** New directions in ion exchange, *Environ. Sci. Technol.,* 10, 980, 1976.
36. **Dorfner, K.,** *Ion Exchange Properties and Applications,* Ann Arbor Science, Ann Arbor, 1972.
37. **Helfferich, F.,** *Ion Exchange,* McGraw-Hill, New York, 1962.
38. **Calmon, C. and Kressman, T. R. E.,** *Ion Exchangers in Organic and Biochemistry,* Interscience, New York, 1957.
39. **Kunin, R.,** *Ion Exchange Resins,* John Wiley & Sons, New York, 1963.
40. **Nachod, F. and Shubert, J.,** *Ion Exchange Technology,* Academic Press, New York, 1956.
41. **Arden, T. V.,** *Water Purification by Ion Exchange,* Butterworths, London, 1968.

SEPARATIONS USING SUPERCRITICAL GASES

C. A. Irani and E. W. Funk

TABLE OF CONTENTS

INTRODUCTION

Dense-gas extraction is a chemical engineering separation process that is still in the developing stage. It is often called gas extraction, supercritical extraction (to emphasize that the solvent gas is above its critical temperature), or in chromatographic separations, fluid extraction. We use the term dense-gas extraction since, for practical separations, high pressures/densities are required for the gaseous solvent to have a reasonable capacity. Dense-gas extraction is presently an active area of research and has the promise of leading to novel and economically viable separation processes.

The most recent extensive review is by Paul and Wise.[1] Their 1971 monograph emphasizes the basic concepts and also areas of potentially important separation processes. Additional reviews, although briefer, have been presented by Valteris,[2] Ellis,[3] Hicks and Young,[4] and Pilz.[5] The review by Booth and Bidwell[6] gives an historical perspective and a description of experimental methods; finally, Rowlinson and Richardson[7] give a development of the theory of dense-gas extraction and a compilation of experimental data. A comprehensive bibliography of critical phenomena has also been compiled.[8]

In this review, we cover the recent advances in thermodynamic analysis, experimental data, and practical separation processes. In particular, we discuss the emerging separation processes in foods, upgrading of heavy hydrocarbons and coal liquids, and miscible displacement techniques for enhanced oil recovery from reservoirs. However, we want to first examine qualitatively why dense-gas extraction is a potentially important and unique separation process.

As a chemical engineering separation process, dense-gas extraction lies between distillation and solvent extraction. As presented by Paul and Wise,[1] it is possible to consider a continuum of physical conditions from distillation to solvent extraction. This concept is based on the idea that

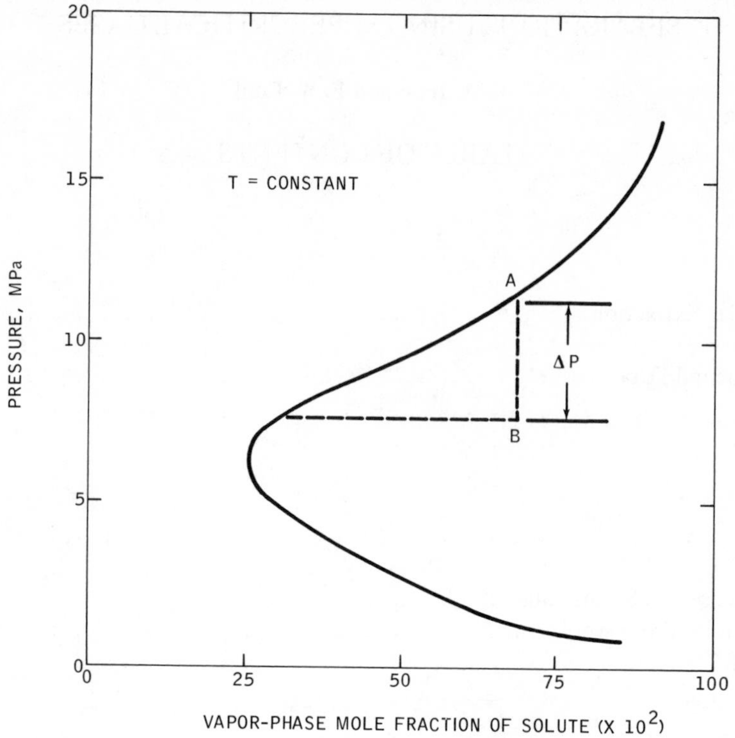

FIGURE 1. Schematic solubility curve for low-volatility solute in a dense gas.

for distillation near atmospheric pressure the dilute gas phase can be considered as the extracting solvent, and one can think of continually increasing the density of this gas phase by increasing the system pressure. When the gas phase becomes a condensed liquid, the separation is then by solvent extraction. As one proceeds along this continuum, dense-gas extraction begins where high-pressure distillation ends.

Dense-gas extraction is clearly differentiated from high-pressure distillation. In distillation, the separation factor (relative volatility) is primarily a function of temperature; pressure is often applied to allow condensation without refrigeration, although this usually has the effect of decreasing slightly the relative volatility. In dense-gas extraction, the separation factor is a strong function of both temperature and pressure.

In comparing the energy requirements for the two processes, we consider a single-stage, dense-gas extraction process in which the solvent gas A is cycled from a high pressure where it is rich in solute to a low pressure where it is lean. The critical variable is the compression ratio (defined as the ΔP through which the solvent is cycled) required for the gas extraction. This can be better understood by analyzing Figure 1 which shows a schematic solubility curve for a low-volatility solute in a dense gas. If the operation between similar pressures A and B allows a high yield of solute, the energy required for compression may be significantly less than energy (heat) required for distillation.

As a specific example, consider the use of propane for the dense-gas extraction of 20% of a hydrocarbon mixture in the 600 to 700°F boiling range. (This simple example is somewhat similar to petroleum deasphalting.) Figure 2 shows the energy required to compress the propane at its critical temperature as a function of the compression ratio. Also shown is a rough estimate of the energy requirement for an equivalent separation by distillation. This is a qualitative calculation based on approximate power plant efficiencies, compressor efficiencies, etc. Thus, for a compression ratio of approximately 3, the energy required for dense-gas extraction is similar to that for distillation. Figure 2 shows the important result that the energy savings for dense-gas extraction only become large if it is possible to work at low compression ratios.

The principle difference between dense-gas

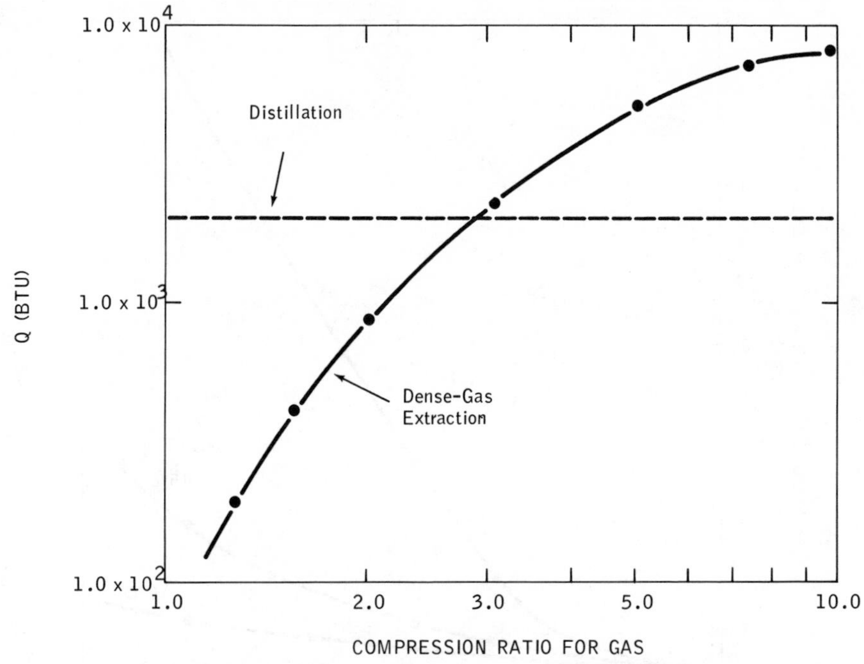

FIGURE 2. Comparison of energy requirements for dense-gas extraction and distillation.

extraction and solvent extraction is in the method of solvent recovery. For dense-gas extraction, reduction in pressure allows a simple recovery of solvent. For solvent extraction, heat is generally used to separate the solvent from solute.

Finally, being on the continuum between distillation and extraction, dense-gas extraction has pressure as a useful variable to affect the separation in addition to temperature and solvent. Figure 3 presents the classic data of Diepen and Scheffer[9,10] for the ethylene-naphthalene system, and it shows the dramatic increase in the vapor phase mole fraction with pressure for temperatures above the critical temperature of ethylene (10°C). Obviously, pressure is a variable that can be used to adjust the phase equilibria over a wide range of values. In addition, it is possible to consider a decompression in stages to give further separation of the extracted material into several fractions.

Distillation and solvent extraction are the common competing separation processes compared with dense-gas extraction. To make a rational selection, it is important to first have an understanding of how dense-gas extraction differs from distillation and solvent extraction and what are its advantages/disadvantages. Next, it is necessary to have an estimation of the phase equilibria. The theory and prediction of dense-gas equilibria are discussed in the following section.

THEORY OF DENSE-GAS EXTRACTION

The need for supercritical temperatures to obtain these wide variations in thermodynamic properties can be intuitively understood as follows. Any pure component at temperatures below the critical temperature behaves as a condensed phase and demonstrates volume changes of only a few percent over pressure gradients as high as 100 MPa. The only physical property affected by pressure at low temperatures is the viscosity; the others remain relatively unchanged. At progressively higher temperatures along the vapor pressure curve, the vapor and liquid properties begin to approach each other until finally at the critical point the difference disappears completely. It is in this region near the critical point that modest pressure changes begin to give rise to large variations in physical properties.

This section reviews the basic theory of dense-gas extraction and provides the quantitative background explaining why high extraction yields are possible with dense gases. Also, it emphasizes the

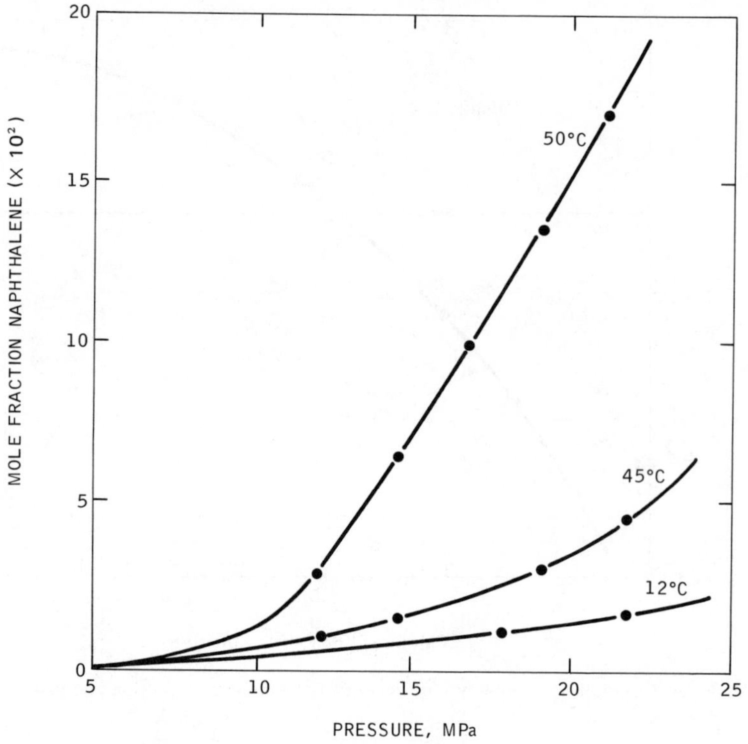

FIGURE 3. Solubility of naphthalene in supercritical ethylene.

new thermodynamic and computational techniques that are available to estimate and extend experimental data.

The theory of dense-gas extraction is easily formulated and understood for a solid solute. This is a particularly simple case because the solubility of the gas in the solid can be considered negligible. Prausnitz[11] gives a derivation of the expression for y_2, the solubility of the solid in the gas; the result is

$$y_2 = \frac{P_2^S}{P} \cdot E \quad (1)$$

where E, the enhancement factor, is defined as

$$E \equiv \frac{\varphi_2^S \exp \int_{P_2^S}^{P} v_2^S \, dP/RT}{\varphi_2} \quad (2)$$

In Equations 1 and 2,

P_2^S = the vapor pressure of pure solid 2;
P = the total pressure;
φ_2^S = the fugacity coefficient evaluated at P_2^S,
φ_2 = the vapor-phase fugacity coefficient of solute in the mixture at system T and P;
v_2^S = the pure component molar volume of 2; and
T = the temperature.

The enhancement factor contains three terms: φ_2^S,φ_2, and the exponential term usually called the Poynting factor. The fugacity coefficient φ_2^S is always near unity due to the low vapor pressure of solids. Also, the Poynting correction seldom gives an enhancement factor of more than 2, even at 10 MPa pressure. It is, however, the fugacity coefficient φ_2 which account for the high enhancement factors encountered experimentally. For example, in the ethylene(1)-naphthalene(2) system shown in Figure 3, $\varphi_2 \ll 1$ giving an enhancement factor of 25,000 at 10 MPa.

Therefore, estimation of dense-gas extraction of solids becomes essentially a problem of describing the vapor phase. The rigorous theoretical approach is to use the virial equation of state; the necessary virial coefficients can be calculated exactly from expressions derived from statistical mechanics. Rowlinson and Richardson[7] have developed this approach.

Beginning with the virial equation of state

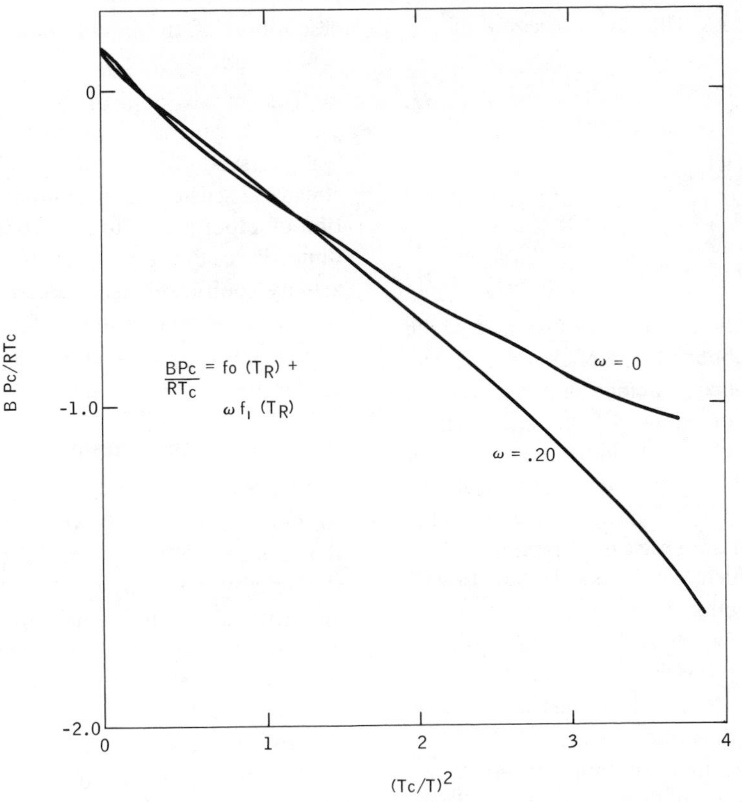

FIGURE 4. Corresponding states correlation for second virial coefficients.

$$\frac{Pv}{RT} = 1 + \frac{B}{v} + \frac{C}{v^2} + \ldots \quad (3)$$

where v is the molar volume, and B, C, . . . the virial coefficients, Rowlinson and Richardson derive the following expression for the enhancement factor:

$$\ln E = \frac{v_2^S - 2B_{12}}{v} + \ldots \quad (4)$$

The derivation of Equation 4 assumes $\varphi_2^S = 1.0$; also, the higher order terms in $1/v^2$, $1/v^3$, . . . are only important at very high pressures.

In Equation 4, it is often the second virial coefficient B_{12} which is large and negative, thus giving a large enhancement factor. The coefficient B_{12} expresses interactions between solute 2 and dense gas 1; the greater the potential energy of interaction between solute and solvent, the more negative B_{12}.

For simple systems, the virial coeffient can be calculated using an intermolecular potential energy function such as the Lennard-Jones 6-12. Ewald et al.[12] discuss such a calculation for the air-carbon dioxide system. When this calculation is not practical, virial coefficients can be estimated from the corresponding states correlation of Pitzer and Curl.[13] This correlation has the form

$$\frac{BP_c}{RT_c} = f_0\ (T/T_c) + \omega f_1\ (T/T_c) \quad (5)$$

where

P_c = the critical pressure;
T_c = the critical temperature; and
ω = the acentric facor.

The acentric factor is a measure of the extent to which the force field around a molecule deviates from spherical symmetry. Reid and Sherwood[14] give an extensive list of acentric factors. The two empirical functions are given by Tsonopoulos.[15] Figure 4 shows Equation 5 for nonpolar or slightly polar gases. Tsonopoulos[15,16] has recently extended Equation 5 to polar and hydrogen bonding molecules.

Equation 5 can be extended to cross-virial coefficients B_{12} by using mixing rules for the pure component properties. The most successful mixing rules to date are

$$T_{c_{12}} = (T_{c_1} T_{c_2})^{1/2} (1 - k_{12}) \quad (6)$$

$$P_{c_{12}} = \frac{4(Z_{c_1} + Z_{c_2}) RT_{c_{12}}}{(v_{c_1}{}^{1/3} + v_{c_2}{}^{1/3})^3} \quad (7)$$

$$\omega_{12} = 1/2 (\omega_1 + \omega_2) \quad (8)$$

where Z_c is the critical compressibility and v_c the critical volume (tabulated in Reference 14). The constant k_{12} is a binary interaction parameter and must be estimated or obtained from experimental mixture data. Chueh and Prausnitz[13] give a compilation of k_{12} for numerous systems. Equations 1 through 8 are easily programmed for digital computation of dense-gas extraction.

A practical problem with the virial equation of state for the calculation of dense-gas extraction is that it does not converge as the critical density of the solvent gas is approached. As a rule of thumb, the virial equation is useful for densities below approximately 1/2 the critical density.

For higher pressures, an empirical or semi-empirical equation of state must be used. There are many such equations in the chemical engineering literature. Prausnitz and Chueh[18] have developed a modified form of the Redlich-Kwong equation of state for calculations involving essentially nonpolar components; computer programs are given in Reference 18 for fugacity coefficients. Prausnitz[18] shows that this modified Redlich-Kwong equation gives excellent prediction of the solubility data of naphthalene in ethylene shown in Figure 2 for pressures up to 25 MP2.

The thermodynamic analysis for the solubility of a liquid in a dense gase is considerably more complicated than the gas-solid system discussed above. The equation of phase equilibrium for liquid solute 2 is

$$f_2^L = f_2^V \quad (9)$$

which is more conveniently expressed in terms of a liquid-phase activity coefficient γ_2 and the vapor phase fugacity coefficient φ_2. Introducing these auxiliary variables into Equation 9 gives

$$x_2 \gamma_2 f_2^0 = y_2 \varphi_2 P \quad (10)$$

where f_2^0 is the pure component fucacity of component 2. Thus, the calculation of y_2 requires description of the liquid phase in addition to the vapor phase.

The monograph of Chueh and Prausnitz[18] presents a general thermodynamic framework for high-pressure vapor-liquid equilibrium. We have already discussed their approach for the calculation of vapor-phase fugacity coefficients. Also, the Chueh-Prausnitz equations for the liquid-phase activity coefficients can be used for calculation of the dense-gas extraction of low-volatility liquids.

For dense-gas extraction, calculation of liquid-phase activity coefficients is complicated by the fact that they depend on temperature, composition, and pressure.

Chueh et al. use the dilated van Laar model[19] to describe the composition dependence of the liquid-phase activity coefficients. The model fits the activity coefficients adjusted to zero pressure and with different normalization used for solute and solvent activity coefficients. The thermodynamic model is very approximate but does aim to describe liquid-phase activity coefficients up to and including the critical region; the model contains two binary interaction parameters, one of which is only important at temperatures approaching the critical temperature of the solution. The utility of the dilated van Laar model for dense-gas extraction is that it provides a good description of liquid-phase activity coefficients over a wide range of temperature, composition, and pressure.

Hsu and Lu[20] have presented a thermodynamic analysis similar to the Chueh-Prausnitz approach where the Redlich-Kwong equation is used to describe both the vapor and the liquid. Thus, complications are eliminated due to the use of different standard states for solute and solvent. For supercritical components, the Redlich-Kwong parameters are considered to be temperature dependent. The authors show that for various systems their correlation gives a good fit to experimental data.

The calculation of dense-gas extraction for liquid-gas systems generally requires use of a computer for the trial and error calculations. However, the calculation is quite simple for a high-boiling liquid and a sparingly soluble gas. For this case, the heavy liquid, component 2, obeys Raoult's law and the gas, component 1, obeys Henry's law. Applying Equation 9 to both components leads to

$$E = \frac{x_2 \varphi_2^S \exp \int_{P_2^S}^{P} v_2^L \, dP/RT}{\varphi_2} \quad (11)$$

$$x_1 H = y_1 \varphi_1 P \quad (12)$$

where H is Henry's constant for the gas dissolved in the liquid. A more detailed development of Equations 11 and 12 is given in Reference 11.

Equations 11 and 12 can often be solved by assuming $y_1 \approx 1.0$ in Equation 12 and then calculating E in Equation 11 by assuming $y_2 = 0.0$ for the estimate of φ_2. Equation 1 is used to check the assumption of $y_1 = 1.0$. At the most, a few iterations are required to solve Equations 11 and 12.

In summary, we can look at the factors that give a high solute yield by dense-gas extraction:

1. The greater the attractive interaction between solute and solvent, the larger B_{12} and hence the larger the enhancement factor (see Equation 4). In the absence of virial coefficient data, the critical temperature of the gas gives an approximate measure of its potential energy. Figure 4 shows that, for a given temperature, gases with high critical temperatures have large negative values of B_{12} and therefore are better solvents than those with low critical temperatures.

2. For moderate pressures, the solute concentration in the gas phase increases due to the increase in the solute vapor pressure. At higher pressures, two opposing factors become important. As T increases, P_2^S increases but B_{12} decreases in magnitude (see Figure 4), and consequently, E becomes closer to unity (see Equation 4). The maximum solubility is a compromise between these two effects. There is no simple analytical expression available for estimating the temperature of maximum solubility; it is necessary to solve the equations of equilibrium for various temperatures to find the maximum.

3. The solute solubility in the gas phase generally first decreases with pressure and then increases. Hinckley and Reid[21] have shown that since this minimum occurs at moderate or low pressures, it is possible to derive simple expressions for the point of minimum solubility.

$$P_{(min)} = -RT/(B_{11} + 2B_{12}) \quad (13)$$

$$y_{(min)} = -5.44\, B_{12} P_2^S/RT \quad (14)$$

Equations 1 and 2 were used in the derivation neglecting φ_2^S, the Poynting correction, and virial coefficients beyond the second.

Equations 13 and 14 can be used to obtain an estimate of the maximum solute yield for a dense-gas extraction operating between some pressure P and $P_{(min)}$.

It is interesting to note in conclusion that much of the thermodynamic analysis useful in dense-gas extraction has been developed during the last decade. This, coupled with the availability of high-speed computers, has led to a dramatic advance in the general area of phase equilibria at high pressure and dense-gas extraction as a particular application. It is expected that this decade will produce a better physical understanding of supercritical gases at high pressures; from this should emerge new techniques for predicting dense-gas extraction.

REVIEW OF EXPERIMENTAL DATA

Much of the early research dealt with the use of hydrocarbon components as the dense-gas phase for extracting primarily organic solutes or for altering the miscibility conditions in hydrocarbon mixtures. It is only more recently that inorganic components have received greater attention, either as solvents by themselves or in admixture with hydrocarbon solvents. The last half decade has also seen the emergence of large-scale field tests of dense-gas drives as a means for tertiary oil recovery. Furthermore, as the effort to move away from dependence on foreign energy sources intensifies, the applicability of dense-gas processes in the area of upgrading refractories will take on additional significance. In this review, we plan to limit ourselves primarily to the more recently disclosed systems, many of which have not received previous reviews.

Methane

The nonidealities associated with the critical region can give rise to anomolous behavior, including the onset of immiscibility in otherwise perfectly miscible systems. Perhaps the most interesting example of this type of behavior is the recent discovery that lower paraffinic hydrocarbons demonstrate partial immiscibility with their higher homologues due primarily to a difference in their sizes. Thus, methane is immiscible with *n*-hexane across a narrow temperature range,

TABLE 1

Selectivities for System Methane + Nitrogen – Isopentane – *n*-Pentane

Temperature (K)	Initial ratio of iso- to normal parrafin (x_{iso}/x_{norm})	Solvent/paraffin ratio	β*
110	1.0	0.33	1.08
114	1.73	0.75	1.06
114	2.5	1.0	1.06
123	0.83	0.61	0.79
123	1.21	0.61	0.60
129	1.5	0.61	0.8
131	2.5	1.0	0.79
131	3.1	1.0	0.89

$$*\beta = \text{selectivity} = \left(\frac{x_{iso}}{x_{normal}}\right)_{\text{extract phase}} \left(\frac{x_{normal}}{x_{iso}}\right)_{\text{raffinate phase}}$$

though it is completely miscible with all paraffinic compounds C_5 and smaller.[22] With ethane, immiscibility is first witnessed with n-C_{19},[23] and with propane, it is anticipated that n-C_{37} is the smallest homologue that will first show immiscibility. Guy et al.[24] used an interesting variation on this type of immiscibility to attempt to develop a separation scheme for isopentane. Thus, a methane (80 mol %)-nitrogen (20 mol %) mixture was found to be partially miscible with C_5 paraffins, and based on the fact that the branched paraffins are more soluble than the straight chained paraffins of the same carbon number, a separation of normal from isopentane was attempted. Their results are shown in Table 1 and lead to the following conclusions. For a fixed solvent/paraffin ratio and initial ratio of iso- to normal paraffin, an increase in temperature caused the selectivity (β) to decrease. Additionally, for a fixed solvent/paraffin ratio, increasing the initial ratio of iso- to normal paraffins causes β to decrease at 123 K, but increase at 131 K. Even though the selectivities obtained by this process are only comparable to those obtainable by normal distillation, the authors point out that such a scheme might have value in the separation of isomers whose boiling points are much closer to each other.

Kohn and co-workers[25-27] have investigated the use of supercritical methane to enhance the solubilization of solid, high molecular weight hydrocarbons in a lower molecular weight liquid hydrocarbon. The two ternary systems they studied were methane-decane-dotriacontane and methane-decane-phenanthrene. By studying both a high molecular weight paraffin and an aromatic, the applicability of this type of enhanced solubilization for different chemical species was determined. The authors evaluated their experimental data in terms of two process variables ξ_1 and ξ_2. For the all-paraffin model system, the variable ξ_1 is defined as

$$\xi_1 \equiv \left[\frac{\partial(x_{32}/x_{10})}{\partial P}\right]_T \tag{15}$$

where x_{10} is the liquid-phase mole fraction of n-decane, and x_{32} is the mole fraction of n-dotriacontane. The second process variable ξ_2 is defined as

$$\xi_2 \equiv \frac{[\partial N_{32}/\partial P]_T}{[\partial N_j/\partial P]_T} \tag{16}$$

where N_j is the moles of species j in the liquid phase. The process variable ξ_1 determines whether n-dotriacontane dissolves or precipitates with increased methane pressure. A value of ξ_1 greater than zero indicates that n-dotriacontane dissolves upon methane pressurization. Conversely, a value of $\xi_1 < 0$ indicates that the long-chain paraffin precipitates. ξ_2 is a measure of how much $C_{32}H_{66}$ is dissolved per mole of methane in the liquid phase. Again, a high positive value is desirable from a process viewpoint. Equations similar to Equations 15 and 16 can be written for the second model system where the solid phase is aromatic.

TABLE 2

Phase Equilibrium Data for Methane – *n*-Decane – *n*-Dotriacontane at 340 K[25]

Pressure (MPa)	Moles CH_4 in solution	Moles *n*-dotriacontane in solution
0	0	841.2
0.5	39.0	1009.6
1.0	94.7	1246.4
1.5	180.1	1606.0
2.0	326.8	2220.2
2.5	634.7	3504.3
3.0	1089.1	7894.1

Table 2 shows the ternary data from Reference 25 for the methane-decane *n*-dotriacontane system at 340 K. These results demonstrate clearly the large increase in solid solubility due to dissolved methane gas.

For the 340 K isotherm, ξ_1 increases from 0.24 at 0.5 MPa to 12.19 at 3.0 MPa. Over the same pressure range, ξ_2 remains relatively constant at approximately 4.20. This isotherm is just a few degrees below the melting temperature of *n*-dotriacontane. For lower temperatures, the variables ξ_1 and ξ_2 decrease dramatically. For example, at 330 K and 5.0 MPa, $\xi_1 = 0.0036$ and $\xi_2 = 0.3336$. These results indicate that methane pressurization is only useful for enhancing solid solubility when the solid phase is near its melting point. Replacing the dotriacontane with the aromatic phenanthrene gave essentially similar results, though analysis of the two systems demonstrated that the methane-*n*-decane solvent selectively extracts the paraffin over the aromatic. However, no quaternary data were obtained for the two solid phases.

The experimental data for both systems have been modeled using the Flory-Huggins theory. The necessary parameters were obtained from phase-equilibrium data for the constituent binary systems. This thermodynamic analysis should be useful up to pressures where the liquid-phase partial molar volumes are functions of pressure. Qualitatively, the enhanced solubility can be explained in terms of the gaseous methane dilating the liquid solvent and thus giving more space for the bulky solid solute. It is expected that a gas similar to methane, i.e., ethane, could give the same dilation at lower pressures.

In a recent paper, Tan et al.[27] have experimentally studied the system CH_4-*trans*-decalin-*n*-dotriacontane. This study aims to investigate the role of the liquid in changing paraffin/aromatic selectivity.

The experimental work of Kohn and co-workers is an interesting advance in the field of dense-gase extraction. By the combination of supercritical dense gases with normal liquid solvents, they were able to potentially obtain the advantages of both dense-gas and liquid solvents. The authors mention that this methane pressurization concept has application for the removal of high molecular weight hydrocarbons left behind after primary and secondary recovery techniques have been employed on subsurface reservoirs. It is easy to visualize a number of other applications where similar concepts could prove applicable, for example, increasing the solubility of refractory materials during upgrading processes.

Another promising development in dense-gas applications is their use as flooding agents in secondary and tertiary oil recovery from subsurface reservoirs. The various schemes being tested cover a wide range from light hydrocarbon slugs capable of first-contact miscibility to enriched and high-pressure gas drives using methane gas as the displacing agent.[28-31] Some of these processes will be more extensively discussed in a later section.

Ethane, Ethylene

Kay and co-workers[32-34] studied the binary systems ethane-heptane, -cyclohexane, -benzene, while Zhuze[35] studied the systems ethylene-heptane, -cyclohexane, -benzene. Both ethane and ethylene showed similar solvent properties with ethylene having the greater capacity. In both solvents, the paraffinic components were more soluble than the aromatics, while the naphthenic components showed an intermediate solubility. It is interesting to note that this trend towards changing solubility in going from paraffinic to aromatic components is characteristic of a wide class of solvents. Thus, it will be pointed out later that water shows a reverse preference for aromatics over paraffins.

Elgin and co-workers[36-39] have studied a large number of binary and ternary systems involving ethylene and found that most of the binaries can be described in terms of one of three different pressure-composition diagrams depending on the extent to which the components are dissimilar. These dissimilarities arise primarily due to differences in molecular weight, hydrogen bonding, polarity, or other properties of the two components making up the binaries and are usually manifest by the presence of regions of liquid-liquid immiscibility. Perhaps their most interesting findings, however, came out of their study of ternary systems involving compressed ethylene. Thus, they demonstrated that when ethylene was compressed over aqueous organic mixtures, a "salting-out" effect could be realized, resulting in the dehydration of the organic phase. One such system studied by Elgin and Weinstock[38] was the ethylene-water-methyl ethyl ketone (MEK) ternary at 14.9°C. Yorizane et al.[40] studied the same system over a larger range of temperatures and showed that this technique could be used to break the MEK-water azeotrope to almost pure MEK. For example, on the basis of a feed containing 100 lb of MEK saturated with 10 lb of water, the process would give two phases – one containing 8 lb of water and 0.6 lb of MEK, while the other would contain 99.4 lb of MEK and 2 lb of water. Furthermore, the solvent loss associated with the removal of approximately 90% of the water was shown to be only 0.6% of the solvent.

Earlier it was pointed out that the second virial coefficient B_{12} played an important role in defining the solvent power of a dense gas. When dealing with solid substrates which usually have very low vapor pressures, gases as chemically dissimilar as carbon dioxide and ethylene can still show similar solvent power, as demonstrated in Figure 5 which compares carbon dioxide and ethylene as dense-gas solvents for naphthlene. At the same reduced temperature carbon dioxide is a better solvent than ethylene, though raising the extraction temperature for ethylene minimizes this difference. However,when dealing with complex liquid substrates having higher vapor pressures, the resulting phase equilibria is more complicated and this in turn gives rise to differing solvent behavior. Thus, work undertaken at Exxon[41] on an Arabian gas oil substrate has demonstrated a reversed solvent action between ethylene and carbon dioxide. For any set of conditions, ethylene was found to dissolve more oil than carbon dioxide on either a mole or weight bases (Figure 6), with the solvent power of ethylene now decreasing with an increase in extraction temperature. Furthermore, as the complexity and boiling point of the hydrocarbon increases, the capacity of carbon dioxide as an extractive solvent falls off rapidly. Additional studies have confirmed that dense gases can separate low molecular weight, low density components from high molecular weight and high density components, and that choice of proper solvent can result in good selectivity for polar over non- or less polar constituents.

Propane

Propane has been extensively investigated in the petroleum industry as a solvent for deasphalting heavy hydrocarbon fractions, and commercial deasphalters using liquid propane are in common use. Figure 7 shows a simplified flowsheet for a propane deasphalter. Generally, the propane/oil treat rate is quite high, in the range of 6 to 8 volumes of solvent per volume of oil. This solvent extraction provides an oil which is substantially asphalt-free.

The separation is based on the fact that the very high molecular weight fractions of the oil (often called asphaltenes) are not soluble in propane. It is desirable to extract these asphaltenes from the oil since they contain many of the components that poison hydrotreating catalysts. An important example is metals (Ni, V, Fe).

With the commercial introduction of subcritical propane deasphalters, the possibility of using supercritical propane for deasphalting began to receive serious attention. In more recent years, the Russians[42] have been the main proponents for a dense gas propane-propylene system for deasphalting petroleum stocks, claiming as advantages over the conventional liquid propane process (1) a lower solvent/oil ratio, (2) easier solvent recovery, and (3) a smaller plant. Perhaps the most emphasized advantage is that only a small part of the solvent needs to be vaporized by steam heating unlike liquid-phase deasphalting where solvent recovery represents a large utility cost. While this

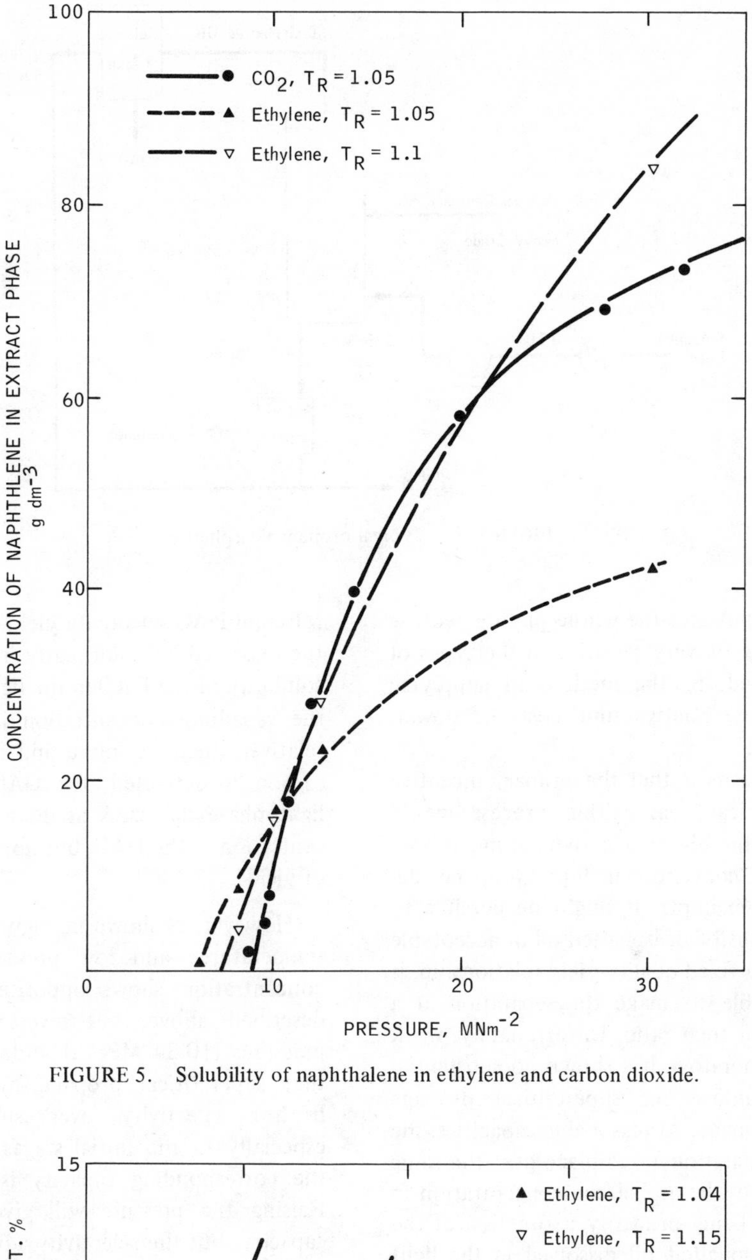

FIGURE 5. Solubility of naphthalene in ethylene and carbon dioxide.

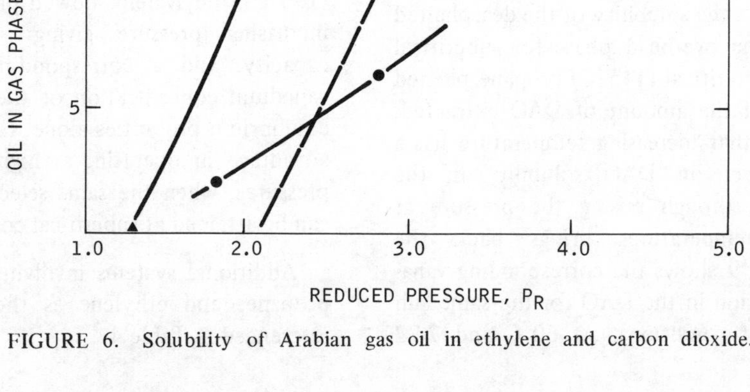

FIGURE 6. Solubility of Arabian gas oil in ethylene and carbon dioxide.

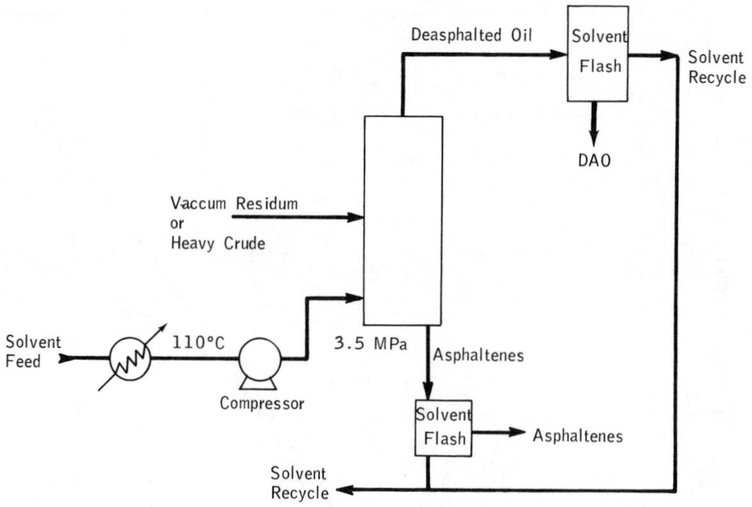

FIGURE 7. Typical propane deasphalter.

is true, it does not give the whole picture because the utility costs are very sensitive to the types of compressors used, to the method of supplying heat, and to the relative unit costs of power, steam, and heat.

What this means is that the primary incentive for a supercritical deasphalting process would probably lie in the higher selectivity it might have to offer over conventional liquid-propane deasphalting: for example, it might be possible to obtain high yields of deasphalted oil of acceptable quality, or for a fixed quality-yield relationship, it could be possible to make the separation at a lower solvent/oil treat ratio. Unfortunately, work done at this laboratory has shown no substantial selectivity advantage for supercritical propane versus liquid propane. At reasonable capacities, the deasphalting separation takes place over the same two-phase region, the asphaltene concentration in the light phase being primarily a function of the amount of deasphalted oil dissolved in the light phase.[43]

Figure 8 shows the solubility of the deasphalted oil (DAO) in the overhead phase for subcritical (60°C) and supercritical (115°C) propane plotted as a function of the amount of DAO extracted. The data show that increasing temperature has a detrimental effect on DAO solubility in the overhead phase, though raising the pressure at supercritical temperatures brings back the capacity. Figure 9 shows the corresponding vanadium concentration in the DAO for the same sub and supercritical conditions. At 60°C and 7.72 MPa and DAO selectivity-yield relationship follows the expected behavior; early in the extraction, the solubility of the DAO in the light phase is high and the vanadium concentration in the DAO is also relatively high. As more and more of the hydrocarbon is extracted, the DAO solubility in the light phase decreases as does the vanadium concentration in the DAO, but not as a linear function of yield.

However, as shown in Figure 9, at supercritical temperatures and low pressures the vanadium concentration shows opposite behavior to that described above, but reverses again at higher pressures (10.34 MPa). The data seem to indicate that supercritical propane may indeed have a higher selectivity over subcritical propane, especially in the initial stages of extraction, but the corresponding capacity is also much lower. Raising the pressure will give back the higher capacity, but the selectivity advantage is no longer substantial. At the highest temperature studied (150°C), the system showed predictable behavior, increasing pressure giving rise to increasing capacity, and a corresponding increase in the vanadium concentration of the extract. Based on equilibrium properties alone, there seems to be no advantage in operating at high temperatures and pressures, when the same selectivity and capacity can be attained at subcritical conditions.

Additional systems involving methane, ethane, propane, and ethylene as the dense phase are referenced in Table 4.[44-59]

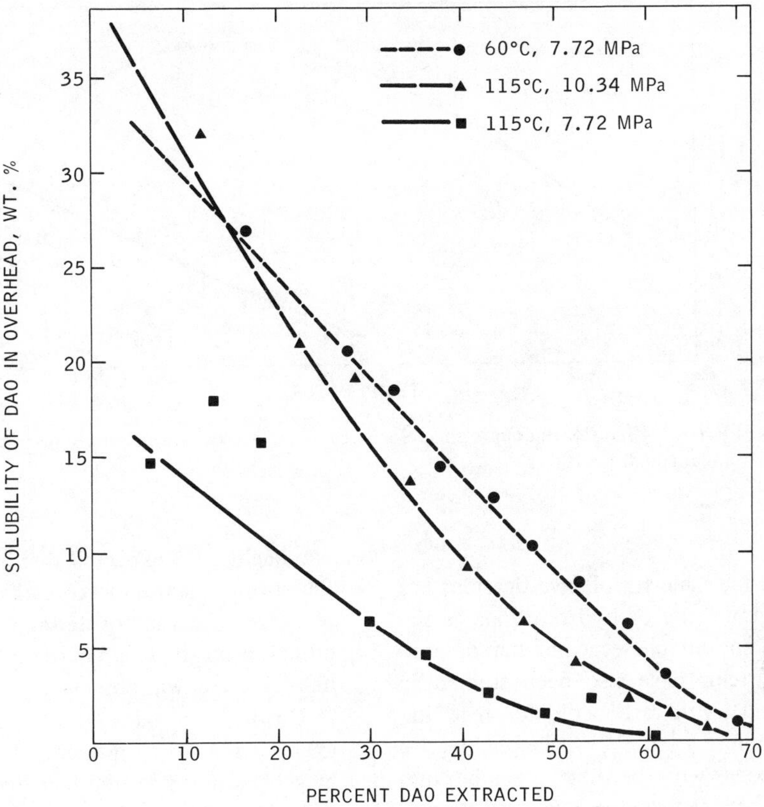

FIGURE 8. Deasphalted oil (DAO) solubility in propane phase as a function of temperature.

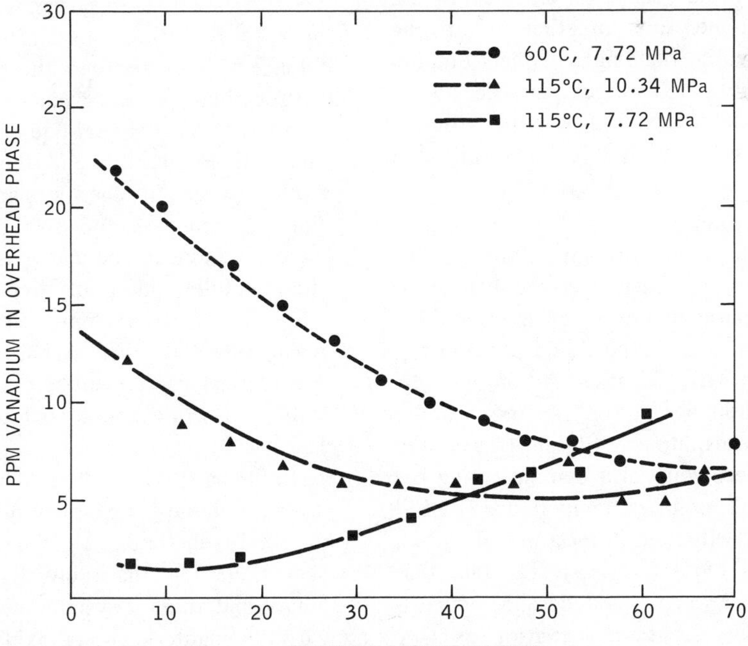

FIGURE 9. Vanadium concentration in propane phase as a function of temperature.

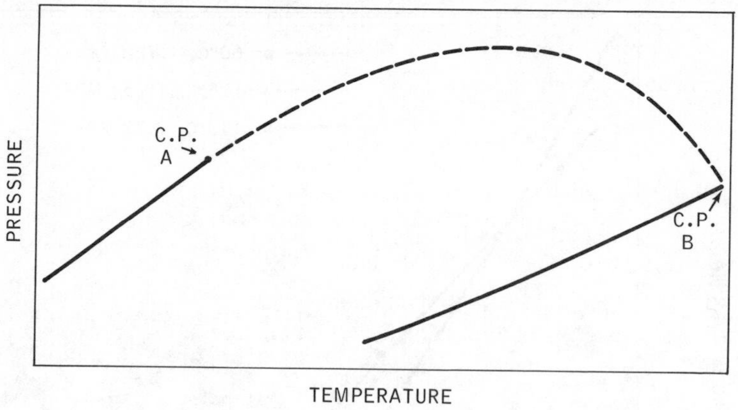

FIGURE 10. Continuous critical locus connecting critical end points of two similar components.

Carbon Dioxide

Even though the majority of investigations has centered around the use of hydrocarbons as the compressed gas solvent phase, a number of non-hydrocarbon systems have also been studied as extractive solvents with carbon dioxide receiving the most attention.[49,51,53,60–70] Simple binaries of carbon dioxide with benzene, cyclohexane, *n*-hexane and 1-hexene all show a classical type of continuous locus between the pure-component critical end points (Figure 10).[71] A break in the critical locus (Figure 11) is usually the result of a large difference in size, shape, or chemical nature of the two components, or sometimes due to the presence of hydrogen bonding in either component. The absence of a break in the above-mentioned systems indicates that shape, aromaticity, or the presence of double bonds plays an insignificant role in such simple systems.

Binaries of carbon dioxide with more complex hydrocarbons do show discontinuities in the critical locus, but even then it is size differences rather than chemical nature which is responsible for the formation of a second liquid phase. Thus, for example, the two binaries carbon dioxide-tetrahydronaphthlene (tetralin) and carbon dioxide-decahydronaphthlene (decalin) have very similar critical loci while also demonstrating the same upper critical solution temperature (UCST) type behavior as witnessed in mixtures of carbon dioxide-*n*-alkanes (with $C > 13$). The fact that tetralin, which is aromatic, and decalin, which is naphthenic, show the same behavior as C_{14} *n*-alkanes points to the minimal role played by chemical structure in such systems. Additionally, one might have expected that interaction between the strong quadrupole of carbon dioxide and the aromatic structure of tetralin would have some influence on the phase behavior of the system, but no such effect was observed.

On the other hand, the case for size differences exerting the major influence in such systems can be substantiated by the fact that the UCST in the carbon dioxide-decalin system can be dropped to lower temperatures and even eliminated (Figure 12) by the addition of benzene to the hydrocarbon phase. There is a strong similarity between the above-mentioned system where the addition of benzene to decalin minimizes the relative difference in size between the carbon dioxide and hydrocarbon phase, giving a transiton from a condition of liquid-liquid immiscibility to complete miscibility, and the earlier mentioned work[24] where nitrogen was added to methane in order to increase the size difference between methane and pentane and thus effect a transition from complete miscibility to liquid-liquid immiscibility. These two examples serve to point out the remarkable flexibility available in systems where supercritical components are involved, and where additional work could lead to novel separation schemes.

In the past, carbon dioxide has been extensively used as a dense-gas phase to increase the volatility of solid substrates. More recently, Kohn and co-workers[72,73] have investigated a number of binary and ternary systems with carbon dioxide, where the lighter carbon dioxide phase was used to selectively extract one hydrocarbon component over another. In the ternary system carbon

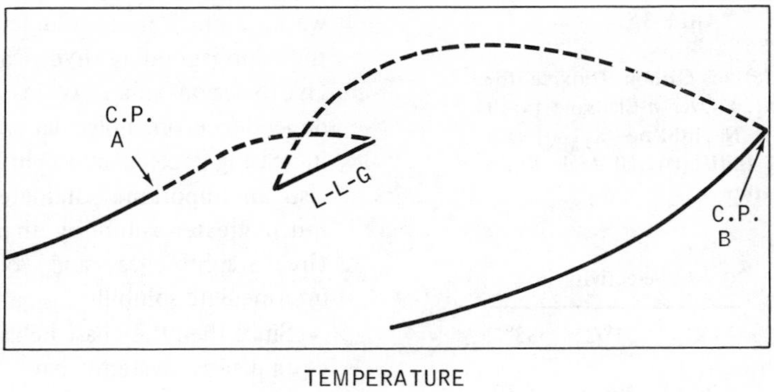

FIGURE 11. Break in continuous critical locus due to dissimilarities in the two components.

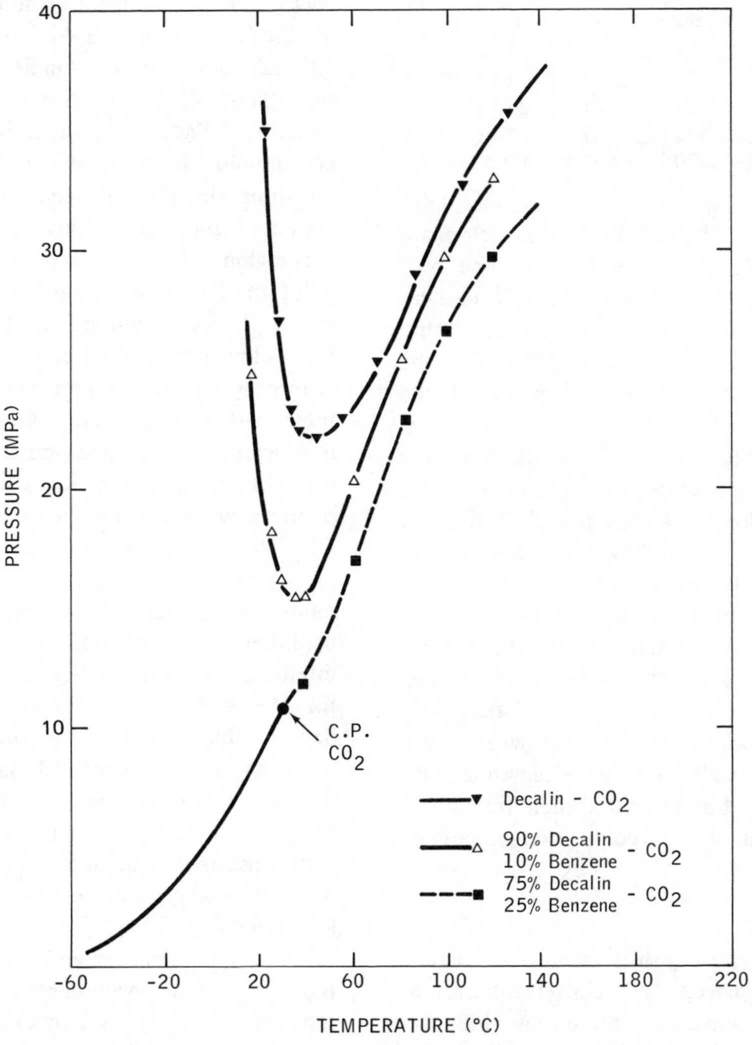

FIGURE 12. Pressure-temperature projections of the critical loci of decalin-benzene-carbon dioxide mixtures.

TABLE 3

Selectivity (β) of Carbon Dioxide for *n*-Decane (x_{10}) Over *n*-Eicosane (x_{10}) and 2-Methyl Naphthlene ($x_{2\,MN}$) as a Function of Initial Overall Mole Ratio and Temperature

Initial mole ratio	Selectivity		
x_{10}/x_{20}	29°C	31°C	33°C
0.1	4.2	4.6	5.3
0.2	4.3	4.7	5.4
0.4	4.4	4.8	5.6
0.7	4.7	5.0	6.0
0.9	4.9	5.3	6.4
$x_{10}/x_{2\,mn}$	15°C	20°C	30°C
0.15	2.76	2.67	2.64
0.25	2.40	2.24	2.06
0.35	2.25	2.07	1.84
0.40	2.20	2.01	1.78

dioxide-*n*-eicosane, the carbon dioxide rich phase showed a greater preference for *n*-decane over *n*-eicosane. When the *n*-eicosane was replaced by 2-methylnaphthlene, an aromatic structure with a melting point similar to that of *n*-eicosane, the carbon dioxide rich phase still preferred the *n*-alkane. Some of their ternary results are presented in Table 3 and lead to the following conclusions. The capacity of carbon dioxide as a solvent is very low, and even though it shows a distict preference for the lower molecular weight *n*-alkane, there is no consistent trend in its selectivity as a function of temperature or initial hydrocarbon mole fraction. Thus, the solvent selectivity showed opposing tendencies, increasing with increasing temperature and initial mole fraction of *n*-decane for the case where both components are *n*-alkanes; and decreasing with increasing temperature and intial mole fraction of *n*-decane when the second component is 2-methylnaphthlene.

Water

More recently water has received increasing attention as a cheap and convenient solvent capable of demonstrating interesting phase behavior with various hydrocarbon types. The earlier work dealt mainly with the mutual solubility of water-hydrocarbon systems at elevated temperatures,[74-77] clearly showing that on a mole basis water is much more soluble in hydrocarbons than the corresponding hydrocarbons are in water. Hydrocarbon solubility in water shows a strong dependence on molecular weight, decreasing with increasing molecular weight. Hydrocarbon type is also an important parameter, aromatics showing much greater solubility than the paraffins, with the naphthlenes and olefins demonstrating intermediate solubility.

Since then the phase behavior of a large number of aqueous systems have been studied in the vicinity of the critical point of water so that in many instances the quantitative aspects of the critical loci are known. While the critical loci of most hydrocarbon-water systems are quite involved, their evolution can be explained in terms of the simpler critical loci by introducing additional dimensions of complexity brought on by the chemical dissimilarity of the two components.[79] Basically, hydrocarbon-water mixtures are immiscible at ambient temperatures and pressures. In the low temperature range such systems show distinct three phase (liquid-liquid-gas) regions which terminate at a lower critical end point in the vicinity of the hydrocarbon critical point. The hydrocarbon critical point is connected to this lower critical end point by means of a short critical locus made up of the loci of points in pressure-temperature-composition space where the hydrocarbon phase goes critical (Figure 13). A more important critical locus starts at the critical point of water and for the aromatic components, falls to a temperature minimum before rising rapidly to very high pressures. For paraffins this minimum is much less pronounced, while for naphthenic and olefinic components it has an intermediate value. In Figure 13 the critical loci for the systems water-benzene, 1,3,5-trimethyl benzene and *n*-heptane are shown. Each critical locus shown in Figure 13 has a very specific significance for the binary pair it represents, in that it demarcates regions of partial solubility from regions of complete miscibility, a condition that arises when the loci are crossed going from left to right.

O'Grady[80] has extensively investigated the ternary system water-benzene-*n*-heptane as a function of increasing temperature in the region where the miscibility boundary for the water-benzene binary is crossed. However, the industrial applicability of such a process is also dependent on how selective water is in extracting benzene from a

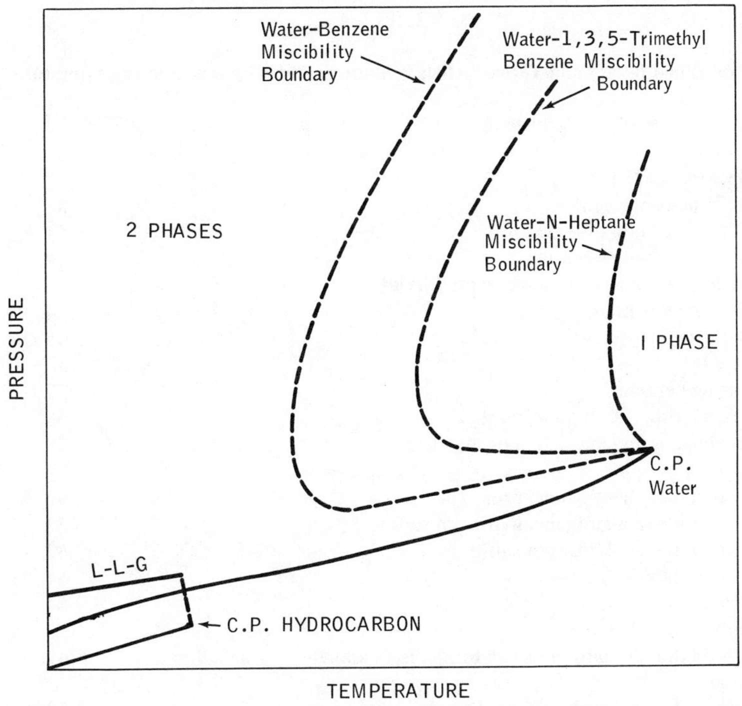

FIGURE 13. Pressure-temperature projections for various hydrocarbon-water binaries.

branched paraffin. Connolly[81] had previously pointed out that paraffin solubility would increase with decreasing chain length, but that branching would have little effect. Preliminary work at this laboratory has indeed verified that replacing the straight chain paraffin in the water-benzene-heptane system with a branched paraffin of the same carbon number (3-methyl hexane) does not substantially alter the phase diagram.

Additional water-hydrocarbon systems have been referenced in Table 4.[82-84]

DEVELOPMENT OF DENSE-GAS SEPARATIONS

Extraction of Lanolin From Wool

The process for extraction of the valuable lanolin from wool grease is based on the use of supercritical propane or propane-propylene mixtures to selectively extract the lanolin without dissolving the albuminous and acidic components of the wool grease. Valteris[2] gives a detailed discussion of the process.

Basically, the process is similar to petroleum deasphalting. Propane gas at approximately 100°C is compressed to a level between 6.0 and 10.0 MPa and contacted with wool grease at a solvent/wool ratio of 5 to 8. The lanolin is recovered from the supercritical gas by reducing the pressure to 4.0 to 5.0 MPa.

The lanolin obtained is valuable to the cosmetic industry; it is classified as a wax but contains free alcohols and cholesterol which give it a hydrophilic character and which is the key property for its cosmetic use.

The development work in the U.S.S.R. on the extraction of ozocerite is very similar to that on lanolin. Basically ozocerite is a very heavy wax obtained from shale in Eastern Europe; the present extraction technology uses boiling water to extract ozocerite. For a dense-gas extraction, the raw ore is contacted with supercritical propane at 100°C and at 8.0 to 10.0 MPa pressure. A propane/wax ratio of above 6 is used and the ozocerite is recovered by reducing the pressure to 4.0 to 5.0 MPa. It is not believed that this has become a commercial process.

Decaffeination of Coffee

Vitzthum et al.[85-87] have proposed the use of carbon dioxide for the removal of caffeine. Pressures in the range of 8.0 to 35.0 MPa are

TABLE 4

Additional Binary and Ternary High Pressure Systems Reported in the Literature

System	Ref.
Methane-methanol	49
Methane-naphthlene	50
Methane-carbon dioxide	51
Methane-ethane-n-butane	52
Methane-hydrogen sulfide-carbon dioxide	53
Methane-*n*-pentane	54
Methane-nitrogen	55, 56
Ethane-benzene	57
Ethane, propane, butane, pentane-polyethylene	58
Propane, propylene-aliaphatic alcohols	59
Carbon dioxide-ethylene, propylene	60, 61
Carbon dioxide-methane, hydrogen sulfide	53
Carbon dioxide-hydrogen sulfide	62
Carbon dioxide-methane	51, 63
Carbon dioxide-nitrous oxide	64
Carbon dioxide-water	65, 66
Carbon dioxide-carbon tetrachloride, isoocatane, toluene	67
Carbon dioxide-methanol	49
Carbon dioxide-isopentane	68
Carbon dioxide-methane, *n*-decane	69
Carbon dioxide-*n*-octane, *n*-tridecane, *n*-hexadecane	70
Water-benzene	82
Water-benzene, toluene, ethyl benzene, propylene, etc.	83
Water-ethane, *n*-butane	84
Water-propane, butane, *n*hexane, cyclohexane, benzene	85
Water benzene, *n*-heptane, *n*-pentane, 2-methyl pentane, toluene	81
Water-benzene, 1,3,5-trimethyl benzene, ethane, *n*-butane, nitrogen, argon, carbon dioxide, ammonia	70

proposed in the patents. The caffeine is removed from the carbon dioxide gas by adsorption on activated charcoal. Thus, for this separation the incentive for dense-gas extraction is the selectivity obtained and is not associated with the energy costs for solvent recovery. The authors believe that this coffee process is still in the development stage.

Oil Recovery

An interesting development in dense-gas processes is their application to tertiary oil recovery from petroleum reservoirs. These cover the range from first contact miscibility drives using propane slugs wherein the injected fluid and the in-place fluid form a miscible solution at all compositions, to the enriched gas-drive and the high-pressure gas process, both of which require the mass transfer of intermediates to occur before miscibility in the reservoir can be achieved. The injected gas for the enriched gas-drive process contains methane, together with intermediate hydrocarbons like ethane, propane, and butanes which dissolve in the oil, sufficiently enriching it to the point where it becomes one phase with the injected gas. In this instance the transfer of species is from the injected fluid to the in-place fluid. In the high-pressure gas process, however, single components like methane or carbon dioxide are used as the injected fluids, which achieve miscibility with the in-place oil through the transfer of C_2 to C_6 intermediates from the reservoir fluids into the gas phase.

Even though the propane slug and enriched gas-drive processes achieve miscibility at moderate pressures (7 to 25 MPa), they still require substantial amounts of expensive hydrocarbons which tend to make them impractical for most reservoirs. The high-pressure gas drive can use cheaper injection fluids like lean gas or flue gas, but these require pressures in excess of 28 MPa to achieve miscibility with the reservoir fluid. Carbon dioxide and methane can also be used via a high-pressure gas-drive process, and it has been pointed out that carbon dioxide requires substantially lower pressures than methane to achieve miscibility with some reservoir fluids.[88] Not surprisingly, carbon dioxide is being injected in a number of reservoirs in an attempt to improve the oil recovery.[89,90] Of course, the applicability of the process is largely dependent on the ready availability of substantial and cheap supplies of the injected fluid, which limits its applicability. As an example, the carbon dioxide injection project at the Sacroc unit of the Kelly-Snyder field will require the injection of almost 600 billion ft^3 of carbon dioxide over a 10-year period. In return it is anticipated that an additional 150 million barrels of oil will be recovered from the reservoir.

CONCLUSIONS AND FUTURE TRENDS

In the previous section we have attempted to illustrate some of the recent developments involving dense-gas systems which can lead to novel and practical separations. The ability to tailor the dense gas to adjust phase equilibria[24,71] and the enhanced solubility of solid hydrocarbons in liquid hydrocarbons dilated by supercritical gas are two important examples; neither has been fully explored. The use of supercritical carbon dioxide in oil recovery is being attempted on a limited basis, and may see more extensive use in situations where large quantities of gas are readily available. These experimental studies, coupled with a more complete understanding of the phase equilibria, have widened the field of dense-gas extraction.

Presently, the main emphasis of the research involving supercritical gases is directed towards their use as extraction solvents for heavy hydrocarbons (vacuum residua, heavy crudes, tar sands, shale, and coal liquids). One group very active in this area is the Coal Research Council in England, where they have been studying the extraction of coal with supercritical hydrocarbons and water. Using toluene as the dense gas, they find that only 17 to 20% of a low-volatility coal can be extracted.[91] The extraction yield with supercritical water is significantly less than that for toluene. These results indicate that dense-gas extraction has limited applicability for untreated coal. However, techniques such as those developed by Kohn and co-workers[25-27] could have an important impact.

It is reasonable to expect that in the near future there will be an increasing number of experimental studies on the dense-gas extraction of other heavy hydrocarbons such as the products of coal liquefaction, heavy tar-like crudes from Venezuela and Canada, and shale oil. The interpretation of these data will be much easier if studies are also available of simpler systems that model various aspects of the heavy hydrocarbons.

This review has emphasized the use of supercritical gases as solvents. However, should they be used as solvents for systems undergoing chemical reaction, it is doubtful that the supercritical gas would behave as an inert solvent. This is largely an unexplored area. For example, a number of beneficial effects have been attributed to supercritical water. McCaully[92] has suggested that supercritical water minimizes the production of asphaltenes in a hydrogen-donor coal-liquefaction process; Gatsis[93] has claimed that in the treatment of heavy hydrocarbons water facilitated the conversion of sulfur and nitrogen to H_2S and NH_3; and supercritical water has also been used in catalytic hydrotreating processes for the *in situ* generation of hydrogen.[94] Finally, work in our laboratory[95] has shown that the isomerization of C_4-C_{12} normal paraffins using Lewis acids such as $AlCl_3$ is enhanced by carrying out the reaction in dense-gas solvents. There is very little understanding of the effect of dense gases when they can simultaneously affect solubility and chemical reactions. This is a fruitful area of basic research where a reasonable understanding of the phenomena is needed.

For many dense-gas separations, the major economic driving force is the potential energy savings in solvent recovery. Just recently Kerr-McGee[96] announced a new supercritical deasphalting process which is expected to save 50% of the energy required for conventional deasphalting. This appears to be an example of where increased energy costs have stimulated development work on a dense-gas process.

However, along with lower energy costs, dense-gas extraction usually requires more expensive process equipment due to the high pressures required to give the supercritical gas liquid-like properties. Unfortunately, the rise in cost for process equipment[97] has been extremely sharp during the last several years. At present, it is difficult to rationally evaluate the net economic incentive for dense-gas extraction, taking into account both decreased energy costs and increased capital costs. This may have delayed short-term development work.

Looking beyond the short term, it is reasonable to expect considerable research, both university and industrial, in the area of dense-gas extraction of heavy hydrocarbons. This will include reservoir equilibria and more conventional refinery separations. In these emerging areas, dense-gas extraction may find important applications.

ACKNOWLEDGMENTS

The authors would like to thank J. D. Bushnell, R. B. Long, and H. J. Soloman for their helpful suggestions to this work and E. S. Matulevicius for his critical comments on the manuscript.

NOMENCLATURE

B	Second virial coefficient, cm^3/mol
C	Third virial coefficient, cm^6/mol
E	Enhancement factor
f^0	Standard-state fugacity, atm
f^L	Liquid-phase fugacity, atm
f^V	Vapor-phase fugacity, atm
f	Fugacity, atm
H	Henry's constant, atm
k_{12}	Interaction parameter
N	Number of moles
P_c	Critical pressure, atm
P_2^S	Solute vapor pressure, atm
P	System pressure, atm
R	Gas constant, $atm\text{-}cm^3/mol\text{-}K$
T_c	Critical temperature, K
T	System temperature, K
v_c	Critical volume, cm^3/mol
v^L	Liquid molar volume, cm^3/mol
v^S	Solid molar volume, cm^3/mol
v	Gas-phase molar volume, cm^3/mol
x	Liquid-phase mole fraction
y	Vapor-phase mole fraction
Z_c	Critical compressibility factor

Greek

β	Selectivity
ξ	Process variable
φ_2^S	Vapor-phase fugacity coefficient of solute 2 at P_2^S
φ	Vapor-phase fugacity coefficient
γ	Liquid-phase activity coefficient
ω	Acentric factor

Subscripts

1	Dense-gas solvent
2	Solute
5	Pentane
10	n-Decane
19	Nonadecane
20	*n*-Eicosane
32	Dotriacontane
37	Heptatriacontane
2MN	2 Methyl naphthlene

REFERENCES

1. **Paul, P. F. M. and Wise, W. S.,** *The Principles of Gas Extraction,* Mills and Boon, London, 1971.
2. **Valteris, R. L.,** The solubility of materials in compressed hydrocarbon gases, *Birmingham University Chem. Eng.,* 17, 38, 1966.
3. **Ellis, S. R. M.,** Vapor phase extraction processes, *Br. Chem. Eng.,* 16, 358, 1971.
4. **Hicks, C. P. and Young, C. L.,** The gas-liquid critical properties of binary mixtures, *Chem. Rev.,* 75, 119, 1975.
5. **Pilz, V.,** Phase equilibria at high pressure *Verfahrenstechnik (Mainz),* 9, 280, 1975.
6. **Booth, H. S. and Bidwell, R. M.,** Solubility measurements in the critical region, *Chem. Rev.,* 44, 477, 1949.
7. **Rowlinson, J. S. and Richardson, M. J.,** The solubility of solids in compressed gases, *Adv. Chem. Phys.,* 2, 85, 1959.
8. **Michaels, S., Green, M. S., and Larsen, S. V.,** Equilibrium Critical Phenomena in Fluids and Mixtures, National Bureau of Standards, Special Publication 237, June 1970.
9. **Diepen, G. A. M. and Scheffer, F. E. C.,** Solubility of naphthalene in supercritical ethylene, *J. Phys. Chem.,* 57, 575, 1953.

10. **Diepen, G. A. M. and Scheffer, F. E. C.,** Solubility of naphthalene in supercritical ethylene, *J. Am. Chem. Soc.,* 70, 4085, 1948.
11. **Prausnitz, J. M.,** *Molecular Thermodynamics of Fluid-Phase Equilibria,* Prentice-Hall, Engelwood Cliffs, N.J., 1969.
12. **Ewald, A. H., Jepson, W. B., and Rowlinson, J. S.,** The solubility of solids in gases, *Discuss. Faraday Soc.,* 15, 238, 1953.
13. **Pitzer, K. S. and Curl, R. F.,** The volumetric and thermodynamic properties of fluids. III. Empirical equation for the second virial coefficient, *J. Am. Chem. Soc.,* 70, 2369, 1957.
14. **Reid, R. C. and Sherwood, T. K.,** *The Properties of Gases and Liquids,* McGraw-Hill, New York, 1966.
15. **Tsonopoulos, C.,** An empirical correlation of second virial coefficients, *AIChE J.,* 20, 263, 1974.
16. **Tsonopoulos, C.,** Second virial coefficients of polar haloalkanes, *AIChE J.,* 21, 827, 1975.
17. **Chueh, P. L. and Prausnitz, J. M.,** Vapor-liquid equilibria at high pressures. Vapor-phase fugacity coefficients in nonpolar and quantum mixtures, *IEC Fundam.,* 6, 492, 1967.
18. **Chueh, P. L. and Prausnitz, J. M.,** *Computer Calculations for High Pressure Vapor-Liquid Equilibria,* Prentice-Hall, Englewood Cliffs, N.J., 1968.
19. **Chueh, P. L., Muirbrook, N. K., and Prausnitz, J. M.,** Multicomponent vapor-liquid equilibria at high pressures. Part II. Thermodynamic analysis, *AIChE J.,* 11, 1097, 1965.
20. **Hsi, C. and Lu, C. Y.,** Prediction of gas solubilities and phase equilibria of normal fluid mixtures with one supercritical component, *Can. J. Chem. Eng.,* 19, 134, 1971.
21. **Hinckley, R. B. and Reid, R. C.,** Rapid estimation of minimum solubility of solids in gases, *AIChE J.,* 10, 416, 1964.
22. **Davenport, A. J. and Rowlinson, J. S.,** The solubility of hydrocarbons in liquid methane, *Trans. Faraday Soc.,* 59, 78, 1963.
23. **Kohn, J. P., Kim, Y. J., and Pan, Y. C.,** Partial miscibility phenomena in binary hydrocarbon systems including ethane, *J. Chem. Eng. Data,* 11, 333, 1966.
24. **Guy, K. W. A., Malanowski, S. K., and Rowlinson, J. S.,** Liquid methane as an extractive solvent for the separation of hydrocarbons, *Chem. Eng. Sci.,* 22, 801, 1967.
25. **Cordeiro, D. J., Luks, K. D., and Kohn, J. P.,** Process for extracting high-molecular-weight hydrocarbons from solid phase in equilibrium with liquid hydrocarbon phase, *Ind. Eng. Chem. Process Des. Dev.,* 12, 47, 1973.
26. **Cordeiro, D. J., Luks, K. D., and Kohn, J. P.,** A process for extracting high molecular weight hydrocarbons from a solid phase in equilibrium with a liquid hydrocarbon phase: Solubility-selectivity behavior of certain organic groups, *AIChE J.,* 19, 168, 1973.
27. **Tan, F. O., Cordeiro, D. J., Luks, K. D., and Kohn, J. P.,** Some thermodynamic aspects of petroleum recovery by methane pressurization, *AIChE J.,* 19, 486, 1973.
28. **Koch, H. A., Jr. and Slobod, R. L.,** Miscible slug process, *Trans. A.I.M.E.,* 210, 40, 1957.
29. **Stone, H. L. and Crump, J. S.,** Effect of gas composition upon oil recovery by gas drive, *Trans. A.I.M.E.,* 207, 105, 1956.
30. **Holm, L. W.,** Carbon dioxide solvent flooding for increased oil recovery, *Trans. A.I.M.E.,* 216, 225, 1959.
31. **Griffith, B. L. and Hollrah, U. M.,** New high pressure gas injection method, *Oil Gas. J.,* 51, 86, 1952.
32. **Kay, W. B.,** Liquid-vapor phase equilibrium relations in the ethane-*n*-heptane system, *Ind. Eng. Chem.,* 30, 459, 1938.
33. **Kay, W. B. and Albert, R. E.,** Liquid-vapor equilibrium relations in the ethane-cyclohexane system, *Ind. Eng. Chem.,* 48, 422, 1956.
34. **Kay, W. B. and Nivens, T. D.,** Liquid-vapor equilibrium relations in binary systems, *AIChE Symp. Ser.,* 3, 108, 1952.
35. **Zhuze, T. P. et al.,** Solubility of hexane, cyclohexane, and benzene in compressed ethylene, *Bull. Akad. Sci., U.S.S.R.,* 2, 361, 1960.
36. **Snedeker, R. A.,** Ph.D. thesis, Princeton University, 1955.
37. **Todd, D. B. and Elgin, J. C.,** Phase equilibria in systems with ethylene above its critical temperature, *AIChE J.,* 1, 20, 1955.
38. **Elgin, J. C. and Weinstock, J. J.,** Phase equilibra at elevated pressures in ternary systems of ethylene and water with organic liquids. Salting out with a supercritical gas, *J. Chem. Eng. Data,* 4, 3, 1959.
39. **Chappelear, D. C. and Elgin, J. C.,** Phase equilibria in the critical region. Binary systems with chlorotrifluoromethane, *J. Chem. Eng. Data,* 6, 415, 1961.
40. **Yorizane, M., Masuoka, H., Ida, S., and Ikeda, T.,** High pressure vapor-liquid-liquid equilibrium for the ethylene-MEK-water system, *J. Chem. Eng. Jpn.,* 7, 379, 1974.
41. **Long, R. B.,** Exxon Research and Engineering Co., personal communication.
42. **Zhuze, T. P. and Kapelyushnikov, M. A.,** U.S.S.R. Patent No. 113325, 1958.
43. **Solomon, H. J.,** Propane deasphalting in the neighborhood of the critical point of propane, A.C.S. Meeting, Washington, D.C., September 1971.
44. **Dastur, S. P. and Thodos, G.,** Critical temperatures and pressures of the ternary system, ethane-*n*-pentane-*n*-heptane, *Can. J. Chem. Eng.,* 43, 73, 1965.

45. **Grieves, R. B. and Thodos, G.,** The critical temperatures and pressures of binary systems: Hydrocarbons of all types and hydrogen, *AIChE J.,* 6, 561, 1960.
46. **Grieves, R. B. and Thodos, G.,** The critical temperatures of multicomponent hydrocarbon systems, *AIChE J.,* 8, 550, 1962.
47. **Grieves, R. B. and Thodos, G.,** The critical pressure of multicomponent hydrocarbon mixtures and the critical density of binary hydrocarbon mixtures, *AIChE J.,* 9, 25, 1963.
48. **Grieves, R. B. and Thodos, G.,** Critical temperatures and pressures of ternary hydrocarbon mixtures: The ethane-propane-*n*-butane system, *J. Appl. Chem.,* 13, 466, 1963.
49. **Robin, S. and Vodar, B.,** Solubility in compressed gases, *Faraday Soc. Disc.,* 15, 233, 1953.
50. **King, A. D. and Robertson, W. W.,** Solubility of naphthalene in compressed gases, *J. Chem. Phys.,* 37, 1453, 1962.
51. **Zaalishvili, D.,** A modified theorem of corresponding states for gas mixtures and its test on hydrocarbon mixtures, *Zh. Fiz. Khim.,* 26, 970, 1952.
52. **Forman, J. C. and Thodos, G.,** Experimental determination of critical temperatures and pressures of mixtures: The methane-ethane-*n*-butane system, *AIChE J.,* 8, 209, 1962.
53. **Sobocinski, D. P.,** Phase Behavior of the Hydrogen Sulfide-Carbon Dioxide System from the Critical of Hydrogen Sulfide to the Eutectic Temperature at −140°F and of the Methane-Hydrogen Sulfide-Carbon Dioxide System Between −75°F and 148°F, Dissertation, University of Kansas, 1963.
54. **Stegemeier, G. L. and Hough, E. W.,** Interfacial tension of the methane-normal pentane system, *Prod. Mon.,* 25, 6, 1961.
55. **Bloomer, O. T. and Parent, J. D.,** Liquid-vapor phase behavior of the methane-nitrogen system, *Chem. Eng. Prog.,* 6, 11, 1953.
56. **Ellington, R. T., Eakin, B. E., Parent, J. D., Gami, D. C., and Bloomer, O. T.,** Vapor-liquid phase equilibria in the binary systems of methane, ethane, and nitrogen, in *Thermodynamics and Transport Properties of Liquids and Solids,* McGraw-Hill, New York, 1959, 180.
57. **La Ricerca,** *Scientifica,* 29, 2609, 1959.
58. **Ehrlich, P. and Kurpen, J. J.,** Phase equilibria of polymer-solvent systems at high pressures near their critical loci: Polyethylene with *n*-alkanes, *J. Polym. Sci.,* 1A, 3217, 1963.
59. **Close, R. E.,** Vapor-Liquid Equilibrium in the Critical Region: Systems of Aliphatic Alcohols with Propane and Propylene, Dissertation, Princeton University, 1953.
60. **Haselden, G. G., Newitt, D. M., and Shah, S. M.,** Two-phase equilibrium in binary and ternary systems. V. Carbon dioxide-ethylene. VI. Carbon dioxide-propylene, *Proc. R. Soc. London,* 209A, 1, 1951.
61. **Haselden, G. G., Holland, F. A., King, M. B., and Strickland-Constable, R. F.,** Two-phase equilibrium in binary and ternary systems. X. Phase equilibria and compressibility of the systems carbon dioxide/propylene, carbon dioxide/ethylene and ethylene/propylene and an account of the thermodynamic functions of the system carbon dioxide/propylene, *Proc. R. Soc. London,* 240A, 1, 1957.
62. **Bierlein, J. A. and Kay, W. B.,** Phase equilibrium properties of system carbon dioxide-hydrogen sulfide, *Ind. Eng. Chem.,* 45, 618, 1953.
63. **Donnelly, H. G.,** Two-Phase Equilibria in the System: Carbon Dioxide-Methane, Dissertation, University of Michigan, 1952.
64. **Cook, D.,** The carbon dioxide-nitrous oxide system in the critical region, *Proc. R. Soc. London,* 219A, 245, 1953.
65. **Takenouchi, S. and Kennedy, G. C.,** The binary system water-carbon dioxide at high temperatures and pressures, *Am. J. Sci.,* 262, 1055, 1964.
66. **Todheide, K. and Franck, E. U.,** Two-phase region and the critical curve of the system carbon dioxide-water at pressures up to 3500 bar, *Z. Phys. Chem. (Frankfurt),* 37, 387, 1963.
67. **Prausnitz, J. M. and Benson, R. C.,** Solubility of liquids in compressed hydrogen, nitrogen, and carbon dioxide, *AIChE J.,* 5, 161, 1959.
68. **Besserer, G. J. and Robinson, D. B.,** Equilibrium-phase properties of isopentane-carbon dioxide system, *J. Chem. Eng. Data,* 20, 93, 1975.
69. **Yudovich, A., Robinson, R. L., Jr., and Chao, K. C.,** Phase equilibrium of carbon dioxide in the methane-carbon dioxide-*n*-decane system, *AIChE J.,* 17, 1152, 1971.
70. **Schneider, G.,** Phase equilibria in binary fluid systems of hydrocarbons with carbon dioxide, water and methane, *Chem. Eng. Prog. Symp. Ser. 88,* 64, 9, 1968.
71. **Leder, F. and Irani, C. A.,** Upper critical solution temperatures in hydrocarbon-carbon dioxide systems, *J. Chem. Eng. Data,* 20, 323, 1975.
72. **Huie, N. C.,** Dissertation, University of Notre Dame, Notre Dame, Ind., 1972.
73. **Huie, N. C., Luks, K. D., and Kohn, J. P.,** Phase equilibria behavior of systems carbon dioxide-*n* eicosane and carbon dioxide-*n*-decane-*n*-eicosane, *J. Chem. Eng. Data,* 18, 311, 1973.
74. **Jaeger, A.,** Über die Löslichreit von flüssiegn kohlenwasserstoffen in überhitztem Wasser, *Brenst. Chem.,* 4, 259, 1923.
75. **Griswold, J. and Kasch, J. E.,** Hydrocarbon-water solubilities at elevated temperatures and pressures, *Ind. Eng. Chem.,* 34, 804, 1942.
76. **Kobayashi, R. and Katz, D. L.,** Vapor-liquid equilibrium for binary hydrocarbon-water systems, *Ind. Eng. Chem.,* 45, 440, 1953.

77. **Leland, T. W., McKetta, J. J., Jr., and Kobe, K. A.,** Phase equilibrium in 1-butene-water system and correlation of hydrocarbon-water solubility data, *Ind. Eng. Chem.*, 45, 1266, 1955.
78. **Arnold, G. B. and Coghlan, C. A.,** Toluene extraction from petroleum with water, *Ind. Eng. Chem.*, 42, 177, 1950.
79. **Rowlinson, J. S.,** *Liquids and Liquid Mixtures,* Butterworths, London, 1969, chap. 6.
80. **O'Grady, T. M.,** Liquid-liquid equilibria for the benzene-*n* heptane-water system in the critical solution region, *J. Chem. Eng. Data,* 12, 9, 1967.
81. **Connolly, J. F.,** Solubility of hydrocarbons in water near the critical solution temperatures, *J. Chem. Eng. Data,* 11, 13, 1966.
82. **Rebert, C. J. and Kay, W. B.,** The phase behavior and solubility relations of the benzene-water system, *AIChE J.,* 5, 285, 1959.
83. **Danneil, A., Todheide, K., and Franck, E. U.,** Verdempfungsgleichgewichte und kritische Kurven in den Systemen Äthan/Wasser und *n*-Butan/Wasser bei hohen Drücken, *Chem. Ing. Tech.,* 39, 816, 1967.
84. **Rebert, C. J. and Hayworth, K. E.,** The gas and liquid solubility relations in hydrocarbon-water systems, *AIChE J.,* 13, 118, 1967.
85. **Roselius, W., Vitzthum, O., and Hubert, P.,** Process for the Extraction of the Aroma Fraction from Coffee, German Patent 2106133, 1972.
86. **Vitzthum, O. and Hubert, P.,** Process for Decafination of Coffee, German Patent 2212281, 1973.
87. **Vitzthum, O. and Hubert, P.,** Process for Decafination of Coffee, German Patent 2357590, 1975.
88. **Rathmell, J. J., Stalkup, F. I., and Hussinger, R. C.,** A laboratory investigation of miscible displacement by carbon dioxide, Paper SPE 3483, presented at SPE-AIME 46th Annual Fall Meeting, New Orleans, La., October 3 to 6, 1971.
89. **Hull, P.,** SACROC: An engineering conservation triumph, *Oil Gas J.,* p. 57, August 17, 1970.
90. **Holm, L. W. and O'Brien, L. J.,** Carbon dioxide test at the Mead-Strawn field, *J. Pet. Technol.,* p. 431, April 1971.
91. **Whitehead, J. C. and Williams, D. F.,** Solvent extraction of coal by supercritical gases, *J. Inst. Fuel,* 48, 182, 1975.
92. **McCaully, J. J.,** Atlantic Richfield Co., U.S. Patent 3,660,269, 1962.
93. **Gatsis, J. G.,** Universal Oil Products, U.S. Patent 3,453,206, 1969.
94. **Hoffman, E. J.,** University of Wyoming, U.S. Patent 3,505,204, 1970.
95. **Kramer, G. M. and Leder, F.,** U.S. Patent 3,880,945, 1975.
96. *Oil Gas J.,* p. 93, April 5, 1976.
97. **Faltermayer, E.,** The hyperinflation in plant construction, *Fortune,* 15, 102, 1975.

AUTHOR INDEX

A

B

F

G

H

I

J

K

T

U

V

W

Y

Z

SUBJECT INDEX

D

E

F

G

H

I

J

K

L

M

N

O

P

R

S

T

U

V

W

X

Y

Z

CRC PUBLICATIONS OF RELATED INTEREST

CRC HANDBOOKS

CRC HANDBOOK OF TABLES FOR APPLIED ENGINEERING SCIENCE, 2nd Edition
Edited by **Ray E. Bolz, D.Eng.,** Case Western Reserve University and **George L. Tuve, Sc.D.,** Case Institute of Technology.
This Handbook is designed to provide a wide spectrum of data covering many fields of modern engineering with reference to more complete sources and includes presentation of data in metric as well as in conventional units.

CRC HANDBOOK OF CHEMISTRY AND PHYSICS, 58th Edition
Edited by **Robert C. Weast, Ph.D.,** Consolidated Natural Gas Co., Inc.
This Handbook is the definitive reference for chemistry and physics and maintains the tradition that has earned it the reputation as the best scientific reference in the world.

CRC HANDBOOK OF CHROMATOGRAPHY, Vols. I and II
Edited by **Gunter Zweig, Ph.D.,** Chief, Chemistry Branch, EPA and **Joseph Sherma,** Lafayette College.
This two-volume set provides comprehensive information concerning chromatographic data, methods and literature. It also contains a Compound Index that lists the more than 12,000 compounds referenced in this data collection.

CRC HANDBOOK OF LABORATORY SAFETY, 2nd Edition
Edited by **Norman V. Steere.**
This Handbook is a complete treatise on personal hazards and safety for laboratory personnel and includes eight color pages on accidents and safety hazards in the laboratory.

CRC UNISCIENCE PUBLICATIONS

CHEMISTRY AND PHYSICS OF SOLID SURFACES
Edited by **Ralf Vanselow, Ph.D.,** University of Wisconsin, and **S. Y. Tong, Ph.D.,** Naval Research Laboratory.
This book is based on the proceedings of the 1975 International Summer Institute on Surface Science held at the University of Wisconsin, Milwaukee.

FUNDAMENTAL MEASURES AND CONSTANTS FOR SCIENCE AND TECHNOLOGY
By **Frederick D. Rossini,** Rice University.
Invaluable to working scientists, as well as students in science or engineering, who need to know the basis and current status of the measurements involved in their respective disciplines.

CRC CRITICAL REVIEW JOURNALS

CRC CRITICAL REVIEWS™ IN ANALYTICAL CHEMISTRY
Edited by **Bruce H. Campbell, Ph.D.,** J. T. Baker Chemical Co.

RETURN TO → CHEMISTRY LIBRARY
100 Hildebrand Hall 642-3753
LOAN PERIOD 1 | 2 | 3
7 DAYS
4